THE TREASURY OF ETHAN ALLEN AMERICAN TRADITIONAL INTERIORS

Ethan Allen is dedicated to the creation of beautiful environment in the American home . . . the foundation of our strength as individuals, as families and as a nation.

To this end, we present this Treasury of American Traditional Interiors. The broad spectrum of styles and moods as expressed in the Ethan Allen Collection of homefurnishings blends the design and craftsmanship of the past with modern skill and technology. Its diversification offers a unique opportunity for personal interpretation. Here are the grace and beauty of traditional designs keyed to the life we live today. We hope this Treasury of Ethan Allen American Traditional Interiors will provide inspiration for all who love the historical heritage of beauty in our homes.

74TH EDITION
THE ETHAN ALLEN TREASURY
by Ethan Allen Inc., Danbury, Conn.

Price $7.50

Table of Contents

Numerical Index

Index by type of room

Decorating and Home Planning features

Ethan Allen Home Fashions to help you have the home you want

John Ruskin said, "This is the true nature of home—it is the place of Peace; the shelter, not only from all injury, but from all terror, doubt and division."

Today with mounting pressures on our lives, we fully appreciate the truth of these words. Today means change . . . in our life style, our environment, our culture and our values and, while still a haven of peace and shelter, home is emerging as a vital focal point for many other aspects of family life.

Home today is a fountainhead for cultural and educational enrichment. Many new leisure time pursuits are home-oriented. Today our children learn at home, not only of man's knowledge, but of history as it shapes the real world today. The environmental content of home can establish meaningful values and insights for the entire family.

We find a greater need than ever to create an environment that is warm, gracious and personal. To that need American Traditional design brings dignity, good taste and meaningful stability. American Traditional is a style eminently suited to the living needs of the contemporary family and the decoration of today's home. With scale and proportion highly compatible with today's architecture, its quiet charm adds character and personality to the rooms of a typical modern floor plan. It's flexible—easy to decorate with and easy to live with.

Ethan Allen offers you the widest collection of American Traditional home furnishings in the world. Here you will find every conceivable kind and style of American Traditional furniture, lamps, accessories and decorative accents—plus draperies, textiles, floor coverings, wall paper, paint, color television and bedding. Ethan Allen not only expresses the quality of traditional craftsmanship with the efficiency of modern technology—it also provides you with many of today's furniture concepts interpreted in the American Traditional style.

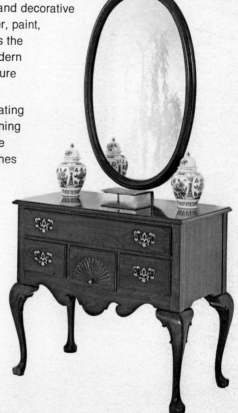

If you're on a budget, you may want to complete your decorating plans by making purchases gradually. Our policy of maintaining Ethan Allen styles over a long period of time assures you the opportunity to make future purchases with designs and finishes compatible with those you acquire today.

Ethan Allen Galleries offer their services and the Ethan Allen Collection throughout the United States and in several Canadian cities. These Galleries are chosen for their high standing in the community, their fine service and reputation for integrity, their ability to offer you trained decorating assistance, and their excellent displays which are rich in decorative ideas.

A beautiful home that expresses your taste and your personality is truly a fine investment. Year after year, you will enjoy its beauty and comfort. The purpose of this Treasury is to help you have the home you want.

Here's the Ethan Allen way to put it all together

What makes a beautiful room? It's your dreams and your ideas brought to life with skill and imagination. It's a synthesis of separate furnishings or elements into a whole that is both handsome and harmonious. The striking whole or "total look" that is always the goal of interior design is shown on these next few pages along with the separate parts that compose them. Here are a living room, dining room and bedroom that are each a pleasing and different addition of furniture, rugs, wallcoverings, draperies, lamps and accessories . . . all available at every Ethan Allen Gallery. On this page is a living room of gracious traditional charm.

Ethan Allen's total look

The whole should be greater than the sum of its parts—certainly when it comes to furnishing a room. Handsome carpeting, beautifully detailed and crafted furniture, delightful accessories mean very little when they fail to complement each other or blend together in a balanced arrangement. At the Ethan Allen Galleries one can find furnishings that really go together, because all the Ethan Allen Collections—furniture, fabrics, floor coverings, draperies, lamps and accessories, etc.—were planned that way. On this page are the elements that add up to the classic 18th Century dining shown opposite.

What adds up to a beautiful bedroom

A world of homefurnishings at your fingertips at every Ethan Allen Gallery! The room settings throughout this Treasury were created almost entirely from the spectacularly comprehensive selection of Ethan Allen homefurnishings—and you too will find it easy to combine, correlate and coordinate whatever you need to complete your room or your home. On this page is a bedroom reminiscent of a New England wayside inn—only one of the many possible looks available in Ethan Allen bedroom homefurnishings.

ETHAN ALLEN
LIVING ROOMS

Once a special occasion room, the living room is now at the center of family life and the hub of entertaining activities. Pride of appearance and warmth of hospitality are, of course, important for any family who entertains, but personal comfort and a style keyed to the requirements of that family are uppermost. What gives comfort to any living room are finely constructed and luxuriously upholstered seating pieces—ranging from large sectionals and sofas down to small occasional chairs and benches. The Ethan Allen collection of living room upholstered furniture offers a spectacular choice of styles, augmented by a wide selection of occasional tables and cabinets designed primarily for living room use.

start with a sofa

Decorating your own home—is it to be a joyous adventure or an exercise in futility? For the achievement of a rich and satisfying family environment is never merely a matter of choosing tasteful furnishings. Color, scale, pattern, texture and arrangement, to name a few, are vital considerations. So is the starting point—often the most difficult decision to reach. To help you past this point we are featuring a series of living rooms designed around several possible starting points: a great sofa, a marvelous print, a fascinating area rug, etc. Sumptuous sectional sofa began the decorating plan of this handsome beige and gold room.

Shown from left to right:
No. 20-7409 **Lounge Chair**
No. 13-8001 **Military End Table**
No. 20-7072 **Sectional Sofa**
No. 20-7075 **Sectional Sofa**
No. 13-9005 **Military End Table**
No. 20-7409 **Lounge Chair**
No. 13-8003 **Military Cocktail Table**

For detailed specifications on:
Upholstery—see pages 392-406
Military Campaign Collection—see page 383

Ethan Allen
AMERICAN TRADITIONAL INTERIORS

start with a sofa

Elegant and urbane, this handsome tufted Tuxedo sofa makes a fine starting point for a room of worldly charm and sophistication. Sable lacquered walls and richly stained parquet floor frame a composition of frosted white and mellow rose, while a consistency of mood lets classicly serene furniture and dynamic contemporary canvas live together in easy harmony.

Shown below from left to right:
No. 11-6210A Duncan Phyfe Chairs
No. 11-8009 Butler's Tray Table
No. 11-9200 Goddard Block Front Chest
No. 20-7189 Tufted Tuxedo Sofa
No. 11-8202 Pembroke Table

Big design effects are easy to come by when space is shy, if this graceful camel-back loveseat starts the decorating plan. A single jewel-bright fabric—splashed everywhere—gives instant impact; its colors are then reversed for area carpet and paneled walls. Chippendale inspired cabinets are space expanders, too, providing storage area as well as table surface.

Shown opposite from left to right:
No. 11-9200 Block Front Chest
No. 11-6211A Queen Anne Arm Chair
No. 20-7122 Loveseat
No. 11-8204 Tea Table
No. 11-9201 Lowboy
No. 20-7606 Queen Anne Wing Chair

For detailed specifications on:
Georgian Court Accents and Tables—see pages 375-376.
Upholstery—see pages 392-406.

Ethan Allen
AMERICAN TRADITIONAL INTERIORS

excitement underfoot

design for living

When a room begins with its floor covering, the results can be subtle or spectacular. Carpeting can proffer an exuberant brush stroke of color or a pale tint of texture. Patterned rugs will stop the eye or quietly define the perimeter of a seating arrangement. Here chrome yellow carpeting is the catalyst for an excitement of color that imparts a young and glowing radiance to formal, traditional living room.

Shown from left to right:
No. 20-7213 **Host Chairs**
No. 15-9010 **Writing Table**
No. 20-7095 **Sofa**

No. 11-8075 **Hexagonal Commode Table**
No. 11-8009 **Butler's Table**
No. 20-7304 **Barrel Chairs**
No. 11-8206 **Nest of Tables**

For detailed specifications on:
Georgian Court Tables—see pages 375-376.
Classic Manor Accents—see pages 388-389 .
Upholstery—see pages 392-406.

Ethan Allen
AMERICAN TRADITIONAL INTERIORS

One exuberant pattern is all it sometimes takes to turn a low key room into a vibrant and memorable interior. Here the master stroke is a brilliantly colored area rug in American Indian design—accenting the ceramic tile floor and providing the palette for the color scheme. Distinctive sofa has bolsters and rope turned base; library units are Royal Charter designs. Playing up the mellow golden tones in the rug are tables in American Foliage Autumn Gold finish.

For detailed specifications on:
Upholstery—see pages 392-406
Royal Charter Accents and Tables—see pages 390-391
American Foliage Colors—see pages 379-383

Shown above from left to right:
No. 16-9007 **Library Cabinet Base**
No. 16-9008 **Library Chest**
No. 16-9009 **Library Upper Cabinet**
No. 24-8020 **Cocktail Table**
No. 20-7443 **Sofa**
No. 24-8083 **End Table**
No. 20-7177 **Lounge Chair**

excitement underfoot

design for living

A room of great verve and vitality borrows both color and mood from its spirited area rug. Richly dark tobacco walls make dramatic foil for silvery white sofa and the intense, electric blues of ottomans, chair, accessories and painting hues. Informal Heirloom bookcase and tables introduce a warming note that tempers and softens the dramatic effect.

Shown from left to right:
No. 20-7744 Sofa
No. 10-8644 Drop Leaf End Table

No. 10-9026 Bookstack
No. 20-7104 Ottomans
No. 20-7937 London Club Chair

No. 10-8640 Cocktail Table
No. 10-8586 Revolving Drum Table

For detailed specifications on:
Heirloom Occasional Pieces—see pages 370-371
Heirloom Accent Pieces—see pages 371-372
Upholstery—see pages 392-406

Oriental rugs impart both pattern and color, yet never in a startling or overpowering way. Which is probably why these rugs are such time-honored favorites for interiors of every mood and description. This Fereghan style rug defines fireplace grouping in gracious, elegant room. Red tones in rug are translated into vibrant, slipper smooth crimson of twin loveseats; decorated bookstacks add suitable accent.

Shown from left to right:
No. 20-7401 **Loveseat**
No. 15-8421 **Pedestal Cocktail Table**
No. 15-8424 **End Table**
No. 14-9026 **Library Book Stacks**

For detailed specifications on:
Classic Manor Occasional Pieces—see pages 387-388
Decorated Furniture—see pages 384-385
Upholstery—see pages 392-406

Ethan Allen
AMERICAN TRADITIONAL INTERIORS

spirited design...
centered on a pattern

Given all options, many choose a patterned fabric as a point of departure for their decorating scheme. And understandably so, for such a fabric—be it print or weave—offers an eye-tested, ready-made color plan as well as a powerful decorating tool. But the patterning of a room can be either free-wheeling or controlled, depending upon personal preference and the ultimate effect to be achieved. Either way it's a great starting point.

Stylized floral print sheathes walls and windows of garden fresh setting below. Pretty, romantically feminine print suggested choice of tufted velvet sofa and curved button back chairs. Two-color prints such as brown and white design on twin sofas, opposite, are enormously versatile. Here the pattern is low-key, and the room itself exuberant, framed in a sparkling backdrop of scarlet walls and white carpeting and draperies.

Shown above from left to right:
No. 16-7439 **Tufted Bench**
No. 11-8067 **Commode Table**
No. 20-7094 **Sofa**
No. 25-9001 **Curio Cabinet**

No. 20-7215 **Curved Button Back Chairs**
No. 11-8075 **Commode Table**
No. 11-8071 **Pedestal Cocktail Table**
No. 15-6001 **Side Chair**
No. 15-9500 **Library Desk**

Ethan Allen
AMERICAN TRADITIONAL INTERIORS

Shown above from left to right:

No. 15-8306 **Nest of Tables**
No. 20-7084 **Sofa**
No. 25-9038 **Console Cabinet**
No. 13-7112 **Chairs**
No. 15-8303 **Lamp Table**
No. 20-7084 **Sofa**
No. 15-8302 **Lamp Table**
No. 15-8671 **Rect. Bunching Table**

For detailed specifications on:
Georgian Court Occasional Pieces—see pages 375-376
Classic Manor Dining Room—see pages 386-387
Classic Manor Antiqued Color Accents—see pages 387-389
Classic Manor Accent Pieces—see pages 388-389
Upholstery—see pages 392-406

spirited design... centered on a pattern

Plaid patterns have always been favorites for casual and easy-going décor. And understandably so—they quickly establish an informal, no-nonsense mood while contributing color and design. Handsome brown and white textured plaid on Tuxedo sofa was the moving spirit behind the decoration of bachelor apartment, below. Rugged Antique Pine designs are fine companions to the plaid; paneled armoire has ample storage capability.

Shown below:
No. 12-6033 **Pedestal Table**
No. 12-6000 **Captain's Chair**
No. 12-8021 **Drop Leaf Cocktail Table**
No. 20-7048 **Tuxedo Sofa**
No. 12-5015 **Armoire**
No. 12-8037 **Commode Table**
No. 20-7703 **Wing Chair**

For detailed specifications on:
Upholstery—see pages 392-406
Antiqued Pine Dining Room—see pages 379-381
Antiqued Pine Bedroom—see pages 378-379
Antiqued Pine Occasional Tables and Accent Pieces—see pages 381-383

Discreet manipulation of pattern can make a room tranquil, yet also animated and colorful. Soft floral weave, used only in one large sweep as sofa cover, is correlated with pillow and chair fabrics. High key background teams kumquat walls with blue carpeting.

Shown above from left to right:
No. 14-7110 Cane Side Chair
No. 20-7262 Crescent Sofa
No. 08-3550 Snack Table
No. 08-3546 Book Trough Table
No. 20-7178 Lounge Chair

For detailed specifications on:
Upholstery—see pages 392-406.

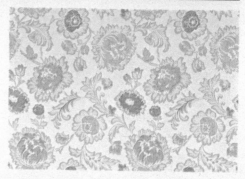

self expression sets the mood
the purists

Those with a keen sense of style—about their lives and about their decor—seldom need to search for a starting point. Their home becomes a personal expression of the mood they prefer...be it a museum calibre or an ecology-oriented environment. A penchant for greenery can give the decoration its focus and direction, so can the memorabilia of a family who travels often, or a very personal collection of paintings or porcelains. Living room, left, reflects a family whose special enthusiasm is an authentic 18th Century look. Summoning up the rich artistry of the period are camel back sofa, Queen Anne chairs, tea table and sideboard, paneled walls and oriental rug.

Shown from left to right:
No. 13-7807 **Chippendale Chair**
No. 11-6207 **Queen Anne Sideboard**
No. 20-7124 **Chippendale Sofa**
No. 11-8203 **Tripod Tea Table**
No. 11-6211A **Queen Anne Arm Chair**
No. 11-8204 **Tea Table**
No. 20-7616 **Queen Anne Wing Chairs**
No. 11-8202 **Drop Leaf Pembroke Table**

For detailed specifications on:
Georgian Court Dining Room—
see pages 374-375.
Georgian Court Accent Pieces—
see page 376.
Georgian Court Occasional Pieces—
see pages 375-376.
Upholstery—see pages 392-406.

Ethan Allen
AMERICAN TRADITIONAL INTERIORS

worldly

Out of town as often as they're home, the family who lives in this apartment enjoys a spirited mix of furnishings and a sophisticated blend of colors—in this case apricot, biscuit and teal blue. What makes the room so very personal is a lively collection of favorite things found in far-off, out-of-the-way places. Tall étagères display and also add architectural enrichment. Slim lined sofa and other furniture are gracefully scaled.

Shown from left to right:
No. 11-6213 **Drop Leaf Table**
No. 20-7245 **Sofa**
No. 11-8205 **Curio Table**
No. 11-8201 **End Table**
No. 15-9040 **Etagere**
No. 20-7104 **Ottoman**
No. 20-7200 **Barrel Chair**

For detailed specifications on:
Upholstery—see pages 392-406.
Georgian Court Accents and Tables—see pages 375-376.
Classic Manor Accent Pieces—see pages 388-389.

Ethan Allen
AMERICAN TRADITIONAL INTERIORS

garden greenery

Glass walls and the easy acquisition of a 'green thumb' have blurred the boundaries of 'indoor' and 'outdoor.' Plantings appear to literally spill over from garden to living area, infusing the room with crisp masses of green and the heady delights of living flowers. Comfortable living room is drenched in garden colors; ample seating provided by loose pillow back sofa and loveseat, in corner arrangement, makes the most of limited space. See-through glass top of coffee table is another space-wise choice.

Shown from left to right:
No. 20-7710 Club Chair
No. 14-7806 Cane Tub Chair
No. 15-8674 Rectangular End Table
No. 20-7184 Three Cushion Sofa
No. 20-7182 Loveseat
No. 24-8081 Square Cocktail Table

For detailed specifications on:
Upholstery—see pages 392-406
Classic Manor Occasional Pieces—see pages 387-388.
American Foliage Colors—see pages 379-383.

romantic

Shown opposite page from left to right:
No. 11-6211A Queen Anne Arm Chair
No. 15-9010 Writing Desk
No. 20-7096 Sofa
No. 15-8303 End Table
No. 15-8304 Coffee Table
No. 15-8306 Nest of Tables
No. 20-7619 Love Seat
No. 13-7807 Chair

Sweeping into her living room in a rustle of long skirts, is a hostess who gives candlelight suppers, collects heirloom jewelry and loves memorable perfumes. An incurable romantic, she warms to jewel bright colors, fresh flowers massed in marvelous containers, gorgeously patterned rugs, and paintings and mirrors, ornately framed. Long, curved sofa, make a gracious focal point in this elegant room, with furniture positioned around the Oriental style rug.

or ethnic

Shown above from left to right:
No. 20-7937 Club Chair
No. 20-7938 Ottoman
No. 16-8000 Cocktail Table
No. 16-9900 Canterbury Cabinet
No. 20-7049 Sofa
No. 16-6013 Flip Top Table
No. 24-8082 Hexagonal End Table

If you prefer the Rockies to the Riviera, collect Indian handcrafts, are a whiz at organic cooking and feel most at home in faded jeans—then it's the natural look for you. Go back to nature with wicker, basketry, neutral hues and fabrics that have a handwoven look. Casual style of the southwest is captured by living room, above; Arresting area rug, hung as a wall tapestry, adds ethnic flavor.

For detailed specifications on: Upholstery—see pages 392-406, Classic Manor—see pages 387-389, Georgian Court—see pages 374-376.
For detailed specifications on: Upholstery—see pages 392-406, Royal Charter, see pages 389-391 American Foliage Colors—see pages 379-383.

Antiques by Vincent Lippe

Ethan Allen
AMERICAN TRADITIONAL INTERIORS

long and narrow room

The long and narrow living room, absorbing a vanished foyer or dining room, or both, poses a special set of decorating problems. Furniture placement and design plan must define the separate areas while maintaining an overall unity, and reshaping, if only visually, the awkward proportions of the room itself.

Shown opposite from left to right:

No. 15-6001 Side Chair	No. 13-8001 Military End Table
No. 16-9007 Cabinet	No. 15-8660 Rectangular Cocktail Table
No. 16-9001 Tall Mirror	No. 20-7411 Lowback "Mrs." Club Chair
No. 15-8676 Nest of Tables	No. 20-7410 Hi-Back "Mr." Club Chair
No. 20-7044 Three Cushion Wing Sofa	

Twin sofas, facing each other across the hearth, compose the central living area and mark off foyer and dining space in room below. Mirrored wall conjures up a glittering illusion of endless space while, gleaming accessories lift the spirit of room, opposite. Tall screen, trimmed with nailheads, defines a small entry area.

Shown below from left to right:

No. 25-9038 Two Door Console Cabinet	No. 20-7743 Sofas
No. 15-6013 Double Pedestal Ext. Table	No. 15-8674 End Table
No. 15-6012 Cane Back Dining Chairs	No. 15-8671 Rectangular
No. 15-6012A Cane Back Dining Arm Chairs	Bunching Table
No. 15-6007/6018 Buffet and China Top	

For detailed specifications on:
Military Campaign Chest Pieces—see page 383
Classic Manor Occasional Pieces—see page 388
Classic Manor Dining Room—see pages 386-387
Upholstery—see pages 392-406

For detailed specifications on:
Classic Manor Antiqued Color Pieces—see pages 388-389
Classic Manor Dining Room—see pages 386-387
Classic Manor Occasional Pieces—see page 388
Upholstery—see pages 392-406

Ethan Allen
AMERICAN TRADITIONAL INTERIORS

with glass walls

Glass walls—today's super windows—flood a room with light and a panorama of the changing seasons. Furniture arrangement must accommodate to the view; window treatment should never obscure it, or attempt to alter the character of the room's architecture.

People who live with glass walls needn't trade privacy for a fine view. Trellised patio screens setting, below, while versatile shade cloth blinds offer masterful light control, right. Ebullient garden hues of both rooms, provide indoor-outdoor continuity of color.

Shown below from left to right:

No. 20-7201 **Barrel Chair**
No. 12-8082 **Hexagonal Lamp Table**
No. 20-7244 **Three Cushion Cap Arm Sofa**
No. 20-7102 **Semi-attached Pillow Ottoman**
No. 24-8080 **Rectangular Cocktail Table**

Shown opposite from left to right:

No. 14-7806 **Cane Tub Chair**
No. 10-6074 **Drop Leaf Table**
No. 15-6021 **Side Chairs**
No. 20-7247 **Sectional Loveseat**
No. 20-7248 **Sectional Sofa**
No. 15-8304 **Corner Table**
No. 11-8071 **Octagon Cocktail Table**

For detailed specifications on:

Upholstery—see pages 392-406
American Foliage Colors—see pages 381-382
Heirloom Dining Room—see pages 366-369

Classic Manor Occasional Pieces—see pages 388-389
Classic Manor Dining Room—see pages 386-387
Georgian Court Occasional Pieces—see pages 375-376

Ethan Allen
AMERICAN TRADITIONAL INTERIORS

the L-shaped room

A popular floor plan, the L-shaped living room offers more than one arrangement. In red, white and blue setting, left, it's a delightful dining area. A small alcove, below, becomes a useful study corner. Comfortable wing sofa teams with rugged Antiqued Pine tables.

Shown left from left to right:
No. 20-7101 Ottoman
No. 11-6211 Queen Anne Side Chair
No. 11-6204 Queen Anne Dining Table
No. 11-8201 Lamp Table
No. 11-8205 Curio Table
No. 20-7334 Pillowback Sofa
No. 11-8202 Drop Leaf Pembroke Table
No. 20-7304 Barrel Chair

Shown below from left to right:
No. 12-8037 Commode Table
No. 20-7363 Wing Sofa
No. 24-9516 Etagere
No. 12-8000 Trestle Cocktail Table
No. 12-6041A Ladderback Chair
No. 24-9506 Pedestal Desk
No. 20-7361 Lounge Chair
No. 12-8034 Drop Leaf Table

small but with charm

Space is only a virtue when you make the most of it; and even the tiniest of rooms can be turned into a memorable interior. Don't choose over-sized pieces or patterns, never crowd or clutter. Slim-lined sofa and decorative Royal Charter tables create an intimate setting flavored by radiant citrus hues.

Shown from left to right:
No. 20-7409 Lounge Chair
No. 20-7213 Host Chair
No. 16-8004 Commode Table
No. 08-3541 Tray Table
No. 20-7193 Pillowback Sofa
No. 08-3546 Book Trough Table

For detailed specifications on:
Upholstery—see pages 392-407.
Georgian Court—see pages 374-376.
Antiqued Pine and American Foliage Colors—
see pages 379-383.
Royal Charter Accents and Tables—see pages 390-391.

color starts the room

Some rooms dazzle with a riot of color; others soothe with a calm leavening of temperate neutrals. Instantly assessed by the eye and the senses, color—or that meld of colors called 'color scheme'—is a sure beginning to a very personalized mood and style. When handled with skill and invention, color can also camouflage, altering the proportions of a room, improving its shape or creating a more spacious flow.

Shown from left to right:
No. 20-7164 **Three Cushion Lawson Sofa**
No. 11-8066 **Octagonal Book Table**
No. 20-7162 **Two Cushion Loveseat**
No. 25-9041 **Game Table**
No. 11-6201 **Side Chairs**
No. 15-9040 **Etagere**
No. 15-8421 **Square Pedestal Cocktail Table**
No. 13-7806 **Cane Tub Chair**

Ethan Allen
AMERICAN TRADITIONAL INTERIORS

For detailed specifications on:
Georgian Court Dining Room Pieces—see pages 374-375 Classic Manor Accents and Tables-see pages 386-387
Georgian Court Occasional Pieces—see pages 375-376 Upholstery—see pages 392-406

Vibrant, incandescent colors can suffuse a room, or be used judiciously in a strategy of disciplined brush strokes. Radiant flower colors pervade small living room, opposite, endowing it with a sunny ambiance and sense of space. Parrot green, an intense and acid-sharp hue, is used sparingly but effectively with dark walls and rich wood tones of living room above.

Shown from left to right:
No. 20-7104 **Square Ottoman with Casters**
No. 15-9200 **Two Door Cabinet**
No. 15-9203 **Upper Cabinet with Grilled Doors**
No. 13-7805 **Chippendale Chair**
No. 15-8666 **Hexagonal Commode Table**
No. 20-7064 **Three Cushion Wing Sofa**
No. 12-8081 **Square Cocktail Table**

For detailed specifications on:
Antiqued Pine Occasional Pieces—see pages 381-383
Classic Manor Occasional Pieces—see page 388
Classic Manor Accent Pieces—see pages 388-389
Upholstery—see pages 392-406

naturals or red/white/blue

A melding of naturals and neutrals composes a tranquil backdrop for casually informal apartment living room that is a restful oasis from city turmoil. Furniture selection and arrangement is mindful of extra-duty requirements of apartment living. Royal Charter flip top table establishes a study corner at one end of the room and also opens for dining. Decorative shelves display accessories.

Everybody's favorite—red, white and blue—can come on strong and vibrant or low key and subdued. Here it's expressed with traditional restraint, so as not to dominate the handsome furnishings that comprise this appealing living room. Large scale floral print is extremely effective on comfortable wing sofa. Royal Charter bowback chairs combine with Heirloom tables and secretary.

Shown below from left to right:
No. 10-7704 **Pub Chairs**
No. 12-8037 **Commode End Table**
No. 12-8031 **Round Pedestal Cocktail Table**
No. 20-7034 **Sofa**
No. 16-6013 **Flip Top Table**
No. 12-7517 **High Back Library Chair**
No. 07-1550 **Shelf System**

Shown opposite from left to right:
No. 16-6000A **Windsor Arm Chair**
No. 10-8354 **Commode Table.**
No. 20-7023 **Sofa**
No. 10-9506 **Nine Drawer Secretary Desk**
No. 10-9507 **Grilled Secretary Top**
No. 10-8350 **Drop Leaf Cocktail Table**
No. 20-7403 **"T" Cushion Chippendale Wing Chair**
No. 10-9042 **Cigarette Pedestal Table**

For detailed specifications on:
Upholstery—see pages 392-406.
Royal Charter Dining Room—see pages 389-390.
Antiqued Pine Occasional Pieces—see pages 381-382.
Heirloom Accents, Tables—see pages 370-372.

Ethan Allen
AMERICAN TRADITIONAL INTERIORS

around a collection

It's fun to be a collector and it doesn't take great riches or a stratified level of taste to be one. Collect anything—quartz, sailing samplers, old needlepoint, posters, clocks, American Indian artifacts or just shells from the beach. Turn the living room into a showcase for your collection; it's a foolproof and fascinating way of making it as personal as your thumbprint. Collection of clocks gives serene setting a sense of whimsy and a unique decorative look.

Shown from left to right:
No. 20-7097 Slope Arm Sofa
No. 25-9038 Console Cabinet
No. 15-8421 Pedestal Tables
No. 13-7113 Chairs

For detailed specifications on:
Classic Manor Antiqued Color Accents—
see pages 388-389
Classic Manor Occasional Pieces—
see pages 388-389
Upholstery—see pages 392-406

Ethan Allen
AMERICAN TRADITIONAL INTERIORS

... seaworthy family room boasting
... morabilia. Lively blue and white
... d white framed loveseats and
... k and bar stools, decorated
... vides the interior into three
... riety of activities.

Shown from left to right:
No. 14-7422 Loveseats
No. 13-9005 Military Bar
No. 14-6111 Button Back Hitchcock Chair
No. 24-6033 Round Center Pedestal Table
No. 24-9004 Two Drawer Dry Sink
No. 24-9505 Swivel Bar Stools
No. 12-8006 Rudder Drop Leaf Table
No. 14-6155 Hitchcock Bench

For detailed specifications on:
Antiqued Pine Occasional Pieces—see pages 381-382
American Foliage Colors—see pages 379-383.
Military Campaign Chest Pieces—see page 383
Decorated Furniture—see pages 384-385
Upholstery—see pages 392-406

a collection of birds

Set up for bird watching indoors is comfortable living room, left, whose cool blues, leafy greens, sunny yellows and tawny browns evoke the hues of a meadow or sanctuary. Imposing Royal Charter library units make a fine showcase for a collection of assortables starring our fine feathered friends—sculpture, porcelains, framed prints and etchings, wall plaques.

Shown opposite from left to right:
No. 16-9005 Library Wall Unit
No. 16-8900 Pub Set
No. 08-3516 Curio Stand
No. 20-7863 Sofa
No. 16-8006 End Table
No. 20-7191 Wing Club Chairs

For detailed specifications on:
Royal Charter Occasional Pieces—see page 390
Royal Charter Accent Pieces—see page 391
Upholstery—see pages 392-406

and needlepoint

Today's enthusiasm for needlework is more than a passing nostalgia for time-honored handicrafts. It is also a way of injecting a warm and personal look into the home, of softening our machine made world with the humanizing qualities of embroidery, crewel, needlepoint and hand knitted and crocheted designs. Room above is cosy retreat for a needlework buff.

Shown above from left to right:
No. 14-9703 Boston Rocker
No. 20-7883 Three Cushion Sofa
No. 12-8034 Drop Leaf End Table
No. 08-3522 Bootmakers Stool
No. 20-7703 High Ladderback Chair
No. 07-1559 Gallery Shelf (over Sofa)
No. 12-8030 Pedestal Oval Cocktail Table

For detailed specifications on:
Antiqued Pine Occasional Pieces—see pages 381-383.
Decorated Furniture—see pages 384-385
Upholstery—see pages 392-406

Ethan Allen
AMERICAN TRADITIONAL INTERIORS

ski lodge or condominium

what's your life style?

Two hundred years ago the choice was limited; today one can live in any home that suits his style—and his pocketbook. Or even have a second home —a weekend and holiday retreat at the seashore, in the country, or near good skiing. Needless to say, the interior design of a year-round house or second home should adapt to the life style of the family and to the special character of the house itself.

Shown below left from left to right:
No.12-7630 Rocker
No.12-7628 Ottoman
No.24-8000 Trestle Cocktail Table
No.12-8026 Dough Box End Table
No.12-7623 Sofa
No.12-6025 Deacon's Bench
No.12-6064 Trestle Table
No.24-6007/6009 Buffet & Hutch
No.12-6002 Ladderback Chairs
No.12-7705 Pub Chairs

For detailed specifications on:
Antiqued Pine Dining Room—see pages 379-381
Antiqued Pine Occasional Pieces—see pages 381-382
American Foliage Colors—see pages 379-383
Upholstery—see pages 392-406

Modern condominiums are a popular choice for vacation retreats—or leisure-time homes. Generously proportioned Antiqued Pine furniture and versatile skipper sofa balance ample dimensions of condominium living room, right. Equally at home in a ski lodge, Antiqued Pine is enlivened by American Foliage accents of Sugarbush Red, a pride of furry accents, and zingy contemporary wall hangings, in room below.

Shown right from left to right:
No. 08-3509 Spindle Magazine Rack
No. 24-7671 Skipper's Lounge Chair
No. 12-9015 Cabinet Bookstacks
No. 12-8034 End Table
No. 12-8030 Pedestal Oval Cocktail Table
No. 12-7673 Three Cushion Skipper's Sofa
No. 16-7439 Tufted Bench

For detailed specifications on:
Antiqued Pine Occasional Pieces—see pages 381-382
Antiqued Pine Accent Pieces—see pages 382-383
Upholstery—see pages 392-406

Ethan Allen
AMERICAN TRADITIONAL INTERIORS

in a split level

Comfort and casual good looks are often primary decorating goals for a young family, especially one that likes the relaxed open style of a split level home. All the essentials of easy informality are present in living room, below, which derives its mood from a play on texture—leather, tweed, wormy chestnut—and beautifully grained Royal Charter designs.

Shown from left to right:
No. 16-9006 Chairside Chest
No. 20-7204 Chair
No. 16-8010 Rectangular Cocktail Table
No. 16-9904 Squire's Chest
No. 20-7343 Sofa
No. 16-8004 Hexagonal Commode Table

AMERICAN TRADITIONAL INTERIORS

For detailed specifications on:
Royal Charter Occasional Pieces—see page 390
Royal Charter Accent Pieces—see page 391
Upholstery—see pages 392-406

or to the manor born

The splendor of Tudor England is translated into a room of contemporary comfort and charm. Handsome Royal Charter furniture, scaled for today's use, is partnered with compatible designs in Antiqued Pine and American Foliage Autumn Gold.

Shown from left to right:
No. 16-6013 Flip-Top Table.
Top is selected veneer.
No. 16-7433 Sofa
No. 16-6011 Side Chair
No. 12-6053 Pedestal Table
No. 16-7432 Loveseat
No. 24-8058 Cogwheel Table

For detailed specifications on:
Royal Charter Dining Room—see pages 389-390
Antiqued Pine Dining Room—see pages 379-381
American Foliage Colors—see pages 379-383
Upholstery—see pages 392-406

remodeled barn

The clear, radiant colors of upholstery fabrics and American Foliage accents turn a remodeled barn into a weekender's cheerful delight. Setting has been furnished as an all-purpose room; trestle table and twin deacon's benches provide dining facilities while Holly Green dry sink stores bar equipment. Sofa featured in this setting is comfortable three cushion wing design in Nutmeg finish, whose informal good looks are most appropriate for a casual mood.

Shown from left to right:
No. 24-7671 **Arm Chairs**
No. 10-7774 **Sofa**
No. 24-8031 **Cocktail Table**
No. 24-8024 **End Table**
No. 24-6055 **Dry Sink**
No. 12-6005 **Trestle Bench**
No. 12-6064 **Trestle Table**

For detailed specifications on
Upholstery—see pages 392-406.
American Foliage Colors—see pages 379-383.
Antiqued Pine Dining Room—see pages 379-381.

at the sea

A cool refreshment after hours of sunworship—come in from the beach to the 'shade' of this cool, calm and collected living room, sparkling with the radiant blues of American Foliage designs. Simple window treatment and scrubbable vinyl flooring keep the maintenance down. A summer delight, this home most comfortably serves the family on fall weekends and winter holidays too. Skipper sofa and loveseat are positioned to allow for passageways and to create a intimate and comfortable seating group around the hearth.

Shown from left to right:
No. 24-7622 Loveseat
No. 10-8346 Spoonfoot Doughbox End Table
No. 14-4552P Three Door Cabinet
No. 24-7623 Sofa
No. 24-9505 Bar Stools
No. 10-8642 Square Pedestal Cocktail Table

For detailed specifications on:
Upholstery—see pages 392-406
Heirloom Occasional Pieces—see pages 370-371
Heirloom Custom Room Plan—see pages 362-363
American Foliage Colors—see pages 379-383

versatile loveseats serve in many ways

Loveseats get around. Smaller than a sofa, yet larger than a chair, loveseats accommodate when space is shy and ample seating is desired. Many Ethan Allen sofas come loveseat size—ready to start a sitting area in any room of the house. Elegant camel back design, in sumptuous white crewel, graces mirrored entry wall, top. Wall space was all taken, so tufted loveseat snuggles at foot of bed, bottom.

Shown at right, from left to right:
No. 11-8008 Wine Stand
No. 20-7122 Chippendale Love Seat
No. 11-9002 Low Boy Base
No. 11-9003 Curio Cabinet

Shown below:
No. 20-7401 Love Seat

For detailed specifications on: Georgian Court Accent Pieces—see pages 375-376, Upholstery—see pages 392-406.

A cosy solution to furniture placement: twin love-seats hugging the hearth. For paneled living room with gracious 18th Century manners, top, a pair of Tuxedo loveseats pattern the room with their stylized, jumbo-scale floral print. To establish an intimate seating oasis in a den or small dining room, flank a loveseat with tall etageres, as in setting at left. Loose pillow back loveseat is covered in flame stitch fabric.

Shown above from left to right:
No. 11-6207 Queen Anne Side Board
No. 20-7042 Love Seat
No. 15-8671 Cocktail Table
No. 20-7042 Love Seat

Shown at left, from left to right:
No. 20-7082 Love Seat
No. 11-9206 Etagere
No. 11-6202A Shield Back Arm Chair

For detailed specifications on:
Georgian Court Dining Room—see pages 374-375.
Georgian Court Accent Pieces—see pages 375-376.
Classic Manor Occasional Pieces—see pages 387-388.
Upholstery—see pages 392-406.

Ethan Allen
AMERICAN TRADITIONAL INTERIORS

sleep sofa magic

The advent of the sleep sofa has turned the disappearance of the separate guest room into a welcome trend. No need to furnish and housekeep an idle room. Now a guest can be bedded down in a room that also serves an active family. At the flick of a wrist, comfortable library-study below turns into delightful guest room for two.

Shown right:
No. 21-7002 Two Cushion Lawson Sleeper.
55"x35"x31"H.
No. 21-7003 Two Cushion Lawson Sleeper.
75"x35"x31"H.

Shown below:
No. 20-7406 Club Chairs
No. 21-7063-5 Sleeper Sofa
No. 16-8004 Hexagonal Commode Table
No. 16-6013 Flip-Top Table
No. 16-6000 Windsor Side Chair
No. 16-9002 Cocktail Cabinet
No. 16-8005 Hi Lo Cocktail Table

Ethan Allen
AMERICAN TRADITIONAL INTERIORS

For detailed specifications on
Royal Charter Dining Room—see pages 390-391.
Royal Charter Accent and Tables—see pages 390-391.
Upholstery—see pages 392-406.
Ethan Allen Sleeper Sofas and Day Beds—see pages 404-405.

No. 21-7023
Two Cushion Pine Trim
Sleeper Sofa. 72"x35"x37"H.
Features a 56"x73" mattress.

Shown above:
No. 12-4037 32" Upper Cabinet Bookcase
No. 12-4030 32" Three Drawer Chest
No. 12-4001 35" Corner Cabinet
No. 12-4000 24" Three Drawer Chest
No. 21-7074 Sleeper Sofa
No. 12-8007 Revolving Octagonal Table
No. 12-8000 Trestle Cocktail Table

Linens on pages 54, 55, 57 by J. P. Stevens, Inc.

Warming neutrals and rugged Antiqued Pine Custom Room Plan units give calm and comfort to all-purpose family room that offers super storage capabilities. All of the room's credentials are not on the surface; pine-trimmed sofa opens to sleep size, lower units are utilized for guests' belongings. High-fashion linens are wise choices for rooms with such dual-purpose character.

For detailed specifications on: Antiqued Pine
Custom Room Plan—see pages 377-378.
Antiqued Pine Occasional Pieces—see pages 381-382.
Ethan Allen Sleeper Sofas and Day Beds—see pages 404-405.

A one-room apartment should live up to its name but not look it. It must supply all the essentials for 'round the clock living yet never seem crowded or cramped. Here it's accomplished in a young and zingy room—just right for a career girl or 'just marrieds'. Compact loveseat sleeps two and is covered in lively but practical chrome yellow vinyl.

Shown above from left to right:
No. 14-6110A Hitchcock Arm Chair.
No. 14-6110 Hitchcock Side Chair.
No. 12-6064 Trestle Table.
No. 24-8037 Commode Table.
No. 21-7043-5 Tuxedo Sleeper Sofa.
No. 13-9006 Wellington Chest.
No. 24-8001 Pedestal Table.

For details on:
Decorated Furniture—see pages 384-385. Antiqued Pine and American Foliage Colors—see pages 379-383. Campaign Chests—see page 383. Sleeper Sofas——see pages 404-405.

No. 21-7034 Loose Pillow Back Sleeper Sofa.

Shown above from left to right:
No. 20-7102 Ottoman.
No. 20-7710 Club Chair.
No. 10-8440P Cocktail Table.
No. 10-9520 Desk.
No. 10-6102 Arm Chair.
No. 21-7053 Sleeper Sofa.
No. 10-8654 End Table.
No. 20-7710 Club Chair.

Extra sleeping quarters—artfully camouflaged by slim lined sleep sofa in comfortable living room. Positioning of sofa in front of window frees long wall for built-in bookcases. Knee-hole desk, finished on both sides, establishes a small study or work corner and also serves as an end table for the sofa, a space-wise idea.

No. 20-7013 Roll Arm
Wing Sleeper Sofa.

For details on: Upholstery—
see pages 392-406. Heirloom—
see pages 366-372. Sleeper Sofas—
see pages 404-405.

Is it a garden room, a family room or a guest room? Actually it's all three combined in one delightful setting. Beautifully scaled and marvelously versatile Ethan Allen daybed offers hidden guest facilities, looks so pretty when made up with patterned sheets. Random plank flooring, whimsically painted, brick wall that's been whitewashed and add-on beams of bright orange, give the room a garden fresh mood all the seasons of the year.

Shown above left to right:
No. 12-7705 Pub Chair
No. 16-7438 Ottoman
No. 24-8026 Magazine End Table
No. 12-7508 Sleeper Sofa
No. 24-6018 Corner Hutch
No. 24-6016 Corner Cabinet
No. 12-9513 Three Drawer Roll Top Desk
No. 24-6002 Ladderback Chair
No. 12-8001 Square Pedestal Cocktail Table

For detailed specifications on:
Upholstery—see pages 392-406.
Antiqued Pine—see pages 381-383.
American Foliage Colors—see pages 379-383.
Sleeper Sofas and Day Beds—see pages 404-405.

No. 12-7507
Sleeper Sofa. Same item as above, except opens to sleep two on separate beds. Thick Urethane mattresses. Matching bolsters included. Old Tavern finish.

Shown above:
No. 12-7508
Sleeper Sofa. 80"x34"x30"H. Sleeps one. Matching bolsters included. Old Tavern finish.

ETHAN ALLEN
CHAIR SHOP

A chair is that one indispensable without which few rooms can be truly comfortable. Add to this the fact that chairs are powerful decorating tools — each design uniquely shaped and proportioned and richly ornamental. Partnered with a table or a twin design, or incorporated into the larger circle of a conversational grouping, chairs participate fully in an active family life.

Shown above:
No. 20-7616 Queen Anne High Back Chair
32"x34"x44"H. Available also in Crewel.

No. 20-7706
Queen Anne Wing Chair
33"x33"x46"H.

No. 20-7703
Ladderback Wing Chair
29"x35"x42"H.

No. 20-7605
Fireside Wing Chair
28"x32"x46"H.

No. 20-7408
Wing Chair
28"x33"x48"H.
Wood trim is selected hardwood
and Royal Charter finish.

No. 20-7403
Chippendale Wing Chair
33"x34"x44"H.

No. 20-7607
Fireside Wing Chair
20"x32"x45"H.

No. 20-7606
Queen Anne Wing Chair
29"x33"x46"H.

No. 20-7208
Fireside Wing Chair
31"x34"x44"H.

No. 20-7204
Chippendale Wing Chair
32"x33"x42"H.

For detailed specifications on:
Upholstery—see pages 392-408

No. 20-7937
London Club Chair.
31"x33"x32"H.
No. 20-7938
London Club Ottoman.
27"x20"x16"H.

No. 20-7409
Lounge Chair.
34"x38"x32"H.
No. 20-7104
Square Ottoman with casters.
24"x24"x15"H.

comfort plus

Deep-seated comfort comes from quality down-under construction, which is what Ethan Allen chairs are all about.

No. 20-7406
Oak Lounge Chair
31"x39"x34"H.

No. 20-7407
Ottoman. 29"x21"x18"H.

No. 20-7414
Roll Back Man's Chair.
29"x40"x39"H.

Appealing dressmaker details distinguish group of chairs on facing page. Seen here are tufted back, loose pillow back, tapered back and swivel rocker designs.

No. 20-7412 Curved Back Lounge Chair. 32"x38"x37"H.

No. 20-7810
Man's Lounge Chair.
34"x38"x37"H.

No. 20-7710
Club Chair.
28″x33″x32″H.

No. 20-7711
High Back Swivel Rocker.
35″x38″x38″H.

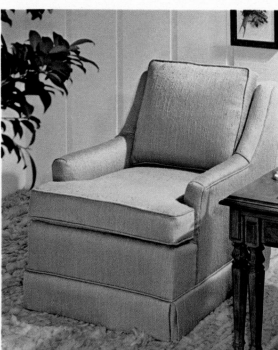

No. 20-7618 Tapered Back Chair. 28″x31″x34″H.

No. 20-7707
Tufted Back Chair.
28″x31″x34″H.

No. 20-7708
Barrel Back Chair.
33″x35″x35″H.

For detailed specifications on Upholstery—see pages 392-406.

Ethan Allen
AMERICAN TRADITIONAL INTERIORS

the perfect pair

Two's company in Ethan Allen Mr. and Mrs. chairs offered in a choice of styles, including club chairs and swivel rockers.

Shown below:
No. 20-7410 Hi Back Mr. Club Chair. 30"x37"x39"H.
No. 20-7411 Low Back Mrs. Club Chair. 29"x33"x34"H.

Shown above:
No. 20-7307 Mr. Club Chair. 30"x35"x37"H.
No. 20-7308 Mrs. Club Chair. 30"x34"x32"H.

For detailed specifications on Upholstery—see pages 392-406.

Shown above:
No. 20-7171 Cap Arm Mr. Club Chair.
30"x35"x31"H.
No. 20-7178 Cap Arm Mrs. Club Chair.
28"x33"x30"H.

Shown at right:
No. 20-7305 Club Chair.
31"x34"x32"H. Semi-attached back.
No. 20-7306 Swivel Rocker.
31"x34"x32"H.

Shown below:
No. 20-7303 Mrs. Swivel Rocker.
29"x35"x38"H.
No. 20-7302 Mr. Swivel Rocker.
29"x35"x40"H.

Ethan Allen
AMERICAN TRADITIONAL INTERIORS

Shown at right:
No. 20-7508-5 Lounge Chair. 31"x34"x33"H.

Shown at far right:
No. 20-7509-5 Swivel Chair. 29"x30"x27"H.
No. 20-7510-5 Lounge Chair. Same as above without swivel feature.

No. 20-7508-5

No. 20-7509-5
No. 20-7510-5

No. 20-7511-5 Swivel Rocker. 30"x34"x34"H.
No. 20-7512-5 Chair. Same without swivel or rocking feature.

No. 20-7501-5 Swivel Chair. 29"x31"x27"H.
No. 20-7502-5 Chair. Same as above without swivel feature.

No. 20-7507-5
Lounge Chair.
36"x38"x34"H.

Ethan Allen offers a wide choice of handsome lounge chairs that also swivel or rock. Some do both if desired. Straight-lined and curved back designs include button and diamond tufted treatment. Most of these chairs are available with or without the swivel or rocker mechanisms.

No. 20-7503-5 Swivel Rocker. 32"x33"x35"H.
No. 20-7504-5 Same as above without, swivel and rocking features.

No. 20-7505-5 Swivel Rocker. 31"x35"x36"H.
No. 20-7506-5 Same as above without swivel and rocking features.

lounge-swivel chairs and ottomans

For detailed specifications on:
Upholstery—see pages 392-406.

Shown at right:
No. 20-7106-1 Ottoman. 21"x30"x15"H.
Available also in Leather.
Not available in -5.

No. 20-7104-1 Square Ottoman with casters.
24"x24"x15"H.   Not available in -5.

No. 20-7201-5 Barrel Chair. 29"x29"x30"H.
No. 20-7202-5 Swivel Barrel Chair. Same item as above. but with swivel feature.

No. 20-7102-1 Ottoman.
17"x22"x15"H. Not available in -5.

Two decorative barrel style chairs, shown on this page, come as swivel chairs. Also shown are three of Ethan Allen's handsome and versatile ottoman styles . . . which can be added to most lounge chairs to create a truly comfortable arrangement. Used alone they fit into conversational groupings, can slide under a tall table and come out when extra seating is needed. They are also fun to use at the end of a bed—in the place of a bench, and work well in front of a picture window as they do not block the view.

No. 20-7215-5 Curved Button Back Chair. 31"x32"x31"H.

No. 20-7314-5 Barrel Swivel Chair.
29"x33"x32"H. Semi-attached back.
Seat cushion not available in -1.

Shown above clockwise:
No. 13-7112-0 Devon Arm Chair.
24"x26"x38"H.
No. 14-7112-0 Same item in decorator finishes.
No. 13-7113-5 Embassy Scroll Arm Chair.
26"x29"x36"H.
No. 13-7115-5 Hampton Wing Chair.
26"x25"x42"H.
No. 14-7115-5 Same item in decorator finishes.
No. 13-7110-5 Cabriolet Arm Chair.
22"x21"x32"H. Cane Back.
No. 14-7110-5 Same item in decorator finishes.

elegant accent chairs

Rich in delicate detail, these graceful chairs offer international charm and sophistication available in glowing Patina finish as shown or in five charming decorator colors.

Shown above:
No. 13-7114-5 DuBarry Wing Chair.
26"x25"x42"H.
No. 14-7114-5 Same item in decorator finishes.

Shown at right:
No. 13-7111-5 Trianon Wing Chair.
28"x30"x40"H.
No. 14-7111-5 Same item in decorator finishes.

No. 10-7421-5 Ladder Back Club Chair.
26"x31"x34"H.
No. 14-7421-5 Same item
in Bone White
finish 427.

Shown at left:
**No. 13-7805-5 Cane
Tub Chair.**
26"x28"x30"H.
No. 14-7805-5 Same item
in decorator finishes.

No. 13-7807-5 Arm Chair.
25"x28"x32"H.
No. 14-7807-5 Same item
in decorator finishes.

**No. 10-7426-5 High Ladder Back
Wing Chair.**
26"x33"x39"H.
No. 14-7426-5 Same item in
Bone White finish 427.

Shown above:
No. 10-7429-5 Bench.
47"x21"x17"H.
No. 14-7429-5 Same item in
Bone White finish 427.

**No. 13-7806-5 Cane
Tub Chair.**
No. 14-7805-5 Same item in
decorator finishes.

Decorator Finishes:
427—Bone White
428—Azure Blue
429—Mimosa Yellow
430—Celadon Green
431—Celery

For detailed specifications on
Upholstery, see pages 392-406.

Ethan Allen
AMERICAN TRADITIONAL INTERIORS

No. 12-7517-3
High Back Library Chair. 27"x36"x44"H.
Old Tavern finish.
*No. 24-7517-3
Same item in American Foliage Colors.

No. 12-7671-1
Skipper's Lounge Chair.
30"x31"x32"H. Old Tavern finish.
*No. 24-7671-1 Same item in
American Foliage Colors.

casual and comfortable

Handsome wood framed Ethan Allen chairs add casual good looks to any informal setting. Highback designs are great for reading; pub designs are ideal for den or family room. For instant extra seating—the decorative stackables, actually four separate benches. Frames come in a choice of wood finishes; some are also offered in colored frames.

No. 10-7704-1
Pub Chair. 25"x30"x28"H.
Available in a choice of Nutmeg,
Georgian Court, Old Tavern or
Classic Manor finishes.

No. 12-7705-1 **Pub Chair.**
25"x30"x28"H. Old Tavern finish.
Available also in leather.
*No. 24-7705-1
Same item in American Foliage Colors.

No. 10-7500 **Stackables.**
17"x17"x9"H. Nutmeg finish.
No. 12-7500 Same item
in Old Tavern finish.

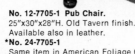

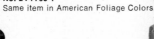

No. 12-7516-3
High Back Chair.
26"x29"x32"H.
Old Tavern finish.
*No. 24-7516-3 Same item
in American Foliage Colors.

No. 16-7514-1 **Pub Chair.**
25"x28"x30"H.
Royal Charter finish.
Available also in leather.

Ethan Allen
AMERICAN TRADITIONAL INTERIORS

the tailored elegance of genuine leather.

Top-grain leather has a look and a quality all its own, used to great advantage by Ethan Allen in an exceptionally diversified collection. Period adaptations such as the Chippendale and Queen Anne wing chairs are at one end of the spectrum, while handsome Club Chairs and Lawson Sofa express a more relaxed mood.

For detailed specifications on upholstered items available in genuine leather, see pages 399-407.

**No. 20-7405-0
Queen Anne Arm Chair.**
26"x28"x43"H.

No. 20-7403-5 Chippendale Wing Chair.
33"x34"x44"H.
No. 20-7404 Ottoman.
25"x18"x17"H.

**No. 20-7810-5
Lounge Chair.**
33"x37"x37"H.

**No. 20-7937-5
London Club Chair.**
31"x33"x32"H.
**No. 20-7938-0
London Club Ottoman.**
27"x20"x16"H.

**No. 20-7204-5
Chippendale Wing Chair.**
32"x33"x44"H.

**No. 20-7956-5
Lawson Sofa.**
83"x34"x32"H.
Available in genuine
leather only.

**No. 21-7912-1
Restocrat Rocker.** 31"x37"
x38"H. Pine wood
arm and wing. Old Tavern
finish only.

**No. 21-7933-1 Cap Arm
Restocrat Recliner.**
31"x37"x37"H.
**No. 21-7930-1 Cap Arm
Restocrat Rocker.**
31"x37"x37"H.

**No. 21-7911-1 Wood-trim
Restocrat Rocker.** 31"x37"x38"H.

No. 21-7910-1 Wing Restocrat Rocker.
31"x37"x40"H.

rest
rock
recline
relax

Ethan Allen Restocrats and Restocrat Rockers offer great comfort and relaxation—based on an improved reclining operation. Available in a wide choice of styles.

No. 21-7928-1 Restocrat Rocker.
30"x37"x38"H.

No. 21-7934-1 Arched Top Restocrat Recliner.
31"x37"x39"H.
No. 21-7931-1 Arched Top Restocrat Rocker.
31"x37"x39"H.

No. 21-7922-1 Restocrat Rocker. 31" x37"x38"H. Urethane Foam Seat only. Old Tavern finish.

No. 21-7921-1 Wing Restocrat Rocker.
35"x36"x40"H.

No. 21-7900-1 Wing Restocrat Recliner.
31"x37"x40"H.

For detailed specifications on Upholstery—see pages 392 through 406.

Ethan Allen
AMERICAN TRADITIONAL INTERIORS

ETHAN ALLEN
GEORGIAN COURT

Taking inspiration from the designs of the great 18th Century cabinetmakers, Ethan Allen Georgian Court is a truly elegant and gracious traditional style. Handsome interpretations of Queen Anne, Chippendale, Duncan Phyfe and Hepplewhite designs distinguish this unique collection expressed in solid Cherry and selected veneers. Cabinets and chests have paneled doors, authentic hardware; dining tables and chairs are distinguished by cabriole or reeded legs. Bedroom designs are also exquisitely detailed, and include adaptations of the chairback bed, the pier chest and the bonnet top highboy. Secretaries, desks, occasional tables and library units round out this comprehensive design series. But for all its traditional eloquence, graceful lines and slender proportions make Georgian Court a style that is beautifully suited to contemporary rooms.

GRACIOUS DINING WITH GEORGIAN COURT

The romance of the past keyed to the needs of the present: Georgian Court dining furniture evoking the elegance of a great era of American craftsmanship, yet adapting with ease to urbane city life or to the informal mood of country dining. Expressed in solid cherry and selected veneers, Georgian Court has been chosen for this spacious apartment setting. Chippendale inspired ladder back and host chairs are given identical silk-like covers. Tall and handsome breakfront appears to be one unit due to continuity of design; actually it is two cabinets—a china with crown glass doors and interior lighting, and a base with symmetrical fielded paneled doors. Classic Queen Anne lowboy is overscored by Chippendale mirror.

Shown from left to right:
No. 11-9205 **Lowboy**
No. 11-9207 **Chippendale Mirror**
No. 20-7312 **Host Chair**
No. 11-6093 **Double Pedestal Extension Table**
No. 11-6212 **Chippendale Side Chair**
No. 11-6212A **Chippendale Arm Chair**
No. 20-7312 **Host Chair**
No. 11-6206 **Breakfront Base**
No. 11-6208 **Breakfront China.** Back is selected veneer.
No. 11-6212A **Chippendale Arm Chair**

For detailed specifications on:
Georgian Court Dining Room—see pages 374-375.
Georgian Court Accent Pieces—see page 376.
Upholstery—see pages 392-406.

Ethan Allen
AMERICAN TRADITIONAL INTERIORS

town or country dining with GEORGIAN COURT

The heritage of gracious country dining makes its point with charming Georgian Court, opposite. Here's country decorating that takes its flavor from splendid cabinetry and rich, welcoming colors—rather than from a synthesis of rough brick flooring, hand hewn beams and homespun furniture. Two apartment dining rooms employ identical table, right. Always an eye-pleaser is the mix of black and white plus one opulent color, as in exhilarating setting, top. For small area, bottom, table nestles between colorfully cluttered étagères.

Shown opposite from left to right:
No. 11-6202 **Shield Back Side Chairs**
No. 11-6227 **Server**
No. 11-6207 **Queen Anne Sideboard**
No. 11-6209 **Queen Anne China Top**
No. 11-6226 **Corner China Cabinet**
No. 11-6214 **Oval Extension Table**
No. 11-6202A **Shield Back Arm Chair**

Shown above from left to right:
No. 11-6201A **Pad Back Arm Chair**
No. 11-6203 **Drop Leaf Extension Table**
No. 11-6200 **Cane Back Side Chairs**
No. 11-6216/6218 **Buffet & China Top**

Shown right from left to right:
No. 11-9206 **Etagere**
No. 11-6211 **Queen Anne Side Chairs**
No. 11-6203 **Drop Leaf Extension Table**
No. 11-6211A **Queen Anne Arm Chair**

For detailed specifications on Georgian Court Dining Room— see pages 374-375.

Accessories by Meiselman Imports

Ethan Allen
AMERICAN TRADITIONAL INTERIORS

for small or spacious areas...

Gracious Georgian Court turns tiny dining areas into settings of immeasurable charm. Key design in these three rooms is expandable dining table, opened, in each instance to the needed size. Pretty but modestly scaled country room, below, shows table fully extended in a spacemaking scheme of stark white and cool blue. Versatile Queen Anne sideboard has ample buffet surface.

Long on impact though short on space are two city dining areas, opposite. With one leaf added, table is partnered with decoratively curving Duncan Phyfe chairs in dining-L, large photo. Compact credenza is space-wise choice as are grilled door curio cabinets in foyer, inset. Now same table is "starter" size, with end leaf dropped so that it hugs the mirrored wall.

Shown below from left to right:
No. 11-6207 Sideboard Base
No. 11-6202A Shield Back Arm Chair
No. 11-6213 Pembroke Drop Leaf Dining Table
No. 11-6202 Shield Back Side Chair
No. 25-9000 Bonnet Top Curio Cabinet

Shown opposite from left to right:
No. 11-6210 Duncan Phyfe Side Chairs
No. 11-6210A Duncan Phyfe Arm Chairs
No. 11-6213 Drop Leaf Table
No. 11-9000 Credenza
No. 11-9002 Lowboy Bases (Inset)
No. 11-9003 Curio Cabinet Tops (Inset)
No. 11-6227 Serving Cabinet (Inset)

Ethan Allen
AMERICAN TRADITIONAL INTERIORS

For detailed specifications on:
Georgian Court Dining Room—see pages 374-375
Georgian Court Accent Pieces—see page 376
Classic Manor Antiqued Color Accent Pieces— see pages 388-389.

apartment dining in a brownstone

Chrome yellow, in gleaming walls and patent-shiny vinyl seats, revitalizes this townhouse room. It's a mingling of moods, however, as nostalgic Georgian Court proffers the graceful past.

Shown from left to right:

No. 11-6217 **Buffet**
No. 11-6219 **China Top**
No. 11-6200 **Cane Back Side Chair**

No. 11-6204 **Round Extension Table**
No. 11-6200A **Cane Back Arm Chair**
No. 13-9006 **Military Wellington Chest**

AMERICAN TRADITIONAL INTERIORS

For detailed specifications on:
Georgian Court Dining Room—see pages 374-375
Military Campaign Chest Collection——see page 383

GEORGIAN COURT
Decorative Accents

Georgian Court designs are more than handsome; they are also spectacularly diverse. There are few pieces whose role is limited specifically to living room, dining room or bedroom use even though they may have been designed primarily for such use. Beyond these are the many accent designs which serve a variety of storage needs and can do so in any number of ways. Desks, consoles, serving cabinets, chests and secretaries are among these distinctive accents. Placed as room dividers are twin étagères which also serve as wall bookcases.

GEORGIAN COURT DECORATIVE ACCENTS

Handsome is as handsome does—Georgian Court accent designs that provide excellent storage or serve a specific role. Exquisite 18th Century style cabinetry marks such designs as block front chest, tall and slender secretary, bonnet top highboy and two lowboys on facing page. Shown on this page are two distinctive new additions—a silver chest on its own base and a leather topped kneehole desk.

Shown at left:
No. 11-6228 Silver Chest. 21½"x16"x41"H. Interior upholstered in Pacific cloth. Lower drawers fitted for both flatware and serving pieces. Removable tray with cut out handles. Holds 8 or more services of silver.

No. 11-9208 Desk. 52"x26"x29½"H. Leather top inserts. Metal file racks in lower left drawer.

No. 11-6212 Chippendale Ladderback Side Chair. 38"H. Upholstered seat.

Shown at right:
No. 11-9202 Chippendale Looking Glass.
Overall 19"x36"H. Fretwork border
is selected veneer.

No. 11-9201 Lowboy. 32"x17"x30"H.
Four Drawers.

Shown at far right:
No. 11-9200 Goddard Block Front Chest.
36"x20"x31"H. Four drawers.

No. 11-9207 Chippendale Mirror.
Overall 25"x44".

**No. 11-5205 Eleven Drawer Bonnet
Top Highboy.** 38"x21"x79"H.

No. 11-9008 Framed Oval Mirror.
Overall 22"x32".

No. 11-9205 Lowboy. 38"x21"x32"H.
Four drawers.

All items are solid Cherry and selected veneers in an
artistically distressed Georgian Court finish.
For detailed specifications on Georgian Court
Accent pieces—see pages 375-376.

No. 11-9203 Drop Front Secretary.
27"x15"x40"H. Four drawers.

No. 11-9204 Secretary Top. 28"x19"x39"H.
Bevelled glass doors.

No. 11-8204 Tea Table. 30"x19"x26"H.
Two pull-out slides. Top is selected veneer.

Georgian Court occasional tables

No. 11-8203 Tripod Tea Table.
30" diameter x 28"H. Top
revolves and tilts to full
vertical position.

**No. 11-8206
Nest of Tables.**
Top table is 23"x
15"x22"H.

No. 11-8205 Curio Table.
24"x22"x21"H. Clear
glass top and sides.
Brass plated ferrules on feet.

No. 11-8202 Pembroke Table.
18"x28"x25"H. Opens
to 35" with leaves extended.

No. 11-8200 Cocktail Table.
46"x21"x18"H. Top
is selected veneer.

No. 11-8201 Lamp Table.
24"x24"x22"H. Two drawers,
top is selected veneer.

No. 11-8165
Commode Lamp Table.
23"x23"x22"H.

No. 11-8009
Butler's Tray Table.
42"x30"x17"H. (shown
bottom with leaves down)

No. 11-8160 Cocktail Table.
49"x21"x15"H. Two drawers.

Shown below:
No. 11-8161 Cabriole Drop Leaf Cocktail Table.
50"x20"x16"H. Opens to 50"x38"
with leaves extended.

No. 11-8164 Pembroke Table. 21"x 27"x22"H.
Opens to 36" with leaves extended.

No. 11-8008
Queen Anne Wine Stand.
15"D. x 21"H.

For detailed specifications on:
Georgian Court Accents and
Tables— see pages 375-376.

Ethan Allen
AMERICAN TRADITIONAL INTERIORS

No. 11-8066 Octagonal Book Table. 26″x26″x22″H.

**No. 11-8070
Hexagonal Pedestal Table.**
20″x23″x17″H.

**No. 11-8067
Square Commode Table.**
26″x26″x22″H. One drawer and large
storage area behind doors.

No. 11-8075 Hexagonal Commode Table.
24″x24″x22″H.
Large storage area behind doors.

**No. 11-8071
Octagonal Pedestal Cocktail Table.**
36″x36″x16″H.

For detailed specifications on Georgian Court
Accents and Tables—see pages 375-376.

Ethan Allen
AMERICAN TRADITIONAL INTERIORS

Shown at left from left to right:
No. 11-9004 Commode Cabinet. 30"x16"x26"H. One adjustable shelf.
No. 11-9005 Library Book Stack. 30"x9"x52"H. Stationary shelves, back is selected veneer.
No. 11-9009 3-Drawer Chest. 30"x16"x26"H.
No. 11-9010 Upper Cabinet Book Stack. 30"x9"x52"H. Adjustable shelves behind doors, back is selected veneer.

Shown at right:
No. 11-9007 Tall Framed Mirror. Overall 17"x46"H.
No. 11-9000 Credenza. 50"x 15"x26"H. One adjustable shelf behind each set of doors.

No. 11-9008 Framed Oval Mirror. Overall 22"x32".
No. 11-9001 Five-sided Console. 36"x12"x30"H. One adjustable shelf behind doors.

For detailed specifications on: Georgian Court Accents and Tables— see pages 375-376.

No. 11-9006 Seven Drawer Ladies' Writing Desk. 34"x18"x40½"H. Extends to 25" deep with folding top extended on pull-out supports. Five letter compartments.

GEORGIAN COURT BEDROOM

romantic, sparkling, one-of-a-kind rooms

Bedrooms with personality and sparkle... rooms with a certain 'one-of-a-kind look... warm, colorful, inviting rooms...these are the bedrooms furnished with Ethan Allen Georgian Court. Celebrating the romance of the past, yet tempered for the life we live today, is furniture that adapts to a variety of moods. Here the look is a romantic one, wrapped in an utterly feminine fabric print, the softening note of bed draperies and pretty ruffles, and the sumptuous sea of tranquil blue carpeting. Splendid triple dresser blends Queen Anne and Chippendale details. Armoire and pier chest provide added storage.

Shown at right from top to bottom:
No. 11-5206 **Night Stand**
No. 20-7215 **Curved Button Back Chair**
No. 11-5215 **Armoire**
No. 20-7178 **"Mrs." Club Chair**
No. 11-5214 **Pier Chest**

Shown opposite from left to right:
No. 20-7178 **"Mrs." Club Chair**
No. 11-5203 **Triple Dresser**
No. 11-5120 **Queen Anne Mirrors**
No. 20-7215 **Curved Button Back Chair**
No. 11-5215 **Armoire**
No. 11-5206 **Night Table**

For detailed specifications on:
Georgian Court Bedroom—
see page 373
Upholstery—see pages 392-406

Ethan Allen
AMERICAN TRADITIONAL INTERIORS

GEORGIAN COURT
colorful, sparkling bedrooms

Saucy floral print, in lively blue, playfully ties together a dormer bedroom, below. Furniture placement puts the chopped up wall area to maximum use, the whole arrangement given added sparkle by the zingy inlaid floor of blue and apricot vinyl. Graceful pediment bed, in true 18th Century styling, has four tall reeded posts, similar in design to nightstand legs. Compact triple dresser and chest-on-chest offer excellent storage potential.

Disarmingly versatile, Georgian Court bedroom furniture accommodates effortlessly to a variety of looks. Teamed below and on preceding page with ruffles and flounces, it takes on a tailored, contemporary mood in setting opposite. Here it mingles with an assorted pride of textures—fur, leather, crushed velvet and lustrous wood. Exquisitely detailed chairback bed with pierced urn shaped splats, lives harmoniously beneath large modern canvas.

Shown below from left to right:
No. 11-5206 **Night Stands**
No. 11-5654 **Bed**
No. 11-5225 **Chest on Chest**
No. 11-5213 **Triple Dresser**
No. 11-6211A **Queen Anne Arm Chairs**

Shown opposite from right to left:
No. 11-5220 **Pediment Mirror**
No. 11-5202 **56" Double Dresser**
No. 11-5650 **Chairback Bed**
No. 13-9005 **Military Bar**
No. 11-5226 **Cabinet Night Table**
No. 11-5204 **Six Drawer Chest**

Ethan Allen
AMERICAN TRADITIONAL INTERIORS

For detailed specifications on:
Georgian Court Bedroom—see page 373
Military Campaign Chests—see page 383

vibrant or

Jewel-bright blend of scarlet and buttercup yellow gives an excitement of color to regal Georgian Court bedroom, whose generous proportions make possible the arrangement of study, sleeping and reading areas. Charming secretary bookcase, chairback headboard, and block front chest are authentic 18th Century adaptations, endowing the bedroom with an old world grace.

Shown left to right:
No. 20-7710 Club Chair
No. 11-5216 Commode Night Table
No. 11-5651 Chairback Headboard
No. 11-6211A Queen Anne Arm Chair

No. 11-9203 Drop Front Secretary
No. 11-9204 Secretary Top
No. 20-7104 Ottoman
No. 11-9200 Goddard Block Front Chest

For detailed specifications on
Georgian Court—see pages 373-376.
Upholstery—see pages 392-407.

Ethan Allen
AMERICAN TRADITIONAL INTERIORS

subtle color

Clear white, balanced by the rich tang of claret—in luxuriously quilted velvet spread and bordered accent rugs—frames a bedroom that is serene but never bland. Imposing, exquisitely detailed Georgian Court designs, such as stately highboy, elegant leather topped writing table and gracefully curved panel headboard provide the room with a quiet elegance that is liveable and comfortable as well.

Shown left to right:
No. 11-5206 Night Stands
No. 11-5652 Panel Headboard
No. 11-5205 Highboy

No. 11-5213 Triple Dresser
No. 11-5210 Mirror
No. 11-9208 Desk
No. 11-6212 Side Chair

For detailed specifications on Georgian Court Bedroom—see page 373.

ETHAN ALLEN
CLASSIC MANOR

A furniture collection that lives up to its name: Classic Manor, distinguished by majestic proportions and a restrained elegance. Its presence imparts the charm of traditional flavor tempered by a simplicity of line and ornamention that's so right for today's living. With generous overhangs, handsome mouldings, massive base details and fluted pilasters, Classic Manor reflects such 18th Century design influences as Queen Anne, Sheraton and Duncan Phyfe. Within the collection are imposing china and buffet designs offering architectural character as well as abundant storage; several styles come in antiqued painted finishes of white, green, blue or yellow—to provide a colorful accent.

the lively elegance of Classic Manor dining

Instant elegance is easy to come by with Classic Manor dining furniture, whose masterful proportions endow a room with the architectural enrichment it so often lacks. Key this elegance to today's tempo by the memorable use of any one of several new decorating looks: bold color, ebullient pattern, darkly lacquered walls, abstract paintings, or the verve of one colored accent. Here glossy brown walls frame rich reds and antique white. Double pedestal table extends easily to seat twelve.

Shown from left to right:
No. 15-6012 Side Chairs
No. 15-6012A Arm Chairs
No. 15-6013 Table
No. 25-9038 Console Cabinet
No. 25-9039 Mirror
No. 15-6007/6018 Buffet and China Top
Back is selected veneer.

For detailed specifications on:
Classic Manor Dining Room—
see pages 386-387.
Classic Manor Antiqued Colors—
see pages 386-389.

Ethan Allen
AMERICAN TRADITIONAL INTERIORS

99

shimmering walls

Use color with a flourish, or apply it with strategy and restraint. Either way is the route to a Classic Manor dining room that gives the tempo of today to designs of time-honored grace. Lustrous Classic Manor finish warms to a broad spectrum of hues.

For detailed specifications on:
Classic Manor Dining Room—see pages 386-387.
Classic Manor Accent Pieces—see pages 388-389.
Upholstery—see pages 392-406.

bright and white

Glowing garden greens shimmer in the gleam of silvery wallpaper for handsome dining room, above. Blue plus white makes an unbeatable yet easy-to-use combination for room, opposite, starring armoire style china cabinet in Antiqued Blue and stately cane back chairs.

Ethan Allen
AMERICAN TRADITIONAL INTERIORS

101

elegant and vibrant

A trio of spirited Classic Manor dining rooms—achieved by zingy, color, graphic pattern or an exuberant area rug. For small dining room, top, twin ètagéres and cane back chairs are in Antiqued White finish, spiced by fabric and wallpaper accents of red and orange. Slim library units accomplish wonders in narrow dining area, below, a composition of black and white. A glowing dining room, opposite is keyed to an ethnic rug design.

Shown at left, from left to right:
No. 15-9200 **Two Door Cabinet**
No. 15-9202 **Library Bookstack**
No. 15-9201 **Three Drawer Chest**
No. 15-9203 **Upper Cabinet
with Grilled Doors**
No. 15-9200 **Two Door Cabinet**
No. 15-9202 **Library Bookstack**
No. 15-6011 **Ladderback Side Chairs**
No. 15-6011A **Ladderback Arm Chairs**
No. 15-6023 **42" Octagonal Extension
Pedestal Table**

Shown above from left to right:
No. 25-6021 **Cane Back Side Chairs**
No. 25-6021A **Cane Back Arm Chairs**
No. 15-6023 **42" Octagonal Extension
Pedestal Table**
No. 15-9040 **Etagere**

Shown from left to right:
No. 15-6006/6008 Buffet with China Cabinet
Back is selected veneer.
No. 15-9035 Two Door Console Commode
No. 15-9007 Tall Mirror
No. 15-6003 Extension Table
No. 15-6011 Ladderback Side Chairs
No. 15-6011A Ladderback Arm Chairs

For detailed specifications on:
Classic Manor Dining Room—see pages 386-387.
Classic Manor Accent Pieces—see pages 388-389
Classic Manor Antiqued Colors—see pages 386-389.

Ethan Allen
AMERICAN TRADITIONAL INTERIORS

Shown above:
*No. 25-9001 Pier Curio Cabinet. 17"x14"x72"H. Three adjustable glass shelves with interior light in top. Back is selected veneer.
No. 15-9001 Same item in Classic Manor finish.

*No. 25-9040 Etagere. 34"x16"x82"H. One adjustable shelf behind doors. All shelves and end panels are selected veneer.
No. 15-9040 Same item in Classic Manor finish.

No. 15-9039 Accent Mirror. 24"x48"H.
*No. 25-9039 Same item in Antiqued Colors.
No. 15-9038 Console Cabinet. 40"x15"x29"H. One adjustable shelf behind doors.
*No. 25-9038 Same item in Antiqued Colors.

DECORATIVE ACCENTS

Elegant and colorful: these handsome and versatile Classic Manor accent designs add so much interest wherever they are used. On opposite page, dramatic dining room is expressed in a rich counterpoint of sepia vinyl walls, vibrant red fabrics and white Classic Manor designs. Extension dining table and game table both come with Classic Manor finish tops. Imposing étagères, above, divide living and dining area with great style. They also serve admirably as wall units, storing books or displaying a collector's hoard. Also for collections: the two delightful curio cabinets. Capacious buffet and china has decorative armoire styling. Antiqued Colors available are White, Yellow, Blue and Green.

***No. 25-9039
Accent Mirror.**
24"x48"H.
No. 15-9039
Same item in
Classic Manor finish.

*No. 25-9000 Bonnet Top Curio Cabinet.
25"x35"x79"H. Three adjustable glass
shelves. Concealed interior light.
Adjustable wood shelf in base.
Back is selected veneer.
No. 15-9000 Same item in
Classic Manor finish.

*No. 25-9041 Game Table.
34"x34"x29"H. Top is
selected veneer.
No. 15-9041 Same item in
Classic Manor finish.

*No. 25-9037P Console Table.
46"x12"x29"H.
Simulated marble top.
*No. 25-9037 Same item
with matching top.
No. 15-9037 Same item in
Classic Manor finish.

Shown below from left to right:
No. 25-6019 China Cabinet.
No. 25-6016 Buffet.
No. 25-6033 Dining Table.
Moulded polyester edge on veneer top.
No. 25-6021 Cane Back Side Chairs.
No. 25-6021A Cane Back Arm Chairs.

*Description of Antiqued Colors:
423—Antiqued white
424—Antiqued yellow
425—Antiqued blue
426—Antiqued green

For detailed specifications on:
Classic Manor Antiqued Colors—see pages 387-389.
Classic Manor Dining Room—see pages 386-387.
Classic Manor Accents—see pages 388-389

Ethan Allen
AMERICAN TRADITIONAL INTERIORS

Classic Manor for the library

Versatile Classic Manor library units provide excellent storage for books, accessories and diversified possessions. They have a sleek, built-in look when used in multiples, while handsome wood graining and beautiful detail can give featureless rooms rich architectural interest. The five accent designs in the Classic Manor collection are shown on the opposite page. Tall secretary desk can enhance any room of the house; seven drawer chest in another very versatile design.

Shown from left to right:
No. 15-9200 **Two Door Cabinet**
No. 15-9203 **Upper Cabinet with Grilled Doors**
No. 15-9201 **Three Drawer Chest**
No. 15-9202 **Library Bookstack**
No. 15-9201 **Three Drawer Chest**
No. 15-9202 **Library Bookstack**
No. 15-9200 **Two Door Cabinet**

No. 15-9203 **Upper Cabinet with Grilled Doors**
No. 20-7184 **89" Three Cushion Sofa.** Loose pillow back.
For detailed specifications on:
Classic Manor Accent Pieces— see pages 388-389.
Upholstery—see pages 392-406.

Shown at left:
No. 15-9507 Grilled Secretary Top. Overall 76"H.
Adjustable shelves behind doors. Back panel is
selected veneer.
No. 10-9507 Same item in Nutmeg finish.
No. 15-9506 Nine Drawer Secretary Desk. 36"x19"x41"H.
Five drawers in base and four behind drop lid. Four
letter compartments. Lock and key for drop lid. Drop
lid only is selected veneer.
No. 10-9506 Same item in Nutmeg finish.
No. 15-6011A Ladderback Arm Chair. 44"H.

Shown below:
No. 15-9035 Two Door Console Cabinet. 39"x14"x28"H.
Adjustable shelf behind doors.
No. 10-9035 Same item in Nutmeg finish.
No. 15-9007 Tall Mirror. Overall 20"x38"H.
No. 10-9007 Same item in Nutmeg finish.

Shown below:
No. 15-9500 Seven Drawer Library Desk. 56"x26"x30"H.
Two file drawers with metal file racks. Pencil tray
in center top drawer. Finished back has simulated center
drawer and one adjustable shelf for each bookcase section.
No. 10-9500 Same item in
Nutmeg finish.

For detailed specifications on
Classic Manor Accents— see pages 388-389

No. 15-5224 Seven Drawer Chest.
23"x17"x52"H. Top drawer is fitted
with felt lined compartments. Perfect
as an accent in living room and
foyer as well as bedroom.

No. 15-9009 Library Book Stand.
26"x17"x32"H. Features ratchet-
operated adjustable stop. Book stand
is mounted on concealed swivel casters
for mobility. One adjustable shelf.
Finished on all sides. Can be used
free standing in a room.

Shown above from left to right:
No. 15-8306 Nest of Tables
No. 15-6001 Queen Anne Side Chair
No. 15-9010 Writing Table
No. 20-7096 Sofa
No. 15-8303 End Table
No. 15-8304 Corner or Cocktail Table

No. 15-8301
Cocktail Table.
68"x32"x16"H. Cane
end shelves.

No. 15-8306
Nest of Tables. 28"x
18"x22"H.

For detailed specifications on: Classic
Manor Occasional Tables—see pages 387-388.
Upholstery—see pages 392-406.

No. 15-8303
End Table. 23¾"x
27"x23"H. Two drawers.

The comprehensive collection of Classic Manor Tables offers a rich variety of design expression shown on these and the following three pages. Here and opposite, the basic theme is a classic architectural influence with recessed molded panels and cove-type frieze molding featuring four-way matched veneers with cross banded borders. The Classic Manor Custom hand rubbed finish offers a mellow warm brown patina. Tops feature moulded polyester edges.

Shown above from left to right:
No. 15-8305 Pedestal Snack Table
No. 15-8302 End Table
No. 13–7113 Embassy Scroll Arm Chair
No. 15-8303 End Table

Classic Manor tables

No. 15-8300
Cocktail Table.
60"x26"x16½"H.

No. 15-8305
Pedestal Snack Table.
22"x22"x16"H.

No. 15-8302 End Table.
25¼"x25¼"x22"H.
Cane shelf.

Ethan Allen
AMERICAN TRADITIONAL INTERIORS

No. 15-8661P Pedestal Cocktail Table.
20"x20"x17"H. Simulated natural
cleft slate top.
No. 15-8661 Same item with wood top
of selected veneer.

Shown below:
No. 15-8660 Rectangular Cocktail Table.
60"x22"x16"H. Wood top is selected veneer.
No. 15-8660P Same item with simulated
natural cleft slate top.

No. 15-9046 Paneled Tall Mirror.
Overall: 25"x46"H.

No. 15-8666P Hexagonal Commode Table 25"x25"x22"H. Storage
compartment with half shelf. Simulated natural cleft slate top.
No. 15-8666 Same item with wood top of selected veneer.

No. 15-9045P Console Commode.
32"x12"x30"H. One adjustable
shelf behind doors. Top is simulated
natural cleft slate. Door panels are
selected veneer.

No. 15-9045 Same item with wood top
of selected veneer.

No. 15-8664 Rectangular Commode End Table.
28"x20"x22"H. Three removable record
partitions. Top is selected veneer.
No. 15-8664P Same item with simulated natural cleft slate top.

Shown at left:
No. 15-8421
Square Pedestal Cocktail Table.
20"x20"x17"H.

Shown at right:
No. 15-8434
Pembroke Drop Leaf Table.
21"x27"x22"H. Opens to
36"x27" with leaves extended.
One drawer.

No. 15-8425
Square Lamp Table.
26"x26"x22"H.
One drawer.

Classic Manor decorative tables

Shown on these and the following pages are still other designs in the diversified Classic Manor table collection. Some are distinguished by fluted Sheraton legs and decorative molding. Other have inlaid marquetry and simulated slate tops and paneled doors.

For detailed specifications on Classic Manor Occasional Tables—see pages 387-389.

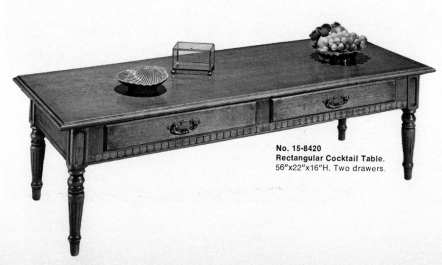

No. 15-8420
Rectangular Cocktail Table.
56"x22"x16"H. Two drawers.

No. 15-8424
Rectangular End Table.
23"x27"x22"H. One drawer.

Ethan Allen
AMERICAN TRADITIONAL INTERIORS

Shown at left:
**No. 15-8673
Square Coffee Table.**
30"x30"x17"H.
Inlaid marquetry
top.

Shown below:
**No. 15-9010
Writing Table.**
58"x26"x30"H.

**No. 15-8671
Rectangular Bunching Table.**
30"x21"x16"H. With casters.

**No. 15-8675
Octagonal Book Table.**
21"x26"x22"H.

No. 15-8674 Rectangular End Table.
23"x27"x22"H.

No. 15-8670 Rectangular Cocktail Table.
60"x22"x17"H. Finished back
with simulated drawers.

For detailed specifications on Classic Manor
Accents and Table Pieces—see pages 387 to 389.

Ethan Allen
AMERICAN TRADITIONAL INTERIORS

**No. 13-9006
Military Wellington Chest.**
18"x15"x42"H.
Seven drawers.
Recessed drawer
pulls.

No. 13-8003 Military Cocktail Table. 48"x22"x16"H.
Three drawers. Finished on all four sides.

**No. 13-9005
Military Bar.** 16"x18"x23"H.
Flip-top attached with sturdy
piano hinge. Compartmentalized
stain-resistant melamine interior
featuring storage for bottles and
gallery rack for glassware.
Finished on all sides.

**No. 13-8001
Military End Table.**
19"x24"x22"H.
One drawer. Deep open
storage shelf.

**No. 13-8002
Military Chest Table**
16"x24"x22"H.
Three deep storage drawers.

Handsome campaign style accent designs are expressed
in yew veneers and imported from England. Bound corners
and recessed hardware distinguish these versatile pieces.

ETHAN ALLEN
CLASSIC MANOR

serene bedrooms offer comfort and calm

Even the most gregarious among us need a private place—an escape hatch from children and household noise. In the master bedroom, one can enjoy those precious solitary moments surrounded by a sense of luxury and creature comforts. A serene retreat, such as this bedroom, includes a super comfortable bed, ample storage, a place to read or take quiet snacks. Soft colors and pastels, and Classic Manor designs impart elegance and calm, while latticed walls are decorative but subtle.

Shown opposite from left to right:
No. 15-5213 72" Triple Dresser
No. 15-5230 Mirror
No. 15-5216 Cabinet Night Stand
No. 15-8671 Coffee Table
No. 15-5655 Cane Headboard
No. 20-7178 Lounge Chair

Shown at right:
No. 15-5215 Chest-on-Chest.

For detailed specifications on:
Classic Manor—see pages 386-389.
Upholstery—see pages 392-406.

Ethan Allen
AMERICAN TRADITIONAL INTERIORS

CLASSIC MANOR
bedrooms designed for comfort and calm

A crisp tableau of blue and white is both soothing and lively, providing just enough panache for a room that serves as a restful retreat from the rest of the world—and the rest of the house. Swivel rockers are comfortable oases for sewing, reading or day-dreaming. Luxurious pink and blue master bedroom, right proffers traditional elegance with contemporary comfort. Handsome Classic Manor storage cabinets are well positioned to take maximum advantage of available wall space in both of these bedrooms.

Shown above from left to right:
No. 20-7304 **Barrel Chairs**
No. 15-5205 **Eight Drawer Chest on Chest**
No. 15-5203 **Nine Drawer Triple Dresser**
No. 15-5220 **Pediment Mirror**
No. 15-5206 **Cabinet Night Tables**
No. 15-5612 **Pediment Bed**

Shown opposite from left to right:
No. 15-5206 **Cabinet Night Table**
No. 15-5637 **Cornice Headboard**
No. 15-5204 **Six Drawer Chest**
No. 15-5202 **Seven Drawer Double Dresser**
No. 15-8421 **Square Pedestal Cocktail Table**
No. 20-7122 **Loveseat**

For detailed specifications on:
Classic Manor Bedroom—see page 385,
Upholstery—see pages 392-406.

Ethan Allen
AMERICAN TRADITIONAL INTERIORS

116

SERENE CLASSIC MANOR BEDROOMS

Pale celadon and shimmering white sanctums have the becalming quality that all monochromatic rooms possess. Space is skillfully utilized by the choice of commodious dressers and the arrangement of comfortable sitting areas, so that the rooms serve as private retreats for the adults of the house. In setting, opposite, seven drawer lingerie chest fits on a narrow slice of wall. Bench facilitates dressing, holds the bedspread at night. Sumptuous white interior, above offers an elegant writing corner. Partition was added to accommodate tall and slender Classic Manor secretary.

Shown opposite from left to right:

No. 11-8205 Curio Table	No. 10-7429 Bench
No. 21-7044 Sofa	No. 15-5634 Spindle Headboard
No. 15-5210 Mirror	No. 15-5216 Commode Night Table
No. 15-5203 Triple Dresser	No. 15-5224 Lingerie Chest

For detailed specifications on:
Classic Manor Bedroom—see page 385,
Classic Manor Accents—see pages 388-389.
Upholstery—see pages 392-406.

Shown below:
No. 15-5627 Sliding Door Bookcase Headboard. 38"H. Available in 6'6" size. Back is selected veneer.
No. 10-5627 Same items in Nutmeg finish.
No. 15-5634 Tall Headboard. 39½"H. Available in 4'6"-5' combination size and 6'6" size.

Shown above from left to right:
No. 15-5625 **Cornice Bed**
No. 15-5206 **Night Table**
No. 15-5202 **Seven Drawer Double Dresser**
No. 15-5200 **Mirror**
No. 15-9507 **Secretary Top**
No. 15-9506 **Secretary Base**
No. 20-7401 **Loveseat**
No. 15-8421 **Pedestal Table**

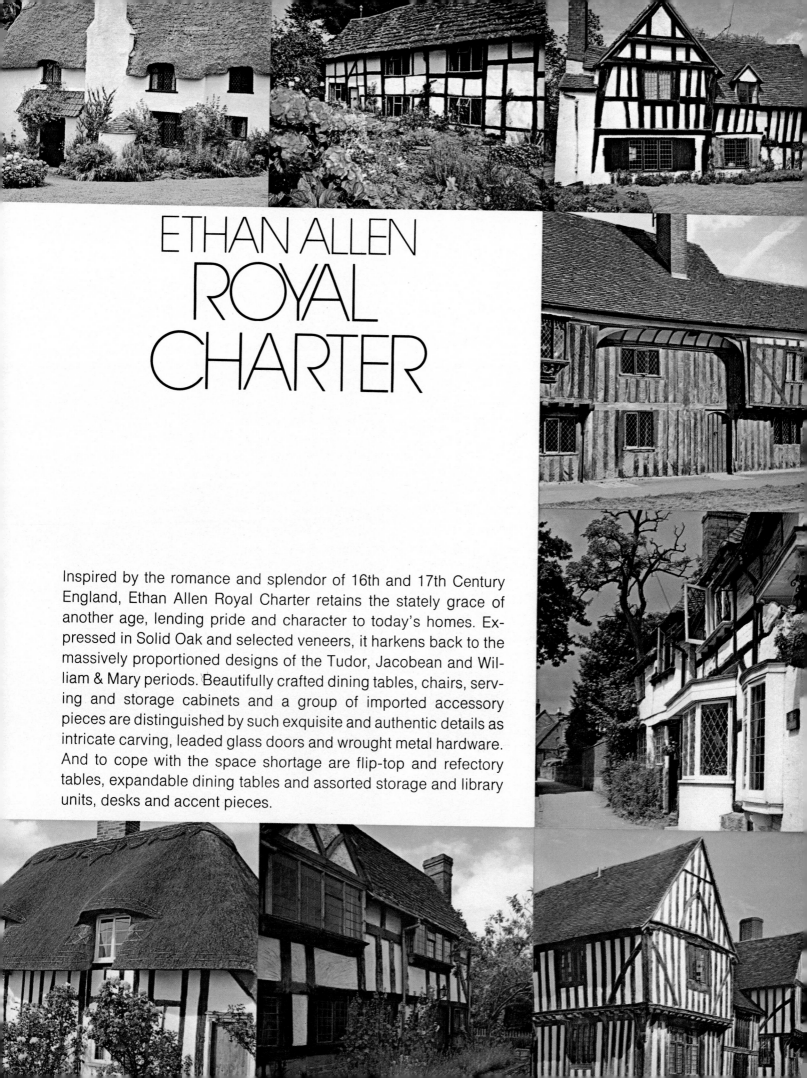

ETHAN ALLEN
ROYAL CHARTER

Inspired by the romance and splendor of 16th and 17th Century England, Ethan Allen Royal Charter retains the stately grace of another age, lending pride and character to today's homes. Expressed in Solid Oak and selected veneers, it harkens back to the massively proportioned designs of the Tudor, Jacobean and William & Mary periods. Beautifully crafted dining tables, chairs, serving and storage cabinets and a group of imported accessory pieces are distinguished by such exquisite and authentic details as intricate carving, leaded glass doors and wrought metal hardware. And to cope with the space shortage are flip-top and refectory tables, expandable dining tables and assorted storage and library units, desks and accent pieces.

splendid dining with
Royal Charter

Imposing and gracious without being pretentious, Royal Charter hosts a handsome dining room that can cater a formal dinner or be a center for family meals. Stately huntboard, made with separate deck and base, has authentic diamond-shaped pendant pulls, valanced shelves and aprons, and carved moulding. Expressing the Spanish influence of the Tudor era are regal high back side and arm chairs. Large and sturdy dining table extends to seat twelve, operates with a slide mechanism so that the top opens independently of the base . . . a process that leaves the carpet undisturbed and even a petite hostess can handle with ease. Above console is Royal Charter accent mirror framed by rope moulding.

Shown at left, from left to right:
No. 16-6011A Arm Chair
No. 16-6003 Extension Table. Top
is selected veneer.
No. 16-9000 Console
No. 16-9001 Mirror
No. 16-6011 Side Chair
No. 16-6006 Hunt Board
No. 16-6008 Hutch. Back is
selected veneer.

Shown below:
No. 16-6006 Hunt Board
No. 16-6008 Hutch. backs are
selected veneer.

For detailed specifications on:
Royal Charter Dining Room—see pages 389-390.
Royal Charter Accents—see pages 390-391.

Ethan 🌸 *Allen*
AMERICAN TRADITIONAL INTERIORS

Royal Charter dining rooms

Mood setting is easy with Royal Charter dining furniture, which lavishly flavors any room with the romance of Tudor England. Choice of fabrics, rugs and accessories can intensify the mood—or play it down.

Shown at right from left to right:
No. 16-6007 Buffet
No. 16-6002 Captain's Chair
No. 16-6004 Octagonal Extension Table

Generating lots of visual interest—the mix of Royal Charter with zingy rug, abstract canvas and lively colors, too. Same octagonal table is shown extended in dining room, bottom, expressed in a crisp blue and white country theme.

Shown below from left to right:
No. 16-9901 Sussex Corner Cabinet
No. 16-6001A Ladderback Arm Chair
No. 16-6004 Octagonal Table
No. 16-6001 Ladderback Side Chair
No. 16-6007 Buffet
No. 16-6009 China Top

Ethan Allen
AMERICAN TRADITIONAL INTERIORS

for a now and then mood

Oriental design rug and traditionally inspired accessories evoke a mood of long ago in stately Royal Charter dining room. Massive designs, such as long huntboard and extension table, are teamed with delicate pieces, including slender corner cabinet and bowback chair.

Shown above from left to right:
No. 16-6006 Huntboard Deck
No. 16-6000 A Bow Back Windsor Arm Chair
No. 16-6003 Rectangular Extension Table
No. 16-6000 Bow Back Windsor Side Chair
No. 16-9911 Nook Cabinet

For detailed specifications on Royal Charter—see pages 389-391.

Royal Charter perfect for dining room or library

The mood of an olde English tavern—the way it might have looked in the Tudor era—is recreated with authentically designed Royal Charter furniture. Long hunt board is an excellent piece for buffet serving.

Shown above from left to right:
No. 16-6000 Bowback Windsor Side Chair.
No. 16-6013 Flip-Top Table. Top is selected veneer.

No. 16-6006 Hunt Board. Lower shelf and back are selected veneer.
Shown at left:
No. 16-6017 Corner China.

Tawny ruby, melon and gold meld into rich surroundings for a comfortable library, right. Knight's chest improvises as window seat between tall library units, flip-top table opens for work surface.

Shown opposite from left to right:
No. 16-6011 Side Chair
No. 16-9003 Secretary
No. 20-7124 Chippendale Sofa

No. 16-6013 Flip Top Table
No. 16-9005 Library Unit
Back is selected veneer
No. 16-9902 Knight's Chest
No. 16-7439 Bench

For detailed specifications on:
Royal Charter Dining Room—see pages 389-390
Royal Charter Accent Pieces—see page 391
Upholstery—see pages 392-406

Ethan Allen
AMERICAN TRADITIONAL INTERIORS

Royal Charter accents and occasional tables

Here's a handsome storage idea that not only organizes books and possessions but adds rich character and architectural flavor. Royal Charter library units can be used in any combination of multiples to fit living room, den or dining room wall. Decorative console and mirror can enhance an entrance hall. Tall secretary, small cabinets and assorted tables on opposite page are all very versatile storage and accessory designs.

Shown above from left to right:
No. 16-9007 Library Cabinet Base.
34"x16"x28"H. Two doors, one adjustable shelf behind doors. Back is selected matching veneer.
No. 16-9009 Library Upper Cabinet.
34"x14½"x52"H. Unit has two antique glass doors and light fixture. The three adjustable shelves have glass insets and are grooved for China display. Back is selected matching veneer.
No. 16-9008 Library Chest Base.
34"x16"x28"H. Three drawers. Back is selected matching veneer.

No. 16-9010 Library Upper Unit.
34"x14½"x52"H. Three adjustable shelves. Shelves grooved for China display. Back is selected matching veneer.
No. 16-8007 Rent Table. 24"x24"x23"H. One door with storage space behind door. One drawer. Back is selected matching veneer.

Shown at right:
No. 16-9900 Canterbury Cabinet. 32"x16"x33"H.
No. 16-9901 Pier Looking Glass. 23"x36"H. Overall.
All items are solid Oak with selected veneers in a deeply-distressed and hand-padded Royal Charter finish.

Ethan Allen
AMERICAN TRADITIONAL INTERIORS

No. 16-9006 Chairside Chest.
Three drawers. 26"x18"x23"H.

**No. 16-9906 Tudor Glazed
Upper Bookcase.** 39"x8"x45"H.
Back is selected veneer.

No. 16-9905 Tudor Secretary.
39"x19"x40"H.

**No. 16-8004 Hexagonal
Commode Table.**
22"x22"x22"H.

Shown below:
No. 16-8010 Rectangular Cocktail Table.
60"x24"x17½"H. Two drawers.
No. 16-8006 End Table. 22"x26"x23"H. Two drawers.

For detailed specifications on
Royal Charter Accents and Tables—
see pages 390-391.

Ethan Allen
AMERICAN TRADITIONAL INTERIORS

recreation room or home office

Here's a colorful room arranged for conversation, relaxation or informal dining—for the family or when company comes. Royal Charter designs create separate activity areas so that various members of the house can enjoy the room at the same time.

Shown opposite from left to right:
No. 16-6011 **High Back Side Chair**
No. 16-8005 **Hi Lo Cocktail Table**
No. 16-9002 **Cocktail Cabinet**
No. 20-7189 **Tufted Tuxedo Sofa**
No. 16-8900 **Pub Set**

For the family it's a comfortable and cozy den—a quiet room for private conversations or solitary reading. But for the man of the house it's a place where he can work, a casual setling of paneled and paper walls, random plank flooring and Royal Charter furniture.

Shown below from left to right:
No. 16-8003 **Nest of Tables**
No. 20-7204 **Chippendale Wing Chair**
No. 16-9003 **Drop Front Secretary Base**
No. 16-9004 **Secretary Top**

No. 16-6011A **High Back Arm Chair**
No. 16-8002 **Gateleg End Table**
No. 20-7163 **Lawson Sofa**
No. 16-8000 **Refectory Cocktail Table**
No. 16-7438 **Ottoman**

For detailed specifications on:
Royal Charter Dining Room, Ocasional Tables and Accents—see pages 389-391
Upholstery—see pages 392-406

Ethan Allen
AMERICAN TRADITIONAL INTERIORS

Shown below:
No. 16-7439
Tufted Bench.
45"x19"x17"H.

No. 08-3545
Library Steps.
19"x19"x42"H.

Shown at top from left to right:
No. 08-3547 Tray Table. 28"x16"x30"H. Black Melamine top. Foldings legs.
No. 08-3551 Curio Cabinet. 16"x13"x72"H. Pewter finish grill with adjustable glass shelves.
No. 16-8007 Rent Table. 24"x24"x23"H. One door with storage space, one drawer. Back is selected matching veneer.
No. 16-9005 Library Wall Unit. 48"x15"x48"H. Leaded glass doors. Removable magazine rack. End panels and back are selected veneer.

For old world flavor and rich decorative impact—add a handsome occasional design in Ethan Allen Royal Charter. Intricate carvings on drawer fronts and legs, dramatic grain configuration and authentically inspired hardware are among the appealing hallmarks of this collection. Some cabinets have leaded glass doors and compartmentalized interiors; other accents include a screen, a candle chest, a desk, library steps, tray tables, console designs, a mini-cabinet and a mirror.

Royal Charter accents & occasional tables

Shown from left to right:
**No. 08-3543
Three Panel Screen.**
48"x78"H. Beveled panels.

**No. 16-9000
Hall Console.** 36"x14"x28"H.
**No. 16-9901
Pier Looking Glass.** 23"x36"H.

**No. 16-9002
Cocktail Cabinet.** 30"x17"x
48"H. Interior mirrored
work-surface and top-actuated
light. Doors have lock
and key.

**No. 16-9904
Squire's Chest.**
26"x15"x30"H.
Four storage drawers.
Flip-top doubles as
writing surface. Top
is selected veneer.

Shown above from top to bottom:
No. 16-9908 Davenport Desk. 25"x20"x
33"H. Five drawers. Storage compartment
under lift-lid. Genuine leather gold-
tooled writing bed. Partioned interior.
Front panels are selected veneer.
**No. 08-3541 Folding Octagonal Tray
Table.** 26" Diagonal x 18"H. Black
Melamine plastic top.

All items are solid Oak with selected veneers
and are deeply distressed and hand padded to a glowing
Patina in handsome Royal Charter finish.

**For detailed specifications on Royal Charter
Accents and Tables—see pages 390-391.**

133

ETHAN ALLEN
HEIRLOOM
COLLECTION

Use Ethan Allen Heirloom—to recreate the style of old New England or to fashion a fresh and contemporary look. Beautifully scaled and executed in a clear Nutmeg brown finish, the Heirloom collection covers a broad spectrum of styles. One design expression achieves its Shaker-like simplicity or country house look by the absence of mouldings, the employment of simple batwing hardware and by the rustic design of open hutch tops. The more formal designs within the collection include several handsome buffet and china cabinets. Delightful adaptations of Duxbury, Duncan Phyfe and Hitchcock chairs are also part of this comprehensive Heirloom collection.

ETHAN ALLEN HEIRLOOM
dining rooms with colonial spirit

Nostalgic, sentimental, yet spare as in the so-called 'keeping rooms' of yesteryear, are the three dining rooms on these next pages. Frills and furbelows are absent; in their place are huge hearths, stencilled or panelled walls, brick floors, rag rugs, ironstone and pewter. With these elements and Heirloom furniture, we have created settings that evoke the appealing simplicity of homespun Colonial life...a soothing balm to the hectic pace we lead today. The trestle dining table is set for a traditional American Sunday supper: shrimp Creole, glazed carrots, rich biscuits, applecake.

Shown left to right:
No. 10-6060A Arrowback Arm Chair
No. 10-6084 End Extension Trestle Table
No. 10-6060 Arrowback Side Chair
No. 10-6056/6058 Buffet & China Top
No. 10-6315 Trestle Bench
No. 10-6027 Server

For detailed specifications on:
Heirloom Dining Room—see pages 366-369.

Ethan Allen
AMERICAN TRADITIONAL INTERIORS

colonial spirit dining

Stencilled decoration, a Colonial art, takes to walls of cheerful dining room, left, happily rearranging the area rug motifs. A patterning of shapes and diverse textures replaces the more obvious forms of pattern below. Tables are set for a summer lunch—clam chowder, corn-on-the-cob and blueberry pie—and a winter dinner—chicken pie, red cabbage, relishes, preserves and orange nut bread.

Shown opposite from left to right:
No. 10-9003 Governor's Cabinet.
No. 10-6106 Dry Sink
No. 10-6016/6059 Buffet & China Top
No. 10-6030A Arm Chair
No. 10-6030 Side Chairs
No. 10-6114 Spoonfoot Oval Table

Shown below from left to right:
No. 10-6067/6069 Buffet W/China Top
No. 10-6020A Duxbury Arm Chair
No. 10-6020 Duxbury Side Chair
No. 10-6113 Pedestal Extension Table

For detailed specifications on:
Heirloom Dining Room—see pages 366-369.
Heirloom Accents —see pages 371-372.

Ethan Allen
AMERICAN TRADITIONAL INTERIORS

the spirit of today

Shown left to right:
No. 14-6085 **Tea Cart**
No. 10-6050A **Ladderback Chair**
No. 10-6105 **Dry Sink**
No. 16-6050 **Ladderback Side Chair**
No. 10-6073 **Drop Leaf Extension Table**
No. 10-6126/6128 **Buffet & China Top**

Artful improvisation can move Heirloom designs in any number of possible directions. Cast in the mold of long ago, as on preceding pages, it recalls that moment in time in which this design genre was born. But it's also a natural for now—with lightly scaled proportions that solve the problems of smaller rooms. Here it takes on a fresh and free-wheeling style generated by a cachet of mixed-mood accessories

For detailed specifications on:
Heirloom Dining Room— see pages 366-369.
Decorated Furniture—see pages 384-385.

Heirloom dining

Shown left to right:
No. 10-6100 Spindleback Formal Side Chair
No. 10-6100A Spindleback Formal Arm Chair
No. 10-6114 Spoonfoot Table
No. 10-4552P Three Door Cabinet
No. 10-4066 Upper Bookcase
No. 10-4513P Two Door Cabinet
No. 10-4029 Armoire. Full glass doors

Heirloom can invite romantic, dramatic decor. Chameleon-like, it adapts painlessly to an unbelievably broad range of moods. Old world one moment, sprightly contemporary the next, now it takes to a richly romantic look. Armoire shaped cabinets, royal purple walls, white velvet chair seats and intricately patterned rug all contribute. When not in service for dining, room also doubles in brass as library and study area.

For detailed specifications on: Heirloom Dining Room—see pages 366-369.
Heirloom Custom Room Plan—see pages 362-363.

Ethan Allen
AMERICAN TRADITIONAL INTERIORS

FAR EAST...................FAR WEST

The mood potential of backgroud design and accessorization is literally unlimited. Two cases in point are these interiors, both furnished with Ethan Allen Heirloom, but there the resemblance ends. Shoji screens on window and ceiling, tatami floor covering and oriental-style accents evoke a mood of the Far East, left. Black decorated Hitchcock chairs and library

bookstack units, seemingly born to such a scene, are straight out of our own heritage. High on a hillside, out in the sunny west, is small dining room, above, furnished with space-minded corner cabinet and round extension table with matching lazy susan. Unique wall treatment is actually a super mosaic of assorted barn siding rectangles.

Shown at left from left to right:
No. 14-9026 Bookstacks
No. 10-4521 Apothecary Chest
No. 14-6110 Side Chair
No. 14-6110A Arm Chair
No. 10-6063 Spoonfoot Drop Leaf Table

For detailed specifications on:
Heirloom Dining Room—see pages 366-369.
Decorated Furniture—see pages 384-385.

Shown above from left to right:
No. 10-6027 Server
No. 10-6040 Mate's Chair
No. 10-6024 Round Extension Table
No. 10-6005P Lazy Susan
No. 10-6046 Corner Cabinet

Ethan Allen
AMERICAN TRADITIONAL INTERIORS

an Heirloom country garden

Pretty as a picture in a story book is this colorful country room that lets you get away from it all without stepping out of your own front door. Potted greenery is planted in a row the length of fretwork sheathed window. Flower bower is actually saucy-fresh Ethan Allen print, paving walls and tightly shirred for tent-like ceiling. Set for four here, 48-inch round double pedestal table opens to accommodate ten.

Shown left to right:
No. 10-6016 Six Drawer Buffet
No. 10-6059 China Cabinet
No. 10-6094P Round Pedestal Table
No. 14-6072A Duxbury Arm Chair
No. 14-6072 Duxbury Side Chair
No. 10-6006 Two Drawer Server

For detailed specifications on:
Heirloom Dining Room— see pages 366-369.
Decorated Furniture—see pages 384-385.

Ethan Allen
AMERICAN TRADITIONAL INTERIORS

lively rooms

A delightful way to dine— in colorfully cluttered rooms with casual country manners. It's the kind of mood that Heirloom takes to with ease—sparked by informal patterns and textures, bright colors and greenery, and a bevy of rustic accents.

Shown from left to right:
No. 10-6006 Two Drawer Server
No. 10-9007 Tall Mirror
No. 10-6016 Six Drawer Buffet
No. 10-6028 Grilled China Cabinet
No. 14-6041 Ladderback Side Chairs
No. 10-6013 Round Spoonfoot
Extension Table

Crisp red and stark white give color impact to handsome country room top, an attractive blend of Nutmeg and Decorated finishes. Unexpected counterpoint of oriental rug with large modern canvas lends charm to dining room, bottom.

Shown from left to right:
No. 10-6039 Hutch Top
No. 10-6036 Buffet
No. 10-6046 Grilled Corner Hutch
No. 10-6044P Spoonfoot
Extension Table
No. 10-6011 Thumb Back Side Chairs

For detailed specifications on:
Heirloom Dining Room— see pages 366-369.
Decorated Furniture— see pages 384-385.

for dining

A circle of apricot rug punctuates the round extension dining table in this pretty country room, using lightly scaled Ethan Allen Heirloom designs. A remarkable amount of storage area is provided by both the hutch and buffet, each distinguished by decorative louvred doors.

Shown from left to right:
No. 10-6027 **Server**
No. 10-6049 **Hutch Cabinet**
No. 10-6017 **Buffet**
No. 10-5040 **Framed Mirror**
No. 10-6034P **Round Extension Table**
No. 10-6040 **Comb Back Mate's Chairs**

Enough to whet the appetite and warm the soul—a room of colorful country clutter and Heirloom. Terra cotta tile floor keys the delightful bucolic mood, while fake add-on beams were painted a brilliant red. Wallpaper adds a textured look. Unexpected accent—the abstract print.

Shown from left to right:
No. 10-6085 **Drop Leaf Tea Wagon**
No. 10-6017 **Buffet**
No. 10-6018 **China Cabinet**
No. 10-6031 **Captain's Chair**
No. 10-6093 **Spoonfoot Oval Extension Table**

a style

Tiny areas—big impact. Limited space may force us to dine in foyers, alcoves or right in the living room, yet Heirloom lets us do it with style and ease. Born yesterday, it's a great answer today for those dining without a separate dining room. Lighthearted Heirloom furnishes all the essentials, yet never crowds.

Shown above from left to right:
No. 14-6085 Tea Cart
No. 10-6102 Side Chairs
No. 10-6044P Extension Table
No. 10-6017/10-6039 Buffet with Hutch Top

Shown at left from left to right:
No. 10-6101 Mate's Chairs
No. 10-6124P Pedestal Table
No. 10-6027/10-6048 Server with China Top

For detailed specifications on:
Heirloom Dining Room—see pages 366-369.
Decorated Furniture—see pages 384-385.

for all spaces

It's how you dine, not where you do it that makes the difference. Windowed corner of a family room, opposite top, becomes a crisp blue and white setting for dining. Lightly scaled hutch has serving surface, copious storage capabilities. Colorful area off the kitchen, opposite bottom, tiny country room, right, and sparkling dining foyer, below are other examples of 'big impact' areas.

Shown at right from left to right:
No. 10-6002 Concord Chairs
No. 10-6083P Center Extension Table
No. 10-6006/10-6009 Server with China Top

Shown below from left to right:
No. 14-6111 Button Back Hitchcock Chairs
No. 10-6104P Round Extension Table
No. 10-6017/10-6018 Buffet with China Top

For detailed specifications on:
Heirloom Dining Room—see pages 366-369.
Decorated Furniture—see pages 384-385.

Heirloom lends charm to

It's only a nook under the stairs, but for the family that lives here it's a cosy and festive place to dine. Pert and decorative painted chairs and round table are perfect choices for diminutive dining room, left. Compact dry sinks offer storage and serving surface for both of these small dining areas.

Shown above from left to right:
No. 10-6106 Dry Sink
No. 10-6000 Squire's Chair
No. 10-6074P Drop Leaf Harvest Table

Shown at left, from left to right:
No. 14-6301 Farmhouse Chair
No. 10-6103P Drop Leaf Extension Table
No. 10-6105 Dry Sink

For detailed specifications on:
Heirloom Dining Room—see pages 366-369.
Decorated Furniture—see pages 384-385.

small dining areas and alcoves

Exuberant décor compensates for lack of space in handsome dining alcove, above, which continues mood and color scheme of adjacent living room. Trestle table is partnered with deacon's bench and a pair of ladder back chairs. For dining under the beams, left, a compact corner hutch and spoonfoot extension table.

Shown above from left to right:
No. 14-6085 Tea Cart
No. 10-6112 Ladderback Side Chair
No. 10-6123P Trestle Table
No. 10-6025 Deacon's Bench

Shown at left, from left to right:
No. 10-6046 39" Corner Hutch
No. 10-6011 Thumb Back Chair
No. 10-6004P Rectangular Spoonfoot Table
No. 10-6036 48" Buffet
No. 10-6039 48" Hutch Top

buffet or otherwise...

Lightly scaled and beautifully proportioned for small areas and alcoves are the many expandable tables in the Heirloom collection. These drop leaf or extension styles expand easily to accommodate a company evening or to serve a buffet spread. Here they are teamed with Duxbury and comb back chairs in Nutmeg and painted finishes.

Shown above:
No. 10-6034P Round Extension Table
***No. 14-6040 Comb Back Mate's Chairs**

For detailed specifications on:
Heirloom Dining Room—
see pages 366-369.
Decorated Furniture—
see pages 384-385.

Shown above:
No. 10-6014P Round Drop Leaf Extension Table
No. 10-6051 Comb Back Swivel Mate's Chairs

Shown at right:
No. 10-6053P Spoonfoot Drop Leaf Table
No. 10-6090 Comb Back Mate's Chair

Shown below:
No. 10-6133P Round Spoonfoot Extension Table
No. 10-6072 Duxbury Side Chair
No. 10-6072A Duxbury Arm Chair

*Description of Decorated Finishes:
400—Alabaster White
409—Antiqued Blue
411—Daffodil Yellow
604—White Decorated with Nutmeg
610—Black Decorated with Nutmeg

Ethan Allen
AMERICAN TRADITIONAL INTERIORS

HEIRLOOM
Decorated Accents
& Occasional Tables

You will find traditional charm combined with a world of practicality in this collection of cabinets, book shelves, occasional tables, desks, and consoles. Cherished ideas from the past combined with modern day needs for versatile storage. Ethan Allen's warm mellow Nutmeg color enhances authentic details throughout this collection. Many of the designs are available in dramatic and colorful hand decorated finishes. Each will enhance the decorative as well as the functional potential of any area of the home.

Shown above from left to right:
No. 14-8344 Drop Leaf Table
No. 20-7332 Loveseat
No. 14-9026 Book Stack
No. 14-6092 Chancellor's Chair
No. 14-9218 Snack Table

HEIRLOOM

Heirloom dry sinks—a charming traditional idea for today. Design, left, has felt-lined silver compartments, removable copper plated tray. Dry sink below, comes in Decorated finishes.

Shown at far left:
No. 10-6105 Four Drawer Dry Sink. 40"x20"x35"H. Felt lined compartment, adjustable shelf behind doors. Matching wood grained plastic top. Removable copper tray. Swivel casters.

Shown at left:
No. 10-6095 Swivel Bar Stool. 21"x20"x42"H. Height may be shortened at any of three places marked by rings. Tubular steel footrest with brushed brass finish. Nutmeg finish.

Shown below:
No. 10-6106 Dry Sink. 34"x18"x40"H. One drawer. Adjustable shelf behind doors. Felt lined compartments. Door panels are selected veneer.
*No. 14-6106 Same item in Decorated Finishes 604 or 610.

Shown at left:
No. 10-9007 Tall Mirror. 20"x38"H.
No. 15-9007 Same item in Classic Manor Finish.
No. 10-9035 Two Door Console Cabinet. 39"x14"x28"H. Door panels only, Selected veneer.

No 15-9035 Same item in Classic Manor Finish.

For detailed specifications on:
Heirloom Dining Room—see pages 366-369.
Heirloom Decorative Accents—see pages 371-372.
Decorated Furniture—see pages 384-385.

AMERICAN TRADITIONAL INTERIORS

154

*Description of Decorated Finishes:
601—Nutmeg Decorated
603—White Decorated
604—White Decorated with Nutmeg
609—Black Decorated
610—Black Decorated with Nutmeg

No. 10-9026 Bookstack. 30″x14″x80″H.
Adjustable shelves behind doors.
Cabinet backs are wood-grained
balanced hardboard.

*No. 14-9026 Same item in
Decorated Finishes 604 or 610.
See pages 371-372.

Add storage with a light touch—by choosing commodious yet compact Heirloom cabinets, ideal for rooms of limited dimensions. Library book-stack units can be used singly; a wall can be sheathed with two or more of them. Drop leaf cellarette, with worktop of durable Formica® plastic, accommodates bar essentials.

All items shown are
Solid Maple and/or
Birch and selected
veneers in a warm
brown Nutmeg finish.

No. 10-9040P Drop Leaf Cellarette.
30″x17″x33″H. Opens to 53″x17″.
Selected veneer on top, sides and
door panels. Set of eighteen matched
glasses for side compartments.
Formica® plastic top.

No. 10-9003 Governor's Cabinet.
26″x15″x28″H. Finished back.
Two drawers, adjustable
shelf behind doors.

Ethan Allen
AMERICAN TRADITIONAL INTERIORS

HEIRLOOM

A desk for every purpose, room or available wall space—in the extensive collection of versatile Heirloom desk designs. There are tall, graceful secretaries for the living room, a small decorative writing table for bedroom or entry. Handsome kneehole desks are great for den, library or family room. Many designs come with practical wood-grained plastic writing surfaces; several are also available in decorated finishes.

No. 10-9506 Nine Drawer Secretary Desk.
36"x19"x41"H. Five Drawers in base and four behind drop lid. Four letter compartments, pencil tray in top drawer. Lock and key for drop lid. Drop lid is selected veneer. Back is wood-grained balanced hardboard.
No. 15-9506 Same item in Classic Manor finish.
No. 10-9507 Grilled Secretary Top. Overall 76"H. Adjustable shelves behind doors.
No. 15-9507 Same item in Classic Manor finish.
No. 16-6000A Armchair

No. 10-9508 Six Drawer Secretary Desk. 33"x17"x40"H. Four Drawers in base and two behind drop lid. Three letter compartments. Drop lid is selected matching veneer.
No. 10-9509 Secretary Top. Overall 72"H. Cabinet back is wood-grained balanced hardboard.

No. 10-9520P Eight Drawer Double Pedestal Desk.
43"x21"x30"H. End panels are selected veneer. Formica® plastic top.
File Drawer lower right.

No. 10-4550P Four Drawer Student Desk.
40"W x 30"H. Formica plastic top.

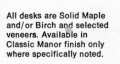

All desks are Solid Maple and/or Birch and selected veneers. Available in Classic Manor finish only where specifically noted.

*Description of Decorated finishes:
400—Alabaster White
409—Antiqued Blue
411—Daffodil Yellow
604—White Decorated with Nutmeg
610—Black Decorated with Nutmeg

For detailed specifications on:
Heirloom Accent Pieces—
see pages 371-372.
Heirloom Custom Room Plan—
see pages 362-363.
Decorated Furniture—
see pages 384-385.

DESK VARIETY

*No. 14-9514 Three Drawer Decorated Accent Writing Table.** 32"x18"x40"H. Pencil Tray. Available in Decorated finishes 604 and 610. Writing surface in Nutmeg.

*No. 14-6155 Hitchcock Bench.** 24"x15"x19"H. Fiber seat. Decorated Finishes 601, 603 or 609.

No. 10-9500 Seven Drawer Library Desk. 56"x26"x30"H. Two file drawers with metal file racks, pencil tray in center drawer. Finished back.

No. 15-9500 Same item in Classic Manor finish.

No. 10-4571P Four Drawer Dresser Desk. 48"x18"x30"H. Formica® plastic top.
*No. 14-4571P** Same item in Decorated finishes 400, 409 or 411.

No. 10-9521 Four Drawer Single Pedestal Desk. 40"x21"x30"H. One file drawer. End panels are selected veneer. Formica® plastic top.

No. 10-9522 Heirloom Desk. 46"x23"x30"H. Eight drawers. Lower left drawer has metal file rack.

No. 14-9026 Library Bookstacks. 30"x14"x80"H.
Back is wood-grained balanced hardboard.
No. 10-9026 Same item in Nutmeg finish.

No. 10-9512 Sliding Door Bookcase.
36"x9"x37"H. One adjustable shelf.
Back is wood-grained
balanced hardboard.

No. 10-9510 Bookcase. 32"x11"x51"H.
Back is wood-grained
balanced hardboard.

No. 10-9012 Bookcase with Grilled Doors.
36"x12"x48"H. Two adjustable shelves
behind doors. Back is wood-grained
balanced hardboard.

No. 10-9513 Bookcase. 36"x9½"x36"H.
Back is wood-grained balanced hardboard.

No. 10-8302 Bookcase Table.
27"x13"x23"H.

No. 10-8627
Hexagonal Commode Table.
29"x25"x20"H. Large storage
area behind doors. Door
panels are selected veneer.

No. 10-8635
Square Commode Table.
27"x27"x20"H. Large
storage area behind doors. Door
panels are selected veneer.

No. 10-8626
**Hexagonal Pedestal
Table.** 29"x25½"x20"H.
One drawer.

No. 10-8625 **Square Lamp Table.** 26"x26"x20"H. One drawer.
No. 10-8620 **Hexagonal Cocktail Table.** 60"x23½"x16"H.

For detailed specifications on:
Heirloom Accents and Tables
—see pages 370-372.

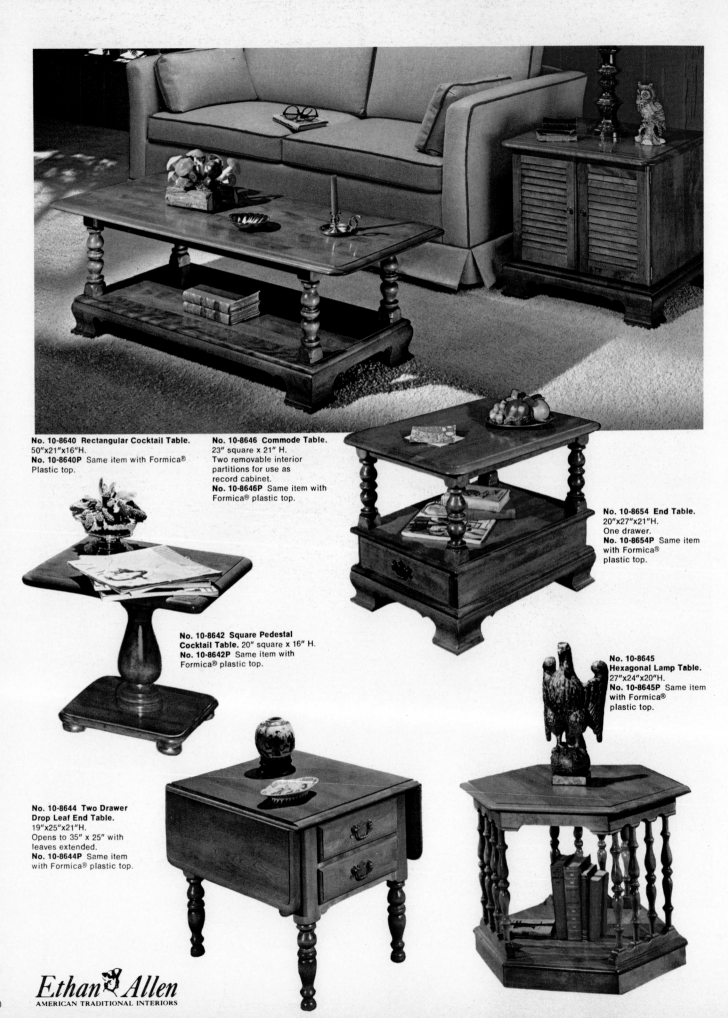

No. 10-8640 Rectangular Cocktail Table.
50"x21"x16"H.
No. 10-8640P Same item with Formica®
Plastic top.

No. 10-8646 Commode Table.
23" square x 21" H.
Two removable interior
partitions for use as
record cabinet.
No. 10-8646P Same item with
Formica® plastic top.

No. 10-8654 End Table.
20"x27"x21"H.
One drawer.
No. 10-8654P Same item
with Formica®
plastic top.

**No. 10-8642 Square Pedestal
Cocktail Table.** 20" square x 16" H.
No. 10-8642P Same item with
Formica® plastic top.

**No. 10-8645
Hexagonal Lamp Table.**
27"x24"x20"H.
No. 10-8645P Same item
with Formica®
plastic top.

**No. 10-8644 Two Drawer
Drop Leaf End Table.**
19"x25"x21"H.
Opens to 35" x 25" with
leaves extended.
No. 10-8644P Same item
with Formica® plastic top.

Ethan Allen
AMERICAN TRADITIONAL INTERIORS

No. 10-8586 **Revolving Drum Table.** 28" diameter x 26"H.

No. 10-8354 **End Table.** 18"x23"x23"H.

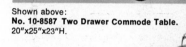

Shown above:
No. 10-8587 **Two Drawer Commode Table.** 20"x25"x23"H.

Shown at left:
No. 10-8582 **Step End Table.** 18"x28"x26"H. Storage area under lid.

Shown above:
No. 10-8584 **Magazine End Table.** 18"x28"x24"H. Deep storage area under lid.

No. 10-9042 **Pedestal Table.** 15" diameter x 21"H.
*No. 14-9042 Same item in Decorated Finishes 601, 603 or 609.

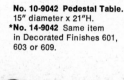

No. 10-8581 **Clover Leaf Cocktail Table.** 36" diameter x 16"H.

No. 10-9019 **Cloverleaf Magazine Rack.** 18"x 12"x15"H. Nutmeg finish (not shown).
*No. 14-9019 Same item in Decorated finishes 601, 603 or 609.

No. 10-8580 **Cocktail Table.** 42"x18"x18"H. Storage area under both lids.

No. 10-9022 **Gossip Bench.** 33"x16"x29"H.
*No. 14-9022 Same item available in Decorated Finishes 604 or 610.

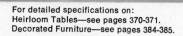

All items are Solid Maple and/or Birch with selected veneers in warm brown Nutmeg. Also available in Decorated Finishes where specifically noted.

For detailed specifications on:
Heirloom Tables—see pages 370-371.
Decorated Furniture—see pages 384-385.

No. 10-8303
Nest of Tables.
Top table is
25"x17"x23"H.

No. 10-8445P Lamp Table. 23" square x 23"H.
One drawer. Formica® plastic top.

For detailed specifications on
Heirloom Occasional Tables—see pages 370-371.

No. 10-8444P End Table. 19"x27"x23"H.
One drawer. Formica® plastic top.

No. 10-8442P Step End Table. 19"x27"x25"H.
One drawer. Formica® plastic top.
No. 10-8440P Cocktail Table. 44"x20"x15"H.
One drawer. Formica® plastic top.

Ethan Allen
AMERICAN TRADITIONAL INTERIORS

No. 10-8355 Spoonfoot Cloverleaf Lamp Table. Opens to 27″ diameter. 24″H.
*No. 14-8355 Same item in Decorated Finish 610.

No. 10-8350 Spoonfoot Harvest Drop Leaf Cocktail Table. 44″x18″x15″H. Opens to 44″x32″ with leaves extended.
*No. 14-8350 Same item in Decorated Finish 610.

No. 10-8344 Spoonfoot Drop Leaf End Table. 18″x25″x24″H. Opens to 36″x25″ with leaves extended.
*No. 14-8344 Same item in Decorated Finish 610.

No. 10-8346 Spoonfoot Doughbox End Table. 18″x24″x24″H. Deep storage area under lid.

No. 10-8340 Spoonfoot Cocktail Table. 42″x18″x15″H.
*No. 14-8340 Same item in Decorated Finish 610.

ETHAN ALLEN
HEIRLOOM
bedrooms of vintage charm

Bedrooms that capture the spirit of a bygone era—an easy accomplishment with Ethan Allen Heirloom furniture. Here are designs derived from authentic Colonial pieces, refined and adapted for use in today's homes. Start with Heirloom and then add all the delightful Early American elements that are readily available in Home Fashion Center designs —wallpaper, oriental design rugs, quilted bedspread, tôle lamps and accessories. Design of triple dresser and chest-on-chest follow authentic Colonial styling as do heavily moulded landscape mirror and arrow splat back. Pair of swivel rockers compose a cosy sitting corner.

Shown opposite page from left to right:
No. 10-5654 **Arrow Bed**
No. 10-5316 **Night Stand**
No. 10-5315 **Chest**
No. 10-6050 **Ladderback Side Chair**
No. 10-5323 **66" Triple Dresser**
No. 10-5210 **Mirror**
No. 20-7302 **Mr. Swivel Rocker**
No. 10-9042 **Cigarette Pedestal Table**
No. 20-7303 **Mrs. Swivel Rocker**

For detailed specifications on:
Heirloom Bedroom—see pages 364-366.
Heirloom Accents—see pages 371-372.
Upholstery—see pages 392-406.

Ethan Allen
AMERICAN TRADITIONAL INTERIORS

Heirloom bedrooms of colonial charm

Step into this delightful bedroom and you are wafted back in time —to a bygone era when life was simpler, sweeter and more serene. You might find rooms like this in Williamsburg or Sturbridge Village; with blue paneled walls, plank floors, oriental accent rugs and lacy canopy bed it purveys the spirit of another age. And so does Ethan Allen Heirloom furniture with Colonial inspired design detail, authentic hardware and warm, appealing Nutmeg finish. Compact and lightly scaled chest-on-chest and triple dresser are easy to use in this modest-sized bedroom, leaving space for a sitting arrangement.

Shown above left to right:
No. 10-5302 Double Dresser
No. 10-5040 Mirror
No. 10-5612 Pediment Bed
No. 10-5304 Chest
No. 07-1550 Shelves
No. 24-6002A Ladderback Arm Chair
No. 10-5306 Night Stand

Shown opposite left to right:
No. 10-5622 Canopy Bed
No. 10-5316 Night Stand
No. 10-5305 Chest on Chest
No. 14-6111 Button Back Hitchcock Chair
No. 10-5303 Triple Dresser
No. 10-5100 Pediment Mirror
No. 10-6085 Tea Cart

For detailed specifications on:
Heirloom Bedroom—see pages 364-366.
Decorated Furniture—see pages 384-385.
American Foliage Colors—see pages 379-383.

Once an awkward dormer bedroom, now a pretty setting of vintage charm. A few of the furnishings are antique, the rest is mood-setting Heirloom, providing the flavor of long ago. Decoration of the room was simple but effective; lightweight simulated beams, added on, look just like the real thing. Floors were painted bright red; patchwork quilt might inspire a do-it-yourselfer to try her hand at this new craft revival.

the dresser that organizes a woman's world

Super strategy for storage: a dresser that takes all the guesswork out of where to put whatever a woman owns. It's hard to be sloppy when your dresser keeps things organized and separate. With its well planned arrangement of uniquely compartmented doors and drawers, this handsome cabinet contains small compartments for such tiny items as gloves, handkerchiefs and scarves, and larger ones for sweaters, blouses and nightgowns, etc. Removable and adjustable partitions offer flexibility.

A—Top Center Drawer—for gloves, handkerchiefs, lingerie, stockings.
C—Top Left and Right Drawers—for socks, jewelry, belts, handkerchiefs, cosmetics.
E—Left Facing Cabinet—for hats, handbags, shoes.
G—Bottom Row Left Facing—for blouses, shirts, pajamas.

B—Second Row Center—for slips, girdles, nightgowns, pajamas, T-shirts.
D—Third Row Center—for peignoirs, nightgowns, shirts, pajamas.
F—Right Facing Cabinet—for shirts, pullovers, pajamas,
H—Bottom Row Center and Right Facing—for sweaters, scarves, blouses, pajamas.

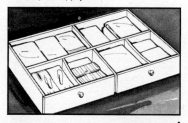

A

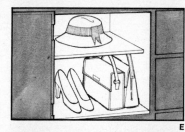

B

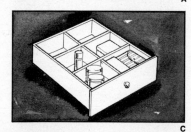

C

D

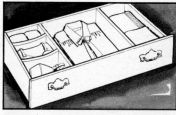

E

F

G

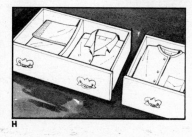

H

Shown from left to right:
No. 10-5013 63″ Fitted Triple Dresser
No. 10-5050 Mirror
No. 10-5056 Night Stand
No. 10-5604 Fiddleback Bed
No. 10-5005 Chest-on-Chest
No. 14-7428 Ottoman

For detailed specifications on:
Heirloom Bedroom—see pages 364-366.
Upholstery—see pages 392-406.

HEIRLOOM BEDROOMS

Shown above from left to right:
No. 10-6112 **Ladder Back Side Chair**
No. 10-6124P **Pedestal Table**
No. 10-5002 **Double Dresser, 50"**
No. 10-5040 **Mirror**
No. 10-5611 **Spindle Bed**
No. 10-5014 **Chest**

Shown at left from left to right:
No. 10-5012 **Double Dresser 52"**
No. 10-5020 **Mirror**
No. 10-5005 **Chest-on-Chest**
No. 10-5638 **Ladder Back Headboard**
No. 10-5036 **Night Table**
No. 20-7938 **Ottoman**

The versatility of Ethan Allen Heirloom never ceases to amaze. Put it into a setting of Colonial-mood background treatment and accessories, and it takes on the character of another age. Then frame it with a modern color scheme or add some contemporary elements, and it assumes a totally different kind of look. Explicit examples of this about face are seen in these two interiors. Master bedroom, left has a luxurious and current-day personality, generated almost entirely by the contemporary wallpaper, and of course the posh of velvet and fur. Saving wall space for dresser and chest on chest, ladder back bed is placed in front of draped window. Zingy blue and lime color scheme gives lively look to bedroom above, a skillful solution to an awkward floor plan. Furniture arrangement maximizes employment of available wall space and invisibly partitions the room as well.

For detailed specifications on:
Heirloom Bedroom—see pages 364-366.
Upholstery—see pages 392-406.

Ethan Allen
AMERICAN TRADITIONAL INTERIORS

ETHAN ALLEN HEIRLOOM

compact designs for the younger set

Young in heart, and lightly scaled, Heirloom bedroom designs are eminently suited to the decoration of a child's room. Unpretentious and adaptable they can accommodate to a variety of decorating approaches as well as to the constantly changing age levels of the specific child that occupies an Heirloom bedroom. Of special interest of the compact and versatile bed designs that offer dual sleep facilities as illustrated on these two pages.

No. 10-5012 **Double Dresser**
No. 10-5040 **Mirror**
No. 10-5600 **Tri-Way Bed**
No. 10-5014 **Chest**

For detailed specifications on Heirloom Bedroom Pieces—see pages 364-366.

Ethan Allen
AMERICAN TRADITIONAL INTERIORS

SHOWN AS BUNK BEDS

SHOWN AS TWIN BEDS

SHOWN AS TRUNDLE BEDS

Sketched above:
**No. 10-5600 Tri-Way Bed
with Side Rails and Slats.**
Overall 61"H; headboard
37½"H. Can be used three ways:
as Bunk Bed, Twin Beds, or in two positions
as a Trundle Bed with casters.
*No. 14-5600 Same item in Decorated
Finishes 400, 409 or 411.
**No. 10-5981 Full Length Guard Rail and
Ladder.** Available for No. 10-5600.
*No. 14-5981 Same item in Decorated
Finishes 400, 409 or 411.

No. 10-5605 Bunk and/or Twin Beds.
Overall 64½"H. Headboard 37"H.
Complete with wood rails, slats,
guard rail and ladder.

No. 10-5633 Captain's Trundle Bed.
Overall 34½"H. 84"L. Lower drawer rolls
out on casters to be used as extra bed
(39"x75" mattress) or as storage
bin for toys, blankets or
linens by placing a piece of
masonite over slats. Use a 39"
x80" mattress for upper bed.
Drawer pulls out either side.

*Description of Decorated Finishes:
400—Alabaster White
409—Antiqued Blue
411—Daffodil Yellow

Crisp and tailored blue and white boy's bedroom shows the Heirloom Tri-way bed in its trundle position. Bed can also be arranged as a bunk bed or as twin beds. Handsome captain's trundle bed has lower drawer which moves out on casters to become an extra bed. Third bed style shown here is the bunk or twin bed. The Tri-way bed is offered in three Decorated finishes as well as in the Heirloom Nutmeg finish.

*No. 14-5641 Hi Rise Trundle Bed. Overall 37"H.
Available in 3'3" size only. Bed comes complete
with Link Springs, uses standard twin mattress.
Second bed pulls out on casters and rises to same
height as first. Bedding height is 21". Available
in Decorated Finishes 400, 409, 411.
No. 10-5641 Same item in Nutmeg Finish.

ETHAN ALLEN
HEIRLOOM
rooms for a junior miss and twin toddlers

If babies could choose their own color schemes, they'd favor bold primary hues over the washed out baby pastels that parents sometimes choose for them. Bright colors attract and intrigue a child, so use them without inhibition such as in crayon red and white setting, above, designed for two toddlers. Yummy bon bon colors turn a young girl's bedroom, left, into a happy place that she enjoys on a non-stop basis. Compact and slenderly-scaled Heirloom storage pieces accommodate to chopped-up wall space.

Shown opposite from left to right:
No. 10-5026 **Night Stand**
No. 10-5614 **Panel Bed**
No. 10-5001 **Five Drawer Dresser**
No. 10-5000 **Tall Pediment Mirror**
No. 10-5060 **Cheval Floor Mirror**
No. 10-5004 **Five Drawer Chest**
No. 20-7101 **Semi-attached Pillow Ottoman**

Shown above from left to right:
No. 10-5624 **Crib**
No. 10-5306 **Cabinet Night Table**
No. 10-5004 **Five Drawer Chest**
No. 10-9703 **Rocker**

Shown in inset:
10-5660 **Crib**

For detailed specifications on:
Heirloom Bedroom—see pages 364-366.
Upholstery—see pages 392-406.

Ethan Allen
AMERICAN TRADITIONAL INTERIORS

Shown from left to right:
No. 10-9521P Four Drawer Single Pedestal Desk
No. 14-6301 Farmhouse Chair
No. 10-5002 Six Drawer Double Dresser

No. 10-5010 Scalloped Mirror
No. 14-5631 Tall Poster Bed
with Canopy frame
No. 10-5046 Cabinet Night Table

ETHAN ALLEN
HEIRLOOM
bedroom collection

No. 10-5627 Sliding Door Bookcase Headboard.
38"H. Available in 6'6" size only.
No. 15-5627 Same item in Classic Manor finish.

Ethan Allen
AMERICAN TRADITIONAL INTERIORS

No. 10-5621 Cannonball Bed. 44"H.
Available in 3'3", 4'6" and 5' sizes.

No. 10-5638 Ladderback Headboard.
Available in 3'3" and 4'6" sizes.
*No. 14-5638 Same item in Decorated
finishes 400, 409, or 411.

No. 10-5637 Cornice Headboard.
42"H. Available in 5' and 6'6" sizes.
No. 15-5637 Same item in
Classic Manor finish.

No. 10-5628 Spindle Headboard. 41"H.
Available in 5' and 6'6" sizes.

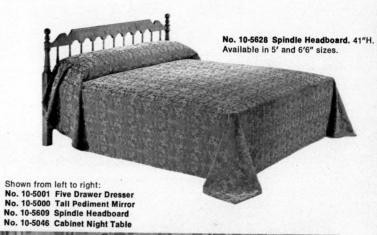

For detailed specification on:
Heirloom Bedroom—see pages 364-366.
Decorated Furniture—see pages 384-385.

Shown from left to right:
No. 10-5001 Five Drawer Dresser
No. 10-5000 Tall Pediment Mirror
No. 10-5609 Spindle Headboard
No. 10-5046 Cabinet Night Table

ETHAN ALLEN CUSTOM ROOM PLAN

Custom Room Plan is the modular system that really puts space to work. Here is comprehensive, engineered storage—upper and lower cabinets—that group together to compose a wall, chosen and assembled to suit your specific room and the needs of your family. In addition to bookshelf and general storage area, Custom Room Plan offers many exciting special purpose units such as the refreshment center, television and stereo units and activity centers for sewing and photography. Use them as "building blocks" to give exceptional storage potential to every room in the house. Available in straight-lined Shaker inspired cabinets or in decorative Provincial styling, Custom Room Plan is offered in the Nutmeg finish and in colors of white, yellow and blue.

ETHAN ALLEN CUSTOM

ROOM PLAN

what it is

.... Custom Room Plan is a modular system with virtually unlimited storage potential. Flawless, beautifully proportioned furniture made by Shaker craftsmen inspired the design of these handsome wall units that work together to compose a storage wall.

Skillfully engineered chests of drawers and cupboards provide storage for assorted possessions. Sizes range from 24-inches to 48-inches in width making it possible to cope with walls of every size and shape.

Louvered doors, patterned after Colonial shutters, wrought metal hinges and apothecary drawers are among the charming design details.

A second expression within the collection features decorative Provincial styling distinguished by armoire-shaped upper units and paneled doors.

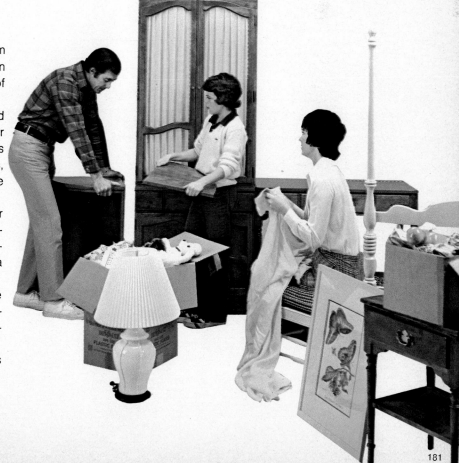

how it works

.... Custom Room Plan units are building blocks with which you can custom design your own storage wall for any room of the house.

There are over 65 units from which to choose, and you can start with a few designs and add on as your needs change and your budget expands. Here is remarkable storage for clothing, linens, china, toys, records, books and all the myriad possessions one accumulates.

Custom Room Plan turns corners, snuggles under windows, sheathes a wall or frames a window. Contributing a built-in effect, it is both flexible and movable and can be rearranged and reassembled for a new home.

These units come in the Nutmeg finish and in three hand-glazed decorated finishes: Antiqued Blue, Alabaster White and Daffodil Yellow. These have matching melamine plastic tops. See pages 204-205.

The Custom Room Plan series in Antiqued Pine is shown on pages 240-247.

CUSTOM ROOM PLAN

activity center for family enjoyment

Good looking and super-functional—an unbeatable combination that makes Ethan Allen Custom Room Plan units a favorite choice—for den, family room or any area that serves a multi-purpose role. Here Custom Room Plan and a lively contemporary plaid sheathe the walls of a spirited family room. An ample complement of general storage and bookshelf cabinets are star studded by special purpose units such as television-stereo, refreshment and refrigerator units, which are shown close up at left. All other tables and chairs are also in the same Nutmeg finish of the wall units—to give cohesion to the room.

Shown opposite from left to right:
No. 10-8644 Drop Leaf End Table
No. 20-7049 Sofa
No. 10-6102A Governor Bradford Arm Chair
No. 10-6124P Pedestal Table
No. 10-4511P Shutter Drawer Cabinet
No. 10-4019 Upper Bookcase
Back is wood-grained balanced hardboard.
No. 10-4532P Corner Chest
No. 10-4037 Upper Corner Bookcase.
Back is wood-grained balanced hardboard.
No. 50-1010 TV Cabinet (See closeup above)
No. 50-1101 Stereo Cabinet (See closeup above)
No. 10-4515P Refreshment Unit Base (See closeup left)
No. 10-4030 Refreshment Unit Top. (See closeup left)
Back is wood-grained balanced hardboard.
No. 10-4516P Refrigerator Unit (See closeup above)
No. 10-4007 Upper Bookcase.
Back is wood-grained balanced hardboard.
No. 10-8642 Snack Table

Simulated T-V reception

Detailed specifications on:
Custom Room Plan—see pages 362-363.
Heirloom Dining Room and Occasional Tables—see pages 366-371.
Upholstery see pages 392-406.
T-V and Stereo—see pages 264-265.

Ethan Allen
AMERICAN TRADITIONAL INTERIORS

ACTIVITY CENTERS
home study

Transform any slice of wall into a compact study area—with the Ethan Allen home study unit. Its compartmentalized interior, which includes file drawers and a pull-up typewriter shelf, is sheathed by louvred doors. Shown below, it's part of a home office arrangement blending Custom Room Plan with Royal Charter and decorated designs. Shown at left is a close up of the same home study unit which establishes a tiny work center on one wall of a large, all-purpose family room.

Shown at left:
No. 10-4556P Study Center. 40"x18½" x30"H. Typewriter storage area, pull out typewriter tray, removable vertical dividers tailored for storage, file drawer with Pendaflex racks; drawer slotted for letter racks, pencil tray; pull out writing board.

Shown below from left to right:
No. 14-6111 Hitchcock Chair
No. 10-4556P Study Center
No. 10-4532P Corner Chest
No. 10-4036 Upper Bookcase
No. 10-4510P Chest
No. 10-4019 Upper Bookcase
No. 16-6000A Windsor Arm Chair
No. 16-6013 Flip Top Table

For detailed specifications on:
Heirloom Custom Room Plan—see pages 362-363.
Decorated Furniture—see pages 384-385.
Royal Charter Dining Room—see pages 389-390.

sewing corner

The woman who sews really needs a special place to work—with storage that organizes fabrics, threads and tools, ample table surface for cutting, and a fine spot for the sewing machine. Ethan Allen's special sewing unit, shown close-up at right, helps solve these problems. The same unit is incorporated into a full Custom Room Plan sewing wall, below—actually part of the master bedroom.

Shown below from left to right:
No. 10-5060 **Cheval Floor Mirror**
No. 14-6301 **Farm Chair**
No. 10-4557P **Sewing Center**
No. 10-4058 **Upper Bookcase**
No. 10-4531P **Extension Table**
No. 10-4511P **2-Door Cabinet**
No. 10-4018 **Upper Cabinet Bookcase**
No. 14-9713 **Valet Chair**
No. 20-7208 **Wing Chair**

Shown at right:
No. 10-4557P **Sewing Center.** 40″ x 18½″ x 30″ H. Storage space for sewing machine plus large flip tray to place machine on when open. Three drawers with dividers; velvet-lined tray for storage; spool rest on inside of door.

For detailed specifications on:
Heirloom Bedroom—see pages 364-366.
Decorated Furniture—see pages 384-385.
Upholstery—see pages 392-406.
Heirloom Custom Room Plan—see pages 362-363.

Ethan Allen
AMERICAN TRADITIONAL INTERIORS

ACTIVITY CENTERS
Photography & MUSIC

Even if it's only a corner of a room, create a private hobby center for the photographer in the house. With the aid of special photo center unit, above, he can store film and cameras, edit, splice, mount albums—and treat the whole family to the joys of the past relived. Small den, opposite, becomes a music center with its wall of Custom Room Plan featuring television and stereo units, and an informal arrangement of furniture.

Ethan Allen
AMERICAN TRADITIONAL INTERIORS

Shown above from left to right:
No. 10-6074P Drop Leaf Table
No. 20-7272-5 Two Cushion Loveseat
No. 20-7104-3 Ottoman
No. 10-4521P 4 Drawer Apothecary Chest
No. 10-4512P Bookcase
No. 10-4532P Corner Cabinet
No. 10-4036 Upper Bookcase
No. 10-4086 TV Upper Unit
No. 10-4510P Three Drawer Chest
No. 10-4059 Photography Center Unit
No. 10-4555P Photography Cabinet
No. 10-4511P Shutter Door Cabinet
No. 10-7500-1 Stackables

Shown opposite from left to right:
No. 10-4510P Three Drawer Chest
No. 10-4086 TV Upper Cabinet
No. 10-4522P Music Cabinet
No. 10-4018 Three Drawer Upper Cabinet
No. 10-4512P Bookcase
No. 10-4088 Record Cabinet Upper Unit
No. 20-7104-3 Ottoman
No. 16-7439-5 Tufted Bench

For detailed specifications on:
Heirloom Custom Room Plan—see pages 362-363.
Upholstery—see pages 392-406.

Activities center for a gourmet cook...

Shown from left to right:
No. 10-6123P Trestle Table
No. 14-6041 Ladderback Side Chair
No. 10-4516P Refrigerator Unit
No. 10-4007 Upper Bookcase
No. 10-4503P Two Door Cabinet
No. 10-4530P Corner Desk
No. 10-4018 Three Drawer Upper Cabinet
No. 10-4511P Shutter Door Cabinet
No. 10-4019 Upper Bookcase
No. 10-4521P Four Drawer Apothecary Chest
No. 14-6182 Deacon's Bench

A personal hobby can turn some corner of your home into a fascinating center of do-it-yourself activity. But it takes the storage expertise of Custom Room Plan to organize the endless assortment of tools, molds, baking and serving ware that are essential to the gourmet's art. Colorful cooking center, above, is right off the kitchen. Trestle table also serves for dining.

or a ceramist

A bright corner near the window—and Custom Room Plan. Just what the ceramist ordered for a work center that's both efficient and compact . . . and delightfully decorative. Versatile compartmentalized desk unit and butcher block table demonstrate here only one of their many possible roles. Brick-look floor is actually easy care vinyl flooring.

Shown from left to right:
No. 10-4556P Study Center
No. 10-4058 Upper Bookcase
No. 10-4558 Hobby Bench
No. 14-6155 Hitchcock Bench

For detailed specifications on:
Heirloom Custom Room Plan—
see pages 362-363.
Decorated Furniture—
see pages 384-385.

CUSTOM ROOM PLAN
Office
Design

Want a business-like office at home, or a comfortable office downtown? Either way, you can't go wrong with Custom Room Plan, the storage formula that turns empty walls into handsome and copious cabinets. Add an Ethan Allen kneehole desk, a few chairs and tailored fabrics and accessories, and voilá—an office that most vice presidents might envy. Armoire style units create an office at home, below. Executive's office, opposite page, has impressive storage capabilities.

Shown below from left to right:
No. 20-7201 Chair
No. 10-4513P Cabinet 30″
No. 10-4026 Upper Bookcase
No. 10-4552P Cabinet 40″
No. 10-4067 Upper Cabinet
No. 10-4513P Cabinet 30″
No. 10-4026 Upper Bookcase
No. 10-9500 Pedestal Desk
No. 20-7606 Wing Chair
No. 10-9035 Console
No. 10-4514P Chest 30″

Shown at right from left to right:
No. 10-4521P Apothecary Chest 30″
No. 20-7213 Host Chair
No. 10-4553P 3-Door Cabinet 40″
No. 10-9500 Pedestal Desk
No. 13-7806 Cane Chair
No. 10-4511P 2-Door Cabinet 30″
No. 10-4018 Upper Cabinet Bookcase
No. 10-4551P 3-Door Chest 40″
No. 10-4059 Upper Cabinet Bookcase
No. 10-4511P 2-Door Cabinet 30″
No. 10-4018 Upper Cabinet Bookcase.

For detailed specifications on:
Heirloom Custom Room Plan—see pages 362-363.
Heirloom Accents and Tables—see pages 370-372
Upholstery—see pages 392-408

Ethan Allen
AMERICAN TRADITIONAL INTERIORS

REMODEL YOUR GARAGE
with Custom Room Plan

"Discovering" space within a home is often easier than and preferable to moving. Such discoveries come out of skillful remodeling—turning wasted or unsightly areas into attractive and useful rooms. Custom Room Plan plays a major decorative role in the conversion of an idle garage into a colorful all-purpose family area.

Shown from left to right:
No. 12-7623 Sofa
No. 24-8034 Butterfly
Drop Leaf End Table
No. 10-4553P Three Door Cabinet
No. 12-7621 Club Chair
No. 10-4555P Base Cabinet
No. 10-4532P Corner Chest
No. 10-4037 Upper Corner Bookcase
No. 10-4522P Music Cabinet
No. 10-4018 Three Drawer Upper Cabinet
No. 10-4512P Bookcase
No. 10-4017 Upper Cabinet Bookcase
No. 10-4522P Music Cabinet
No. 10-4086 TV Upper Unit
No. 10-4531P Console Extension Table
No. 14-6155 Hitchcock Bench
No. 12-9012 Spoonfoot Game Table
No. 24-6020 Mate's Chair
No. 12-7705 Pub Chair

TRANSFORM A PORCH
into a year-round room

Salvaging space from an unused porch adds a tremendous amount of new living area to a house that was bursting at the seams. Perky springtime mood derives from lively print and colorful mix of Antiqued White and Daffodil Yellow Custom Room Plan units—both in decorative armoire styling and in the more classic Shaker-inspired cabinets.

Shown from left to right:
No. 14-4027 Upper Cabinet
No. 14-4511P Shutter Door Cabinet
No. 14-7422 Ladderback Loveseat
No. 14-4027 Upper Cabinet
No. 14-4511P Shutter Door Cabinet
No. 14-4521P Apothecary Chest
No. 14-7421 Ladderback Club Chair
No. 14-6301 Farmhouse Chair
No. 24-8001 Pedestal Cocktail Table

Upper unit backs are lacquered balanced hardboard.

For details specifications on:
Heirloom Custom Room Plan—see pages 362-363.
American Foliage Colors—see pages 379-383.
Decorated Furniture—see pages 384-385.
Upholstery—see pages 392-406.

Ethan Allen
AMERICAN TRADITIONAL INTERIORS

REMODEL AN ATTIC
with Custom Room Plan

A dead attic becomes the private domain of a young teenager who used to share a room with her kid sister. Awkward walls are no problem when Custom Room Plan units take over—turning corners and making the most of whatever wall area is available. Feminine armoire style and paneled cabinets are suitable choices for feminine pink and white bedroom.

Shown from left to right:
No. 10-4524P Vanity
No. 10-4513P Two Door Cabinet
No. 10-4505P Corner Bookcase
No. 10-4028 Upper Cabinet.
Glass doors.
No. 10-4513P Two Door Cabinet
No. 10-4028 Upper Cabinet.
Glass doors.
No. 10-4510P Three Drawer Chest
No. 10-5026P Night Table
No. 10-5631 Tall Poster Bed

For detailed specifications on:
Heirloom Bedroom—see pages 364-366.
Heirloom Custom Room Plan—see pages 362-363.

Ethan Allen
AMERICAN TRADITIONAL INTERIORS

MAKEOVER A BEDROOM
into a children's playroom

An extra bedroom, furnished with leftovers, offered valuable space for a growing family. Now an enchanting playroom, it keeps a toddler and pre-school child out of their mother's hair. Custom Room Plan units, which store an overflowing collection of toys, grows up with the children as room next becomes an upstairs sitting area.

For detailed specifications on:
Heirloom Dining Room—see pages 366-369.
Heirloom Custom Room Plan—see pages 362-363.
Decorated Furniture—see pages 384-385.

Shown from left to right:
No. 10-4503P Two Door Cabinet
No. 10-4511P Shutter Door Cabinet
No. 10-4006 Upper Cabinet Bookcase
No. 10-4503P Two Door Cabinet
No. 10-4018 Upper Cabinet
No. 10-4591P Corner Desk
No. 14-6111 Hitchcock Chair
No. 10-4521P Apothecary Chest
No. 10-6183P Child's Table
No. 10-6180 Child's Chair

Upper unit backs are wood-grained balanced hardboard.

growing up rooms

You can't outgrow Custom Room Plan. From cradle to college Custom Room Plan "grows up" with the child, graduating with him as he reaches a new level of life and a new life style. A dramatic example of Custom Room Plan's amazing grow-up potential is seen in the three settings here—which are actually three versions of the same room. For the new infant right, only five Custom Room Plan units are needed. Growing youngster needs more space for his bulging accumulation of clothing, toys, sports things, so two more units are added, below—one a much needed desk. Guest-minded trundle bed now replaces the crib. Off to high school, our young man gets another upper cabinet—to house his television, records and stereo components. Change of carpeting and tailored window treatment fall in with more mature, no-nonsense mood of this new age level. It's a room that will serve him through the college years and beyond.

Shown at top from left to right:
No. 10-4019 Upper Bookcase
No. 10-4521P Four Drawer Apothecary Chest
No. 10-4510P Three Drawer Chest
No. 10-5624 Crib
No. 10-4511P Shutter Door Cabinet

Upper unit backs are wood-grained balanced hardboard.

Shown at bottom from left to right:
No. 10-5633 Captain's Trundle Bed
No. 10-4522P Music Cabinet
No. 10-4591P Corner Desk
No. 10-6002 Concord Chair
No. 10-4510P Three Drawer Chest
No. 10-4019 Upper Bookcase
No. 10-4521P Four Drawer Apothecary Chest
No. 10-4088 Record Utility Cabinet Upper Unit
No. 10-4511P Shutter Door Cabinet
No. 10-6183P Child's Table
No. 10-6180 Child's Chair

Ethan Allen
AMERICAN TRADITIONAL INTERIORS

Shown from left to right:
No. 10-4019 Upper Unit
No. 10-4511P Shutter Door Cabinet
No. 10-4522P Music Cabinet
No. 10-4591P Corner Desk
No. 10-6002 Concord Chair
No. 10-4019 Upper Unit
No. 10-4510P Three Drawer Chest
No. 10-4088 Record Utility Cabinet Upper Unit
No. 10-4521P Four Drawer Apothecary Chest
No. 10-5633 Captain's Trundle Bed
Upper unit backs are wood-grained
balanced hardboard.

For detailed specifications on:
Heirloom Custom Room Plan—see pages 362-363.
Heirloom Bedroom—see pages 364-366.

Simulated T-V reception.

197

for two girls

Custom Room Plan is a natural for the junior set. For here is furniture that makes it so easy to find everything, and that helps the youngster in learning how to organize his things and to keep his room tidy. Decorative, armoire style units were a fine choice for daffodil and white bedroom for two sisters, above. Units fit around window and turn the corner, providing desk space for both girls, and ample storage and shelf area as well.

Shown from left to right:
No. 14-7428 Ottoman
No. 10-4523P Fitted Vanity
No. 10-4505P Corner Bookcase
No. 10-4029 Armoire
No. 10-4513P Two Door Cabinet

No. 10-4524P Vanity
No. 14-7428 Ottoman
No. 10-4029 Armoire
No. 10-4513P Two Door Cabinet
No. 14-4631 Tall Poster Beds

Ethan Allen
AMERICAN TRADITIONAL INTERIORS

or a boy

Shaker inspired Custom Room Plan units sheathe the walls of a small dormer bedroom, providing fabulous storage potential for an undersized room. What's more, there's room for a guest—trundle bed has pull out drawer containing another mattress. Plaid wall covering, electric blue carpeting and handsome Nutmeg finish cabinets compose a room that's a wonderful domain for a boy in his growing up years.

Shown from left to right:
No. 10-5633 Captain's Trundle Bed
No. 10-4571P Four Drawer Dresser Desk
No. 10-6002 Concord Chair
No. 10-4510P Three Drawer Chest
No. 10-4532 Three Drawer Corner Cabinet

No. 10-4086 TV Upper Unit
No. 10-4511P Shutter Door Cabinet
No. 10-4018 Three Drawer Upper Cabinet
No. 10-4510P Three Drawer Chest
No. 10-4076 Upper Bookcase
No. 10-4551P Three Drawer Dresser

For detailed specification on:
Heirloom Custom Room Plan—see pages 362-363.
Heirloom Bedroom—see pages 364-366.
Upholstery—see pages 392-406.

round-the-clock with custom room plan

Much more than just the master bedroom, it's also a comfortable haven for 'round-the-clock use opposite. Television unit and desk combine with storage cabinets and copious armoire style upper units. Brilliant polished cotton print makes bedspread and headboard, covers walls and table.

Red, white and ironstone—the perfect recipe for country dining. Custom Room Plan wall stores and displays all dining appointments. Ladderback chairs in Sugarbush Red add to scarlet painted pecky cypress walls, patterned vinyl flooring, hurricane lighting fixture.

Shown from left to right:
No. 10-4029 Armoire
No. 10-4510P Three Drawer Chest
No. 10-4591P Corner Desk
No. 14-6111 Button Back Hitchcock Chair

No. 50-1010 TV Cabinet (photo-simulated TV reception)
No. 10-8640 Rectangular Cocktail Table
No. 20-7409 Lounge Chair
No. 20-7101 Ottoman

Shown from left to right:
No. 10-4007 Upper Bookcase
No. 10-4503P Shutter Door Cabinet
No. 10-4086 Upper Cabinet
No. 10-4521P Four Drawer Apothecary Chest

No. 10-4007 Upper Bookcase
No. 10-4503P Shutter Door Cabinet
No. 10-6123P Trestle Table
No. 24-6002 Ladderback Side Chairs
No. 24-6002A Ladderback Arm Chairs

For detailed specification on:
Heirloom Custom Room Plan—see pages 362-363.
Heirloom Dining Room—see pages 366-369.
Upholstery—see pages 392-406.
American Foliage Colors—see pages 379-383.

Upper unit backs are wood-grained balanced hardboard.

AMERICAN TRADITIONAL INTERIORS

all-in-one with custom room plan

Life in a one room apartment can be fun, but it's pretty confining too. One can dream of pushing out the four walls and making it all seem spacious and elegant. Turning the dream into a reality is actually possible—with the aid of Custom Room Plan—which provides abundant storage potential plus all the necessities for a full apartment life. Copious storage is available in wall-to-wall arrangement of bookshelf, door and drawer cabinets and home entertainment and stereo units. Trestle table behind slim-lined sleep sofa is informal dining area.

Shown from left to right:
No. 12-8024 End Table
No. 21-7043-5 Sleeper Sofa
No. 12-6063 Harvest Trestle Table
No. 24-6011A Spindle Back Arm Chairs
No. 24-6011 Spindle Back Side Chairs
No. 10-4019 Upper Bookcase
No. 10-4512P Bookcase
No. 10-4017 Upper Cabinet
No. 10-4510P Three Drawer Chest
No. 10-4532P Three Drawer Corner Chest
No. 10-4037 Upper Corner Bookcase
No. 10-4510P Three Drawer Chest
No. 10-4018 Three Drawer Upper Cabinet
No. 10-4511P Shutter Door Cabinet
No. 10-4086 TV Upper Unit
No. 10-4594P Speaker Cabinet
No. 10-4525P Hi-Fi Cabinet
No. 12-8007 Revolving Octagonal Table
No. 20-7412 Lounge Chair
No. 14-9218 Pedestal Table

Upper unit backs are wood-grained balanced hardboard.

For detailed specifications on:
Heirloom Custom Room Plan—see pages 362-364.
Upholstery—see pages 392-406.
Antiqued Pine Dining Room—see pages 379-381.
Antiqued Pine Occasional Tables—see pages 381-382.
American Foliage Colors—see pages 379-383.

Ethan Allen
AMERICAN TRADITIONAL INTERIORS

storage in glowing color

YELLOW

What a great way to put color into a room—with Custom Room Plan units in a choice of three hues. Use sunny yellow for a radiant living room starring perky print and Georgian Court tables, below. Or blue armoire-style cabinets teamed with plaid carpet and decorated designs. For a girl's room, opposite bottom: the glitter of white cabinets, silvery paper spiced with shocking pink.

Shown from left to right:
No. 11-6213 Drop Leaf Table
No. 20-7192 Loveseat
No. 14-4511P Shutter Door Cabinet
No. 14-4027 Upper Cabinet
No. 14-4553P Three Door Cabinet
No. 14-4066 Upper Bookcase

No. 14-4511P Shutter Door Cabinet
No. 14-4027 Upper Cabinet
No. 20-7202 Barrel Chair
No. 11-8203 Tripod Tea Table
No. 20-7202 Barrel Chair
No. 11-8200 Rectangular Cocktail Table

Custom Room Plan pieces are available in Nutmeg finish or American Traditional Colors: 400—Alabaster White 409—Antiqued Blue 411—Daffodil Yellow Upper unit backs are lacquered balanced hardboard.

For detailed specifications on:
Georgian Court Occasional Tables—see pages 375-376.
Heirloom Custom Room Plan—see pages 362-363.
Upholstery—see pages 392-406.

Ethan Allen
AMERICAN TRADITIONAL INTERIORS

BLUE

Shown above from left to right:
No. 10-6085 Drop Leaf Tea Wagon
No. 14-4008 Upper Bookcase
No. 14-4502P Two Door Cabinet
No. 14-4028 Upper Cabinet with Glass Doors
No. 14-4513P Two Door Cabinet
No. 14-4552P Three Door Cabinet
No. 14-4028 Upper Cabinet with Glass Doors
No. 14-4513P Two Door Cabinet
No. 14-4008 Upper Bookcase
No. 14-4502P Two Door Cabinet
No. 14-4521P Four Drawer Apothecary Chest
No. 14-6080 Bannister Side Chairs
No. 14-6011 Thumb Back Chairs
No. 10-6074P Harvest Drop Leaf Table
No. 14-6182 Deacon's Bench

WHITE

Shown right from left to right:
No. 14-4555P Cabinet
No. 14-4019 Upper Bookcase
No. 14-4006 Upper Cabinet Bookcase
No. 14-4503P Two Door Cabinet
No. 14-4037 Upper Corner Bookcase
No. 14-4530P Corner Desk
No. 14-6111 Hitchcock Chair
No. 14-5010 Mirror
No. 14-4570P Six Drawer Dresser
No. 14-4501P Three Drawer Chest
No. 14-9218 Square Pedestal Cocktail Table

For detailed specifications on:
Heirloom Custom Room Plan—
see pages 362-363.
Heirloom Dining Room—
see pages 366-369.
Decorated Furniture—
see pages 384-385.

Shown from left to right:
No. 10-4553P Three Door Cabinet
No. 10-4056 Upper Cabinet Bookcase
No. 10-4511P Shutter Door Cabinet
No. 10-4019 Upper Bookcase
No. 10-4515P Refreshment Base
No. 10-4030 Refreshment Upper Unit
No. 10-4532P Three Drawer Corner Chest
No. 50-1010 Color TV
No. 50-1101 Upper Stereo Unit

Shown from left to right:
No. 10-4557P Sewing Center
No. 10-4018 Three Drawer Upper Cabinet
No. 14-6041 Ladderback Side Chair
No. 10-4531P Console Extension Table
No. 10-4521P Four Drawer Apothecary Chest
No. 10-4512P Bookcase
No. 10-4019 Upper Bookcase
No. 10-4511P Shutter Door Cabinet
No. 10-4086 TV Upper Unit
No. 10-4511P Shutter Door Cabinet
No. 10-4019 Upper Bookcase

For detailed specifications on Heirloom
Custom Room Plan—see pages 362-363.

custom room plan for family living or a special hobby

How do you turn an empty basement room into a bright and colorful center for family enjoyment? You do it with Custom Room Plan units galore— using a full complement of all that's needed for an informal center: television, stereo and refreshment units plus plenty of bookshelf and storage space area.

An unused upstairs bedroom becomes a splendid sewing center; the transformation achieved by Custom Room Plan furniture. Special sewing unit works in tandem with console extension table to establish efficient sewing corner while additional units store and organize the tools of the trade and all materials.

custom room plan office

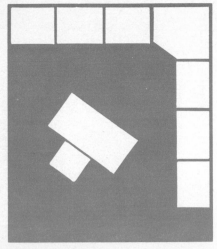

In this age of free-lance, part-time or entirely home-based careers, the at-home office becomes as much a household requisite as a kitchen or living room. For those who live in a spacious home, some room can be set aside for such a purpose. Others with an economy of space have to locate their office within the realm of existing rooms—finding some corner, alcove or bedroom area that can serve the purpose. Then Custom Room Plan units in Antiqued Pine can put the space to work, transforming walls into floor-to-ceiling cabinets, with louvered doors, decorating molding.

Shown from left to right:
No. 16-6000A Bowback Windsor Arm Chair
No. 16-6013 Flip-Top Table
No. 12-4037 Upper Cabinet Bookcase
No. 12-4031 Shutter Door Cabinet
No. 12-4037 Upper Cabinet Bookcase
No. 12-4031 Shutter Door Cabinet
No. 12-4001 Corner Cabinet
No. 12-4006 Upper Bookcase
No. 12-4000 Three Drawer Chest
No. 12-4036 Upper Bookcase
No. 12-4031 Shutter Door Cabinet

Upper Bookcase backs are wood-grained balance hardboard
For detailed specifications on:
Antiqued Pine Custom Room Plan—see pages 377-378.
Royal Charter Dining Room—see pages 389-390.

decorative design for a foyer

Ruggedly handsome, as on the opposite page, Custom Room Plan now takes on pretty and elegant manners in its decorative provincial version—featuring paneled doors and stately armoire shaped upper units. Used in crisp white finish, it composes an impressive foyer with the extra attribute of fabulous storage space. Glass doored cabinets are backed with one's own choice of fabric.

Shown from left to right:
No. 10-4029 Armoire. Full glass door.
No. 10-4513P Two Door Cabinet
No. 10-4505P Corner Bookcase
For detailed specifications on Heirloom Custom Room Plan—see pages 362-363.

ETHAN ALLEN
ANTIQUED PINE

Crafted of solid pine and beautiful veneers.

A marvelous mood for the casual life—Ethan Allen Antiqued Pine, a casual, rustic and handsomely rugged style that's hardy and hearty with mellow informality. Within the collection itself is a diversity of looks. One, a country style, features single paneled doors, plank tops, apothecary doors and drawers, porcelain knobs, dentil molding and ogee bases. Offering a more sophisticated and imposing style are those designs with plinth bases, multi-paneled doors, Colonial arches and prominent hardware. Offered in dining room, bedroom, occasional and Custom Room Plan designs, many styles are available in five dramatic American Foliage colors.

Antiqued Pine

for special events and every day family dining

Some dining rooms are so full of rich hospitality and a warm family spirit that they become stage center rather than merely a place to take meals. The family itself lingers there long after the dinner has ended; the room has an almost chameleon quality that lets it take on the color of any special occasion with the greatest of ease. Such dining rooms could be those furnished with Ethan Allen Antiqued Pine—a rugged, ingratiating style that spells home and joyous occasions. In setting right, the event is an old-fashioned Christmas.

Shown from left to right:
No. 12-6025 **Deacon's Bench**
No. 12-6042 **Side Chairs**
No. 12-6042A **Arm Chairs**
No. 12-6053 **Pedestal Extension Table**
No. 12-6017/12-6028 **Buffet with Hutch Top.**
Back is wood-grained balanced hardboard.

For detailed specifications on:
Antiqued Pine Dining Room—
see pages 379-381.

Ethan Allen
AMERICAN TRADITIONAL INTERIORS

to celebrate a special occasion

Celebrate America's birth date—the Fourth of July—with a colorful barbeque, cooked outdoors but served inside. The flavoring touches of red, white and blue are introduced in dishes and paper accents. Handsome Antiqued Pine hutch has paneled doors and ceramic pulls, ample surface for serving.

Shown opposite from left to right:
No. 12-6033 48" Round Pedestal Table
No. 12-6000 Captain's Chair
No. 24-9010 Drop Leaf Serving Cart
No. 12-6026/6029 Buffet with Hutch Cabinet.
Back is wood-grained balanced hardboard.
For detailed specifications on:
Antiqued Pine Dining Room—see pages 379-381.
American Foliage Colors—see pages 379-383.

Toast the newlyweds with a festive wedding breakfast hosted by a handsome dining area of Ethan Allen Antiqued Pine. Oval table extends, and imposing buffet and china is a handsome ornament on long wall. To spice the crisp green and white color scheme is American Foliage dry sink in Holly Green.

Shown below from left to right:
No. 24-6055 Dry Sink
No. 12-6006/6019 Buffet with China Cabinet.
Back is wood-grained balanced hardboard.
No. 12-6024 Spoonfoot Oval Extension Table
No. 12-6010 Duxbury Side Chairs
No. 12-6010A Duxbury Arm Chairs

Ethan Allen
AMERICAN TRADITIONAL INTERIORS

215

wine-tasting
or housewarming

Give a wine-tasting party—much more interesting than the usual cocktail bash and educational too. Keep it simple rather than elaborate as in setting above. Or have the 'block' in to welcome new neighbors, with cake, coffee and a big pot of flowers than they can take home. Hosting both events is lustrous, informal Antiqued Pine, mixed with American Foliage accents of Autumn Gold and Sugarbush Red, and black decorated chairs.

Shown opposite from left to right:
No. 12-6005 Trestle Bench
No. 12-6044 End Extension Trestle Table
No. 14-6041A Ladderback Arm Chair
No. 24-6006/6009 Buffet with Hutch Top.
Back is wood-grained balanced hardboard.
No. 14-6041 Ladderback Side Chair

Shown above from left to right:
No. 12-6007/6009 Buffet with Hutch Top
Back is wood-grained balanced hardboard.
No. 24-6055 Dry Sink
No. 12-6004 Round Spoonfoot Extension Table
No. 12-6001 Mate's Chairs

For detailed specifications on:
Antiqued Pine Dining Room—see pages 379-381.
American Foliage Colors—see pages 379-383.
Decorated Furniture—see pages 384-385.

say hello or

A clever hostess smartly "bribes" her summer friends into lending a helping hand when spring comes round. Cokes and snacks turn a cooperative house opening into a special event that is cause for celebration. To utilize chopped up space of dining area in summer cottage, below, corner cabinets fit neatly into available corners while dining is provided by round pedestal table. For added spice, mates chairs are in American Foliage Sugarbush Red. Round area rug brightens the arrangement.

Shown from left to right:
No. 12-6016/6018 Corner Hutch.
Back is wood-grained balanced hardboard.
No. 24-6040 Mate's Chairs
No. 12-6013P 42" Round Center Pedestal Table
No. 24-6065 Lazy Susan

For detailed specifications on:
Antiqued Pine Dining Room—see pages 379-381.
American Foliage Colors—see pages 379-383.

happy birthday

Shown from left to right:
No. 12-6011 **High Back Catkin Side Chairs**
No. 12-6011A **High Back Catkin Arm Chairs**
No. 12-9010 **Drop Leaf Serving Cart**
No. 12-6003 **Trestle Table**
No. 12-6005 **Trestle Bench**
No. 12-6026/6029 **Buffet with Hutch Cabinet.**
Back is wood-grained balanced hardboard.

It's a child's birthday party with all the trimmings. Use crepe paper, balloons—loads of traditional party favors. Comfortable dining room, above with trestle table, catkin chairs, expansive hutch, and gay area rug, rises to the occasion.

For detailed specifications on:
Antiqued Pine Dining Room—see pages 379-381.

tropical brunch or après ski

Take the heat out of a summer day with a breakfast starring chilled tropical fruits, adding their glorious colors to the mix of tangy hues, below. Spruce Blue arm chairs are combined with Antiqued Pine designs.

Shown below from left to right:
No. 24-6002A Ladderback Arm Chair
No. 12-6025 Deacon's Bench
No. 12-6064 60″ Trestle Table
No. 12-6002 Ladderback Side Chair
No. 12-6026 56″ Buffet
No. 12-6029 56″ Hutch Top. Back is wood-grained balanced hardboard.

For detailed specifications on:
Antiqued Pine Dining Room—see pages 379-381.
American Foliage Colors—see pages 379-383.

Small wonder that appealing dining room is the center of family fun, opposite. Here it caters a fondue supper after a long day on the trails. Dry sink in Autumn Gold interjects a rich accent to the setting.

Shown opposite from left to right:
No. 24-6055 Stereo Dry Sink
No. 12-6031 Country Chairs
No. 12-6063 Harvest Trestle Table
No. 12-9008 Console Cabinet
No. 07-1522 Homestead Wall Cupboard

Ethan Allen
AMERICAN TRADITIONAL INTERIORS

Antiqued Pine Accents

Here's a lively assortment of Antiqued Pine accent pieces that lend themselves easily to the casual life, and are ideal designs for all-purpose living and family rooms. Shown on these two pages are commodious bar, dry sink, game table, captain's chairs and stool, glass topped coffee table, chair table, folding cellarette and stereo dry sink.

Shown from left to right:
No. 20-7049 **Two Cushion Tuxedo Sofa**
No. 12-9504 **Home Folding Bar**
No. 12-9505 **Swivel Bar Stool**
No. 12-8081 **Square Cocktail Table**
No. 12-6055 **Stereo Dry Sink**
No. 12-9012 **Spoonfoot Game Table**
No. 12-6020 **Swivel Mate's Chair**

For detailed specifications on Antiqued Pine Decorative Accents—see pages 381-383.

All items are solid Pine with selected veneers where noted in a skillfully shaded and hand-distressed in Old Tavern finish "aged" look.

*Description of American Foliage Colors:
402 Sugarbush Red   404 Autumn Gold
403 Pine Cone   405 Holly Green
406 Spruce Blue

No. 12-9004 Two Drawer Dry Sink. 38"x19"x37"H.
Removable partition in left drawer and adjustable shelf behind doors.
Matching woodgrained Formica plastic top.

*No. 24-9004 Same item in American Foliage Colors with black Formica plastic work surface.

No. 12-9515 Chair Table. Shown as chair: 40"x23"x54"H. Shown as table: 40" diameter x 29"H.
*No. 24-9515 Same in American Foliage Colors.

No. 12-9514 Folding Cellarette. 28"x18"x 37"H. Opens to 36"x12". One drawer. Three storage shelves. Stain-resistant Melamine plastic top.

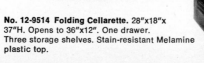

Antiqued Pine accents

Add architectural enrichment and extensive storage capacity with the addition of any of these handsome Antiqued Pine accent designs. Shown on these two pages are decorative étagères, handsome bookstack and gun cabinets, library units, credenza console and console cabinets, and mirrors. Most designs are also available in American Foliage colors.

No. 12-9516 Etagere. 34"x17"x83"H. Bonnet Top is selected veneer. Finished paneled back.
*No. 24-9516 Same item in American Foliage Colors.
No. 12-9015 Bookstacks. 28"x13"x80"H. Center shelves in upper section are adjustable. One adjustable shelf behind doors. Back is wood-grained balanced hardboard.
*No. 24-9015 Same item in American Foliage Colors.
No. 12-9013 Gun Cabinet. 28"x15"x75"H. Two doors. Storage compartment with lock and key. Back is wood-grained balanced hardboard.

Ethan Allen
AMERICAN TRADITIONAL INTERIORS

Shown above:
No. 12-9518 Credenza Console. 52"x15"x28"H.
Door panels are selected veneer. Finished interior.
One adjustable shelf behind doors.
***No. 24-9518** Same item in American Foliage Colors.
No. 12-9517 Oval Framed Mirror. 28"x38"H.
Heavy moulding with shadowbox frame.
***No. 24-9517** Same item in American Foliage Colors.
No. 16-6001A Ladderback Arm Chair. 42"H.
Fiber Seat.
Shown at left:
No. 12-9014 Library Wall Unit. 34"x14"x80"H.
Two adjustable shelves and one adjustable shelf
behind two paneled doors. Back is wood-grained
balance hardboard.
***No. 24-9014** Same item in American Foliage Colors.
Shown at right:
No. 12-9008 Console Cabinet. 30"x13"x30"H.
One drawer. One adjustable shelf.
***No. 24-9008** Same item in American Foliage Colors.
No. 12-9009 Framed Oval Mirror. 24"x36"H.
***No. 24-9009** Same item in American Foliage Colors.

For detailed specifications on:
Antiqued Pine Accent Pieces—see pages 382-383.
American Foliage Colors—see pages 379-383.
Royal Charter Dining Room—see pages 389-390.

a handsome choice of desks.

No. 12-9513
Three Drawer Roll-Top Desk.
40"x21"x43" H. Letter
compartments behind roll-top.
*No. 24-9513 Same item in
American Foliage Colors.

No. 12-9519 Roll Top Desk. 55"x28"x48" H.
Roll Top is equipped with a lock. Two
Pendaflex equipped file drawers. Seven
drawers below, three drawers on top. Cubby
hole interior.

Desks—delightful and useful accents in any room of the house—are expressed in the variety of designs for the Ethan Allen Antiqued Pine collection. Among the styles seen here are charming roll-top desks, rustic pedestal desks and commodious seven drawer desks. Tall, drop-lid Secretary can fit on a narrow wall space. Where designated, desks are offered in American Foliage Colors as well as Old Tavern finish.

No. 12-9503
Four Drawer Pedestal Desk.
32″x25″x35″ H.
***No. 24-9503** Same item in
American Foliage Colors.

Shown at left:
No. 12-9506 Drop Lid
Four Drawer Pedestal Desk.
54″x24″x36½″ H.
Removable partitions and deep
storage area under top lid.
Four·letter compartments.
***No. 24-9506** Same item in
American Foliage Colors.

No. 12-9512 Secretary Top. 24″x10″x43″H. Two
adjustable shelves behind antiqued glass doors
and wooden mullions. Back is wood-grained
balanced hardboard.
***No. 24-9512** Same item in American Foliage Colors.
No. 12-9511 Three drawer Secretary Base.
24″x16″x39″ H. Drop Lid Front
with two pullout slides for support.
Deep file drawer at bottom.
***No. 24-9511** Same item in American Foliage colors.

Shown at right:
No. 12-9509 Seven Drawer
Double Pedestal Desk.
54″x24″x30″ H. Two
deep file drawers with
metal file supports
in bottom left drawer.
Center drawer
has pencil tray.

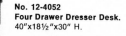

No. 12-4052
Four Drawer Dresser Desk.
40″x18½″x30″ H.

No. 12-4071
Four Drawer Dresser Desk.
48″x18½″x30″ H.

*Description of
American Foliage Colors:
402—Sugarbush Red
403—Pine Cone
404—Autumn Gold
405—Holly Green
406—Spruce Blue

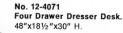

For detailed specifications
on Antiqued Pine Accents
and Occasional Tables—
see pages 381-383

No. 12-8081 Square Cocktail Table.
40"x40"x18"H.
*No. 24-8081 Same item in American
Foliage colors.

with glass tops

No. 12-8083 Rectangular End Table.
27"x22"x22"H.
*No. 24-8083 Same item in American
Foliage colors.

No. 12-8080 Rectangular Cocktail Table.
56"x26"x18"H.
*No. 24-8080 Same item in American Foliage
colors.

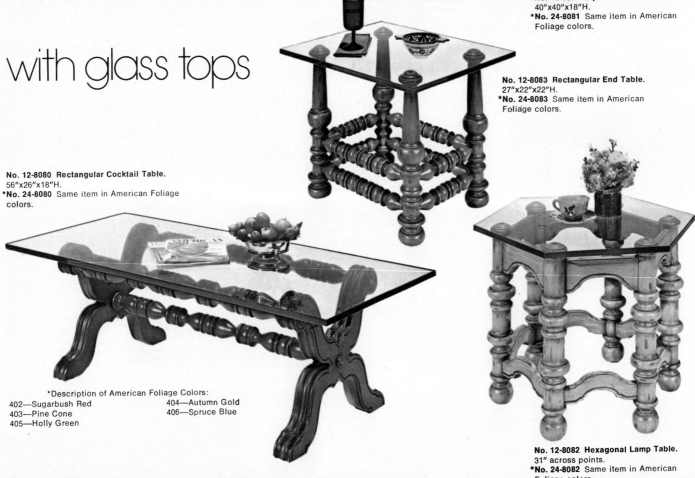

*Description of American Foliage Colors:
402—Sugarbush Red   404—Autumn Gold
403—Pine Cone   406—Spruce Blue
405—Holly Green

No. 12-8082 Hexagonal Lamp Table.
31" across points.
*No. 24-8082 Same item in American
Foliage colors.

228

No. 12-8059 Pedestal Cocktail Table.
56"x22"x22"H. One drop-lid compartment.
*No. 24-8059 Same item in American Foliage colors.

No. 12-8058 Revolving Cogwheel Table.
38" diameter x 17"H.
*No. 24-8058 Same item in American Foliage colors.

Shown below:
No. 12-8075 Square Commode Lamp Table.
26"x26"x22"H.
*No. 24-8075 Same item in American Foliage colors.
No. 12-8074 Hexagonal Lamp Table.
29"x25"x22"H.
*No. 24-8074 Same item in American Foliage colors.
No. 12-8070 Cabinet Cocktail Table.
56"x22"x17"H.
*No. 24-8070 Same item in American Foliage colors.

For detailed specifications on Antiqued Pine Occasional Tables—see pages 381-382.

Ethan Allen
AMERICAN TRADITIONAL INTERIORS

antiqued pine conversation pieces

No. 12-8031
Round Pedestal Cocktail Table.
38" diameter x 16"H. Extra heavy top.
*No. 24-8031 Same item in
American Foliage Colors.

No. 12-8020
Rectangular Cocktail Table.
54"x22"x17"H.
*No. 24-8020 Same item in
American Foliage Colors.

No. 12-8034
Butterfly Drop Leaf Table.
20"x27"x24"H. opens to 37"x27"
with leaves extended. One drawer.
*No. 24-8034 Same item in
American Foliage Colors.

Shown below left to right:
No. 12-8037 Commode Table. 25" Square x 24"H. Two drawers.
*No. 24-8037 Same item in American Foliage Colors.
No. 12-8021 Drop Leaf Harvest Cocktail Table. 54"x20"x17"H
Opens to 54"x26" with leaves extended.
*No. 24-8021 Same item in American Foliage Colors.
No. 12-8024 **End Table.** 21½"x29"x24"H.
*No. 24-8024 Same item in American Foliage Colors.

**For detailed specifications on
Antiqued Pine Tables—see pages 381-382**

Shown at left:
No. 12-8026 Dough Box Magazine End Table. 20″x30″x25″H. Deep storage area under lid.
*No. 24-8026 Same item in American Foliage Colors.

Shown above:
No. 12-8006 Rudder Drop Leaf Table. 28″x13″x23″H. Opens to 28″x32″ with leaves extended. One drawer.
*No. 24-8006 Same item in American Foliage Colors.

Shown below:
No. 12-8032 Two Drawer Step End Table. 20″x30″x24″H.
*No. 24-8032 Same item in American Foliage Colors.

No. 12-8030 Double Pedestal Oval Cocktail Table. 58″x23″x16″H. Extra heavy top.

No. 12-8036 Revolving Drum Table. 28″ diameter x 27″H.
*No. 24-8036 Same item in American Foliage Colors.

*Description of American Foliage Colors:
402 — Sugarbush Red
403 — Pine Cone
404 — Autumn Gold
405 — Holly Green
406 — Spruce Blue

Antiqued Pine accents with country cousin charm

*Description of American Foliage Colors:
402—Sugarbush Red; 403—Pine Cope; 404—Autumn
Gold; 405—Holly Green; 406—Spruce Blue

Delightful and decorative, these distinctive Antiqued Pine designs add flavor and authentic touches wherever they are used. Many were inspired by Colonial favorites—such as the dough box, revolving drum, rudder, sugar bin and bookstand tables. Others shown include a diminutive record cabinet, versatile tea cart, treat tables and butler's tables, pedestal and trestle cocktail tables. Most are available in American Foliage colors.

For detailed specifications on
Antiqued Pine Accents and Tables—see pages 381-383.
American Foliage Colors—see pages 379-383.

Shown from left to right:
No. 12-9003 Sugar Bin End Table.
28"x17"x25"H. One drawer. Large storage bin behind retractable lift-lid.
*No. 24-9003 Same item in American Foliage Colors.
No. 12-8053 Record Cabinet. 26"x15"x 22"H. Vertical removable partition behind doors.
No. 12-9010 Drop Leaf Serving Tea Cart. 20½"x32"x29"H. Opens to 40½"x32" with both leaves extended. One drawer.
*No. 24-9010 Same item in American Foliage Colors.
No. 12-8054 Square Pedestal Cocktail Table. 19½" square x 16"H.
*No. 24-8054 Same item in American Foliage Colors.
*No. 14-9218 Same in Decorated Finishes.

No. 12-8007 Revolving Octagonal Table. 26"x26"x22"H. Table sits on swivel base.
*No. 24-8007 Same item in American Foliage Colors.
No. 12-8000 Trestle Cocktail Table. 54"x22"x17"H.
*No. 24-8000 Same item in American Foliage Colors.
No. 08-3507 Treat Tables. 16"x21"x24"H. Tops are supported by side aprons with movable bar for folding mobility. Set of four with rack.
No. 08-3508 Treat Tables. Same as above. Set of two. No rack included.
No. 12-8001 Square Pedestal Cocktail Table. 23" square x 18"H.
*No. 24-8001 Same item in American Foliage Colors.

233

Antiqued Pine...

colorful country bedrooms

It's a natural look for Antiqued Pine: bedrooms that convey warmth, nostalgia, even an old-fashioned mood. A balm to the emotions as well as to the eye, they blend calico, patchwork, rug rugs and oil lamps with basketry, pewter, copper and ironstone. Walls can be whitewashed stucco, rough hewn paneling or Victorian style wallpaper. These are well lived-in rooms and look it—with vibrant colors and patterns and a goodly peppering of accessories. The handsome bedroom on these two pages interprets the farmhouse look with lively manners. Large room takes imposing, large-scaled furniture including four poster bed, triple dresser, capacious armoire and twin bonnet top mirrors. A zingy blend of two distinct patterns makes for interesting bed dressing; accessories are a rich collection of favorite things.

Shown opposite from left to right:
No. 12-5013 Triple Dresser
No. 12-5020 Bonnet Top Mirror
No. 12-5026 Cabinet Night Tables.
No. 12-5602 Poster Bed with Canopy Frame

Shown at top:
No. 12-5013 Thirteen Drawer Triple Dresser. 72"x21"x34"H. Two tray drawers behind door. Horizontal divider in top end drawers.
No. 12-5020 Bonnet Top Mirrors. Overall 30"x50"H.

Shown center:
No. 12-5015 Armoire. 45"x21"x76"H. Four pull-out trays behind doors. Three drawers in lower section. Molded "Bonnet Top". Massive scale antiqued hinges and hardware.

Shown left:
No. 12-5026 Cabinet Night Tables. 26"x16" x28"H. Two doors. One drawer.
No. 12-5602 Poster Bed. Overall 68"H. Can be extended to 80"H. with extension posts which are included. Available in 4'6 or 5' sizes only.
No. 12-5991 75" Canopy Frame
No. 12-5024 Lingerie Chest. 25"x17"x52"H. Three drawers, adjustable shelf behind doors.

For detailed specifications on Antiqued Pine Bedroom—see pages 378-379.

Antiqued Pine... country bedrooms

Pine paneled walls and a pride of patterns give country house flavor to large and comfortable bedroom. Furniture includes bonnet top spindle headboard and paneled door triple dresser. Trestle cocktail table serves as a useful bench.

Shown from left to right:
No. 20-7161 Lounge Chair
No. 12-5025 Chest on Chest
No. 12-5013 Thirteen Drawer Triple Dresser
No. 12-5020 Mirror
No. 12-5026 Cabinet Night Table
No. 12-5611 Bonnet Top Spindle Headboard
No. 12-5026 Cabinet Night Table

Shown at right:
No. 12-5030 Hutch Mirror. 71"x11½"x 45"H. Six drawers. Mirror: 42"x32" overall.
No. 12-5013 Thirteen-Drawer Triple Dresser. 72"x21"x34"H. Two tray drawers behind door. Horizontal divider in top end drawers.

Ethan Allen
AMERICAN TRADITIONAL INTERIORS

a nostalgic mood

A room to dream in—with old-fashioned Victorian charm and Antiqued Pine furniture. Compact triple dresser and eight drawer chest fit neatly on available wall space. Canonball bed has quilted white throw and matching dust-ruffle. In inset is four drawer nightstand with cheval mirror.

Shown at left:
No. 12-5016 Four Drawer Commode Night Table. 21"x17"x28"H.
No. 06-3506 Cheval Mirror.
18"x18"x24"H. Storage drawer.

Shown from left to right:
No. 12-5600 Cannonball Bed
No. 12-5016 Four Drawer Commode Night Table
No. 12-5003 Eleven Drawer Triple Dresser
No. 14-6110 Hitchcock Side Chair
No. 12-5005 Chest on Chest

For detailed specifications on:
Antiqued Pine Bedroom—see pages 378-379.
Upholstery—see pages 392-406.

Romantic pink, blue and white bedroom contrasts the rich and lustrous finish of Ethan Allen Antiqued Pine with soft, luxurious pastels. Handsome panel-spindle bed is dramatized by drapery panel which matches Victorian-style block print of quilted spread. Colonial rag rug and a mix of antiques flavor the eye-pleasing arrangement. Matching nightstands give balance to the panel design.

Shown above from left to right:
No. 12-4038 Framed Mirror
No. 12-5002 Ten Drawer Double Dresser
No. 12-5004 Seven Drawer Chest
No. 16-6000A Bowback Windsor Arm Chair
No. 12-5006 Two Drawer Cabinet Night Table
No. 12-5601 Panel/Spindle Bed
No. 12-5006 Two Drawer Cabinet Night Table

Shown at right:
No. 12-5604 Spindle Bed.
Overall 41″H. Available in 3′3″, 4′6″ and 5′ sizes.

No. 12-5605 Panel/Spindle Headboard. 41″ H. Available in 5′ and 6′6″ sizes.

Ethan Allen
AMERICAN TRADITIONAL INTERIORS

a boy's domain

Space saving bedroom designs are an important feature of the Antiqued Pine collection. Seen in boy's room, above, is the Tri-Way trundle bed, which can be adjusted to three different positions. Here it's a bunk bed in a rustic and informal room, a position that makes the most out of an awkward floor plan. Playing up the glowing dark brown finish of Antiqued Pine is the rich brown, beige and white color scheme.

Shown above from left to right:
No. 12-5013 Thirteen Drawer Triple Dresser
No. 12-5000 Mirror
No. 12-5614 Bunk Beds
No. 12-9513 Roll Top Desk
No. 12-6041 Ladder Back Side Chair
Shown at left:
No. 12-5023 Eight Drawer
Triple Dresser. 66"x21"x
33"H. Removable partition in
center and bottom drawers.

For detailed specifications on:
Antiqued Pine Bedroom Pieces—see pages 378-379.

Antiqued Pine Custom Room Plan

for family fun

What a great look in modular storage! With its lustrous finish, louvred doors, white pulls and dentil moulding, these Custom Room Plan units build character in any room. All this and a wide choice of storage styles including new refrigerator, refreshment, and television units. These new units are part of the fabulous storage walls of this all-purpose family room, styled as a showcase for a golfer's trophies and an informal living and entertainment area as well.

Shown at left from left to right:
No. 12-6042 Arrow Back Side Chair
No. 12-9012 Game Table
No. 12-4034 Refreshment Base Unit
No. 12-4035 Refreshment Upper Unit.
Back is wood-grained balanced hardboard.
No. 12-4002 Refrigerator Unit
No. 12-4006 Upper Bookcase.
Back is wood-grained balanced hardboard.
No. 50-1011 TV & Base Cabinet
No. 12-4037 Upper Bookcase Cabinet.
Back is wood-grained balanced hardboard.
No. 12-4001 Corner Base Cabinet
No. 12-4007 Upper Corner Bookcase.
Back is wood-grained balanced hardboard.
No. 12-4051 Chest
No 08-3515 Magazine Basket
No. 12-9004 Dry Sink
Simulated T-V reception.

For detailed specifications on:
Antiqued Pine Custom Room Plan,
see pages 377-378.
Antiqued Pine Dining Room and Accent Pieces
—see pages 378-383.

Ethan Allen
AMERICAN TRADITIONAL INTERIORS

241

Antiqued Pine
Custom Room Plan makes

a comfortable office...

It doesn't take much more than a wall of Antiqued Pine Custom Room Plan units to create a small home office or study area. All that was added, below, was roll top desk and a trestle table—for a completely coordinated effect. Rich counterpoint to the furniture is apricot carpeting and robust plaid.

Show below from left to right:
No. 20-7213 Chair
No. 12-9519 Roll Top Desk
No. 12-4002 Refrigerator Base Unit
No. 12-4006 Upper Bookcase. Back is wood-grained balanced hardboard.
No. 12-4034 Refreshment Base Unit

No. 12-4035 Refreshment Upper Unit. Back is wood-grained balanced hardboard.
No. 12-4070 Double Dresser
No. 12-4008 Upper Cabinet Bookcase. Book is wood-grained balanced hardboard.
No. 12-6064 Trestle Table

a dining area in the kitchen

A small dining room—but no lack of vital storage space. Just the opposite, in fact, as handsome Antique Pine Custom Room Plan transforms a small corner into a decorative wall with generous storage potential and serving surface. In matching finish—trestle table, deacon's bench and chairs.

Shown opposite from left to right:
No. 12-6044 Trestle Table
Top is selected veneer.
No. 12-6011 Side Chair
No. 12-4000 Chest
No. 12-4006 Upper Bookcase.
Back is wood-grained balanced hardboard.
No. 12-4001 Corner Cabinet

No. 12-4007 Upper Corner Bookcase. Back is wood-grained balanced hardboard.
No. 12-4031 Shutter Drawer Cabinet
No. 12-4037 Upper Cabinet.
Back is wood-grained balanced hardboard.
No. 12-6025 Deacon's Bench

For detailed specifications on:
Antiqued Pine Custom Room Plan—see pages 377-378.
Antiqued Pine Dining Room, Accents—see pages 378-383.
Upholstery see pages 392-406.

242

rooms with radiant good looks and fine storage

A robust and rugged style, Antiqued Pine Custom Room Plan units display their remarkable versatility as they adapt to rooms with an unquestionably pretty rather than tailored mood. Certainly the two interiors shown on these pages illustrate the point with sparkling clarity. Shown above is a living room in a vacation home that is enjoyed all year long. Walls of Custom Room Plan units provide superb storage and usable shelf space as well. Sumptuous Chippendale wing chairs in cherry velvet and delicate floral print, used on sofa and for intriguing window dressing, combine for a look that is pretty and decorative.

Shown above from left to right:

No. 12-8034 **Drop Leaf End Table**	No. 12-4030 **Chest**
No. 20-7062 **Love Seat**	No. 12-4047 **TV Upper Unit**
No. 12-4030 **Chest**	Back is wood-grained balanced hardboard.
No. 12-4021 **Stereo Speaker Cabinet**	No. 12-4031 **Shutter Door Cabinet**
No. 12-4020 **Stereo Cabinet**	No. 12-4037 **Upper Cabinet Bookcase**
No. 12-4021 **Stereo Speaker Cabinet**	No. 12-4034 **Refreshment Base Unit**
No. 20-7403 **Chippendale Wing Chair**	No. 12-4035 **Refreshment Upper Unit.**
No. 08-3519 **Gate Leg Tray Table**	Back is wood-grained balanced hardboard.

For detailed specifications on:
Antique Pine Bedroom—see pages 378-379.
Antique Pine Custom Room Plan—see pages 377-378.
Upholstery—see pages 392-406.

provided by Antiqued Pine custom room plan

A fine alternative to conventional bedroom furniture—Antiqued Pine Custom Room Plan units—a vertical storage formula that makes the most out of limited wall space. Radiantly pretty bedroom gets a full wall treatment with T-V, refreshment center and even a refrigerator, making a 'round the clock room. There's comfort too and with a flourish, as tufted loveseat is partnered with a pair of ottomans. This charming arrangement plus dense wall-to-wall carpeting and quilted velvet throw add up to a mood of luxury that pampers and pleases the adults of the house in romantic, yet functional room.

For detailed specifications on:
Antiqued Pine Bedroom—see pages 378-379.
Antiqued Pine Custom Room Plan—see pages 377-378.
Upholstery—see pages 392-406.
T-V and Stereo—see pages 264-265.

Shown above from left to right:
No. 12-5006 Night Stand
No. 12-5600 Cannonball Bed
No. 12-4034 Refreshment Base Unit
No. 12-4035 Refreshment Upper Unit.
Back is wood-grained balanced hardboard.
No. 50-1011 TV & Cabinet (photo-simulated T-V reception)

No. 12-4037 Upper Cabinet Bookcase.
Back is wood-grained balanced hardboard.
No. 12-4002 Refrigerator Unit.
No. 12-4006 Upper Bookcase.
Back is wood-grained balanced hardboard.
No. 20-7401 Loveseat
No. 20-7104 Ottoman

Ethan Allen
AMERICAN TRADITIONAL INTERIORS

245

custom room plan for a boy's life

A growing boy needs all the help he can get—in storing possessions and organizing that unwieldly collection of books, games, sports equipment, etc. What better assistance than from Antiqued Pine Custom Room plan units, with its sturdy look and lustrous finish, and seemingly endless assemblage of drawers and shutter door cabinets to keep everything in.

Storage wall, in bedroom below, is 'built' around a window; desk unit, situated at sill height, is a fine spot for daytime study. Compact trundle bed hides guest accommodations. A young man's sporting gear serves as colorful accessories of room, opposite. Custom Room Plan turns the corner of small sitting area; bed has bookcase headboard.

Shown below from left to right:
No. 12-8031 **Pedestal Table**
No. 12-4071 **Dresser Desk**
No. 12-6031 **Chair**
No. 12-4000 **Chest**
No. 12-4006 **Upper Bookcase.**
Back is wood-grained balanced hardboard.

No. 12-4050 **Chest**
No. 12-4057 **Upper Cabinet Bookcase.**
Back is wood-grained balanced hardboard.
No. 12-8026 **Dough Box Table**
No. 12-5607 **Trundle Bed**

Shown opposite page from left to right:
No. 12-6000 **Captain's Chair**
No. 12-6013 **Pedestal Table**
No. 12-4050 **Chest**
No. 12-4056 **Upper Bookcase.** Back is wood-grained balanced hardboard.
No. 12-4001 **Corner Cabinet**

No. 12-4007 **Corner Upper Unit.** Back is wood-grained balanced hardboard.
No. 12-4000 **Chest**
No. 12-4006 **Upper Bookcase.** Back is wood-grained balanced hardboard.
No. 12-5606 **Bookcase Headboard**
No. 24-7671 **Skipper's Lounge Chair**

For detailed specifications on:
Antiqued Pine Custom Room Plan—see pages 377-378.
Antiqued Pine Bedroom, Dining Room and Occasional Pieces—see pages 378-383.
American Foliage Colors—see pages 379-383.
Upholstery—see pages 392-406.

Ethan Allen
AMERICAN TRADITIONAL INTERIORS

American Foliage colors

bright accents to enrich a room

Make your furniture part of the color scheme—with Ethan Allen American foliage colors. Mix one or more of these colorful pieces with wood finishes or do an entire room around them. Except for Antiqued Pine trestle table in room below, all furniture is in glowing color, to spark the weathered brown of barn siding and plank floors. Tall étagères flank fireplace to serve as bookcases. Also shown on these pages are rudder table, octogonal table, hi-fi dry sink, and handsome library units.

Shown below from left to right:
No. 24-6002A **Ladderback Arm Chair**
No. 12-6003 **Trestle Table**
No. 24-9516 **Etagere**
No. 24-8083 **Rectangular End Table**
No. 24-7673 **Skipper's Sofa**
No. 24-6005 **Trestle Bench**
No. 24-9516 **Etagere**
No. 24-6055 **Stereo Dry Sink**

No. 24-6055 Stereo Dry Sink. 38½"x20"x39"H.
No. 12-6055 Same item in Old Tavern finish.

Shown at right:
No. 24-9014 Library Wall Unit.
34"x14"x80"H. Two adjustable shelves
and one adjustable shelf behind two-panel
Back is selected veneer.
No. 12-9014 Same item in Antiqued Pine
with Old Tavern finish.
Back is wood-grained balanced hardboard.

Shown at right:
No. 24-8007
Revolving Octagonal Table.
26"x26"x22"H.
Table sits on swivel base.
No. 12-8007
Same item in Old Tavern finish.

Available in American Foliage Colors:
402—Sugar Bush Red, 403—Pine Cone,
404—Autumn Gold, 405—Holly Green,
406—Spruce Blue.

Shown at above:
No. 24-9008 Console Cabinet. 30"x13"x30"H.
One drawer. One adjustable shelf.
No. 12-9008 Same item in Old Tavern finish.
No. 24-9009 Framed Oval Mirror. 24"x36"H.
No. 12-9009 Same item in Old Tavern finish.

Shown at right:
No. 24-8006 Rudder Table.
28"x13"x23"H. Opens to 28"x32"
with leaves extended.
No. 12-8006
Same item in Old Tavern finish.

All items are solid Pine with selected veneers, or wood-
grained balanced hardboard where noted, in handsome
American Foliage colors. Also available in Antiqued Pine
with Old Tavern finish.

For detailed specifications on: American Foliage Colors—
see pages 379-383.

colorful accents

Rich and vibrant color, partnered with white, create rooms of striking appeal. The white-washed room, below, is a lively mix of Spruce Blue and Holly Green—two of the five sparkling hues offered for many of the diversified Antiqued Pine designs. Spotlighted on these pages are but a few of the many designs offered in glowing color.

*No. 24-6025
Deacons Bench.
64"x20"x34"H.
No. 12-6025 Same item in Old Tavern Finish.

Shown at left:
*No. 24-9010
Drop Leaf Serving Tea Cart.
20"x32"x29"H.
Opens to 40"x32" with leaves extended.
One drawer.
No. 12-9010 Same item in Old Tavern Finish.

Shown at left:
No. 12-8010
Pedestal Candlestand.
18" diameter x 21" H.
*No. 24-8010 Same item in American Foliage Colors
No. 12-8050
Hearth Stool. 14" diameter x 17" H. Extra-heavy seat.
*No. 24-8050 Same in American Foliage Colors.
No. 14-8200 Same in Decorated Finishes.

Shown below left to right:
*No. 24-9008 Console Cabinet
*No. 24-9009 Oval Mirror
*No. 24-9511 Secretary Base
*No. 24-9512 Secretary Top
*No. 24-8080 Glass Top Cocktail Table
*No. 24-7622 Love Seat

*No. 24-8032 Step End Table.
20″x30″x34½″H. Two drawers.
No. 12-8032 Same item in Old Tavern Finish.

*No. 24-9506 Pedestal Desk.
54″x24″x36½″H. Removable
partitions and deep storage
area under top lid.
Four letter compartments.
No. 12-9506 Same item
in Old Tavern Finish.

*No. 24-8020 Cocktail Table.
54″x22″x17″H.
No. 12-8020 Same item in Old Tavern Finish.

*No. 24-8005 Book Stand Table.
16″x14″x27″H.
No. 12-8005 Same item in
Old Tavern Finish.

Shown from left to right:
*No. 24-6000 Captain's Chair
*No. 24-8034 Butterfly Drop Leaf End Table
*No. 24-7622 Two Cushion Loveseat
*No. 24-8020 Rectangular Cocktail Table

*Description of American Foliage Colors:
402—Sugar Bush Red
403—Pine Cone
404—Autumn Gold
405—Holly Green
406—Spruce Blue

For detailed specifications on:
American Foliage Colors—see pages 379-383.
Antiqued Pine Accents and Tables—see pages 381-383.
Upholstery—see pages 392-406.

Ethan Allen
AMERICAN TRADITIONAL INTERIORS

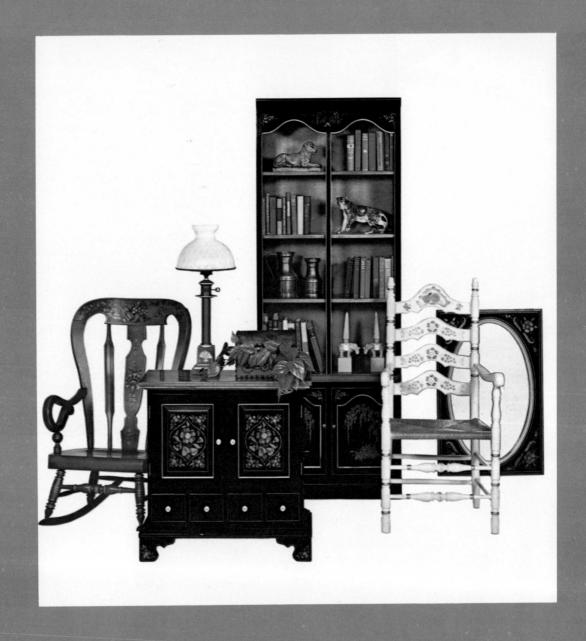

ETHAN ALLEN DECORATED FURNITURE

Colorful, decorative Ethan Allen Decorated Furniture, recreates through the time-honored technique of stencilling, the authentic flavor of cherished designs from our heritage.

The particular art form of stencilled and striped furniture belongs to our American history. It was developed by our forefathers who painted furniture primarily to conceal the similarity of wood and graining; applying decoration for additional interest. Not only did this enhance the appearance of the furniture; it preserved the wood.

Stencilling and decorations used in Colonial times were based on the motifs of the American Indians or folk art brought over by the Swiss and Germans, and on classical subjects seen on English and French imported furniture.

A wine tray once owned by John Hancock inspired the motifs on the Ethan Allen Hitchcock chairs, while Ethan Allen Salem and Boston rockers also have close adaptations of this type of fruit painting. In the golden age of American decorated furniture (1780-1850), Boston rockers, Hitchcock, Thumb Back and Windsor chairs, settees and other furniture were profusely decorated and stencilled—and heavier, more elaborate gold striping became the vogue on the legs and rails of chairs.

METHODS OF HAND-STENCILLING

Furniture is prepared for decorating by applying the many coats of lacquer and stain to bring it into an almost completed state of finish before stencilling.

A design is selected for decoration; then stencils are made from this design. A single design may require ten to fifteen stencils to recapture the detail of the original motif. Artists design each stencil separately on fine architect's linen, cutting the outlines painstakingly with a small scissors and sharp knife. A thin coat of varnish is applied to the surface to be decorated and before it hardens, the first stencil is placed in position, with succeeding stencils meticulously placed in exactly the same position. The varnish holds the stencils in place as well as the powders which are rubbed in it. The artist places a fine piece of chamois around her index finger and transfers a few grains of powder from a palette box which she gently rubs or shaves to the open parts of the stencil, changing colors when required, and achieving subtle shading and refinements that make the decoration look like a painted canvas.

Ethan Allen Decorated Furniture can be grouped together to recreate the pleasant hospitality of a Pennsylvania Dutch farmhouse, or used as specific accents to spice and enliven a room.

hand decorated accents add color & pattern

Ethan Allen hand-decorated furniture proffers a bright spot of color, a dramatic effect or an interesting accent. Versatile and adaptable, this furniture can be used in any room of the house to provide a pretty change of pace—mixing marvelously with wood finishes and tying in with the room's color scheme. An entire room can be designed with decorated furniture—in the same color or in a mélange of colors. One or two decorated pieces can be used strategically for interest or variety. Shown on this page are dry sink, library bookstack unit and console cabinet with oval mirror. Opposite page illustrates accent writing table and bookcase. Seating designs include several Hitchcock styles.

No. 14-6106 Dry Sink.
34"x18"x40"H. One drawer.
Adjustable shelf behind drawer;
felt-lined silver compartments.
Available in Decorated
Finishes 604 or 610
No. 10-6106 Same item in Nutmeg finish.

Shown below from left to right:
No. 14-9216 Console Cabinet.
No. 14-9217 Framed Oval Mirror.
No. 14-9702 Cape Cod Rocker.
No. 14-9709 Gloucester Rocker.
No. 14-9042 Pedestal Table.
No. 14-9026 Library Bookstacks.

Ethan Allen
AMERICAN TRADITIONAL INTERIORS

Shown above from left to right:
No. 14-6182 Deacon's Bench
No. 14-9514 Writing Table
No. 14-9218 Pedestal Table
No. 14-6111 Hitchcock Chair
No. 14-9510 Bookcase. Back is
wood-grained balanced hardboard.
No. 14-9022 Gossip Bench
No. 14-9703 Boston Rocker

Shown below:
No. 14-6155 Hitchcock Bench.
24"x15"x10½"H. Fiber seat.
Available in decorated finishes 601, 603 or 609.

Shown above from left to right:
No. 14-6110A Hitchcock Arm Chair. 33"H.
Fiber seat. Available in decorated finishes 601, 603 or 609.
No. 10-6110A Same item in Nutmeg finish.
No. 14-6110 Hitchcock Side Chair. 33"H.
Fiber Seat. Available in decorated finishes 601, 603 or 609.
No. 10-6110 Same item in Nutmeg finish.

Description of Decorated Finishes:
601—Nutmeg decorated, 603—White decorated,
604—White decorated with Nutmeg, 609—Black decorated,
610—Black decorated with Nutmeg, 612—Red decorated,
614—Green decorated, 616—Blue decorated.

For detailed specifications on:
Decorated Furniture—see pages 384-385.

decorated rockers

For grown-up or youngster, here's that long-time favorite—the versatile rocking chair. Ethan Allen interprets the style in a dozen ways, embellished with hand decoration and offered in a choice of finishes and colors.

No. 14-9710
Litchfield Rocker. 23"x19"x45"H. Available in Decorated finishes 601, 609, 610.
No. 10-9710 Same item in Nutmeg finish.

Shown left and right:
No. 14-9720
Barnstable Rocker. 20"x 24"x45"H. Available in Decorated finish 611.
No. 12-9720 Same item in Decorated finish 618.

*No. 14-9704
Salem Rocker. 24½"x 28"x42"H. Available in Decorated finishes 601, 603, 604, 609, 610, 612, 614, or 616.
No. 10-9704 Same item in Nutmeg finish.

Ethan Allen
AMERICAN TRADITIONAL INTERIORS

*Description of finishes:
212—Old Tavern
601—Nutmeg decorated
603—White decorated
604—White decorated
with Nutmeg
609—Black decorated
610—Black decorated
with Nutmeg
611—Black decorated
with Old Tavern
612—Red decorated
614—Green decorated
616—Blue decorated
618—Old Tavern decorated

For detailed specifications on
Decorated Furniture—
see pages 384-385.

No. 14-9709
Gloucester Rocker. 24"x19"x
42"H. Available in Decorated
finishes 601, 603, 604, 609, 610.

***No. 14-9702**
Cape Cod Rocker. 23"x28"x40"H.
Available in Decorated finishes 601,
603, 609.
No. 10-9702 Same item in
Nutmeg finish.

Shown below center:
***No. 14-9705**
Child's Rocker. 17"x21"x29"H.
Available in Decorated finishes 601,
603, 609.
No. 10-9705 Same item in
Nutmeg finish.

Upper right:
***No. 14-9709**
Gloucester Rocker. Shown
in Decorated finish 601.
No. 10-9709 Same item in
Nutmeg finish.

Lower right:
***No. 14-9709**
Gloucester Rocker. Shown
in Decorated finish 603.
No. 10-9709 Same item in
Nutmeg finish.

From Baby's First High Chair to Grandma's Favorite Rocker, Ethan Allen offers a range of sizes and versatility. In rockers there are Boston, Salem, and Comb Back designs. Seen opposite is a practical Valet Chair—Ideal for Dad.

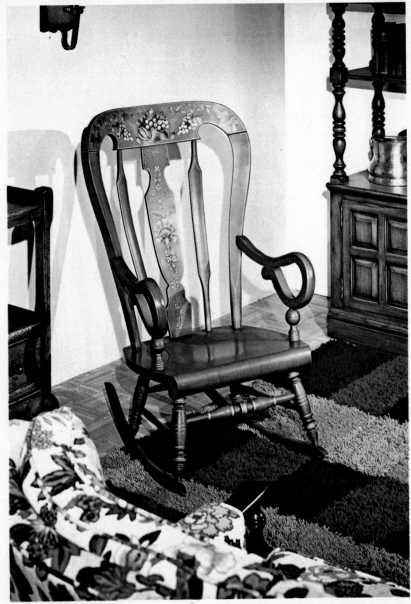

No. 12-9019 Rocker. 26"x27"x45"H. Deep-saddle seat of Solid Pine. Balance of chair solid Maple. Available in Decorated Finish 618.

Shown above:
*No. 14-9706 Homestead Rocker. 25"x28"x40"H. Available in Decorated Finishes 601, 603, 604, 609, 610, 612, 614, or 616.
No. 10-9706 Same item in Nutmeg Finish.

No. 12-6050. General's Chair. Available in Decorated Finish 618.

*Description of finishes:
212—Old Tavern
601—Nutmeg decorated
603—White decorated
604—White decorated with Nutmeg
609—Black decorated
610—Black decorated with Nutmeg
611—Black decorated with Old Tavern
612—Red decorated
614—Green decorated
616—Blue decorated
618—Old Tavern decorated

*No. 14-9715 Comb Back Rocker. 25"W. x 41"H. Available in Decorated Finishes 601 or 610.

For detailed specifications on: Decorated Furniture, see pages 384-385. Antiqued Pine Chairs and Rockers— see pages 380-383.

*No. 14-9713 Valet Chair.
17"x16½"x38"H. Available in
Decorated Finishes 601, 604, 610,
612, 614 or 616.

*No. 14-6120 Hitchock Chair.
16"x34"H. Available in
Decorated Finishes 601 or 611.

No. 12-6120 Same item in
Decorated Finish 618.

Shown below:
*No. 14-9720 Barnstable Rocker.
20"x24"x45"H. Available in
Decorated Finish 610.

No. 12-6170 High Chair.
Features "Safety Belt"
and adjustable
locking tray. Available
in Decorated Finish 618.

*No. 14-6170 High Chair.
Features "Safety Belt"
and adjustable, locking
tray. Available in
Decorated Finish 601.

Ethan Allen
AMERICAN TRADITIONAL INTERIORS

Lively accents from Colonial days can add a romantic note and a storybook flavor when used in today's interiors. Proffering color and design at the same time, these delightful chairs mix beautifully with other designs in the Ethan Allen program. Windsor, ladderback, arrowback, buttonback, and thumb back designs are among those featured. Use a full complement of decorated chairs around a dining table; add one or two for strategic accent in any room.

No. 12-6042
Arrowback Side Chair.
40"H. Available in
Decorated Finish 618.

No. 12-6042A
Arrowback Arm Chair.
40"H. Available in
Decorated Finish 618.

*No. 14-6110
Hitchcock Side Chair. 33"H. Fiber seat.
In Decorated Finishes 601, 603, 609.
No. 10-6110 Same in Nutmeg finish.

*No. 14-6080
Bannister Side Chair.
45"H. Fiber seat. Available
in Decorated Finishes 601, 603,
609, 612, 614 or 616.

*No. 14-6041A
Ladderback Arm Chair. 44"H.
Fiber seat. In Decorated
Finishes 601, 603 or 609.
No. 12-6041A Same in Antiqued
Pine finishes 212 or 618.

Shown at left and above:
*No. 14-6301
Farm House Chair. 33"H.
Available in Decorated
Finishes 601, 603, 609,
610, 612, 614 or 616.
No. 10-6301 Same item in
Nutmeg finish.

*No. 14-6041
Ladderback Side Chair. 44"H.
Fiber seat. In Decorated
Finishes 601, 603 or 609.
No. 12-6041 Same in Antiqued
Pine finishes 212 or 618.

*Description of Decorated Finishes:
212 Old Tavern
400 Alabaster White
409 Antiqued Blue
411 Daffodil Yellow
601 Nutmeg Decorated
603 White Decorated
604 White Decorated with Nutmeg
609 Black Decorated
610 Black Decorated with Nutmeg
612 Red Decorated
614 Green Decorated
616 Blue Decorated
618 Old Tavern Decorated

Ethan Allen
AMERICAN TRADITIONAL INTERIORS

Shown below:
*No. 14-6011 Thumb Back Chair. 35"H.
Available in Decorated Finishes 400, 409,
411, 604 or 610.
No. 10-6011 Same item in Nutmeg finish.

*No. 14-6040 Comb Back Mates Chair.
30"H. Available in Decorated
Finishes 400, 409, 411, 604, 610.
No. 10-6040 Same item in Nutmeg finish.

Shown at right:
*No. 14-6111 Button Back Hitchcock Chair.
33"H. Fiber seat. Available in Decorated
Finish 601, 603, 609, 612, 614 or 616.
No. 10-6111 Same item in Nutmeg finish.

Shown below:
No. 14-6072 Duxbury Side Chair. 39"H.
Available in Decorated Finishes
601, 604 or 610.
No. 10-6072 Same item in Nutmeg finish.

No. 14-6072A Duxbury Arm Chair. 39"H.
Available in Decorated Finishes
601, 604 or 610.
No. 10-6072A Same item in Nutmeg finish.

Shown at right:
*No. 14-6092 Chancellor's Chair.
46"H. Available in Decorated
Finishes 601, 612, 614 or 616.

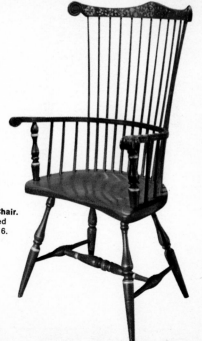

For detailed specifications on
Decorated Furniture—see pages 384-385.

*No. 14-6182
Deacon's Bench.
42"x20½"x34"H.
Available in Decorated
Finishes 604 or 610.

For detailed specifications on
Decorated Furniture—see pages 384-385.

*No. 14-8350
Spoonfoot Harvest Drop Leaf
Cocktail Table. 44"x18"x15"H.
Opens to 32" with leaves extended.
Available in Decorated Finish 610.
No. 10-8350 Same item in Nutmeg finish.

*Description of Decorated Finishes:
601 — Nutmeg Decorated
603 — White Decorated
604 — White Decorated with Nutmeg
609 — Black Decorated
610 — Black Decorated with Nutmeg

*No. 14-8340 Spoonfoot Cocktail Table. 42"x20"x
15"H. Available in Decorated Finish 610.
No. 10-8340 Same item with Nutmeg finish.

*No. 14-8355
Spoonfoot Cloverleaf
Lamp Table. Opens to
27" diameter with leaves
extended. Available in
Decorated Finish 610.
No. 10-8355 Same item
in Nutmeg finish.

*No. 14-8344
Spoonfoot Drop Leaf End
Table. 18"x25"x24½"H.
Opens to 36" with leaves
extended. Available in
Decorated Finish 610.
No. 10-8344 Same item
in Nutmeg finish.

*No. 14-6085
Drop Leaf Tea Wagon. 19"x32"x29"H. Opens
to 42"x32" with leaves fully extended. Large
artillery wheels and swivel casters for mobility.
Wheels are moulded plastic. Handle swings away
under cart when not in use. Available in
Decorated Finishes 604 or 610.
No. 10-6085 Same item in Nutmeg finish.

Ethan Allen
AMERICAN TRADITIONAL INTERIORS

Shown above:
No. 14-9042 Cigarette Pedestal Table. 15" diameter x 21"H. Available in Decorated Finishes 601, 603 or 609.
No. 10-9042 Same item in Nutmeg finish.

Shown at left:
No. 14-9218 Square Pedestal Table. 19½" square x 16"H. Available in Decorated Finishes 604 or 610.

No. 14-9019 Cloverleaf Magazine Rack. 18"x12½"x15"H. Available in Decorated Finishes 601, 603 or 609.
No. 10-9019 Same item in Nutmeg finish.

No. 14-8300 Cigarette Pedestal Table. 15" diameter x 23"H. Available in Decorated Finish 609.

No. 14-9022 Gossip Bench. 33"x16"x 29"H. In Decorated Finishes 604 or 610.
No. 10-9022 Same item in Nutmeg finish.

Shown below:
No. 14-8200 Hearth Stools. 14" diameter x 17"H. In Decorated Finishes 604 or 610.

let us entertain you!

...with free-standing T-V or Custom Room Plan television and stereo units that can convert any room into an all-purpose entertainment area. On this page they are shown in the Antiqued Pine expression, opposite in the Nutmeg finish.

Shown above:
The Yorktown—No. 50-1009 Cabinet: 44⅝"x26"x41"H. (Plus 3" in back for tube.) Old Tavern finish on solid Pine and selected veneers on top and sides. Picture area: 25" visible diagonal (315 sq. in.) Sound Equipment: one 7"x5" and one 6"x4" Dynapower speakers. Features one-touch color and automatic tint lock. (Above photo—simulated T-V reception).

Shown below from left to right:
No. 20-7314 **Barrel Swivel Chair**
No. 15-8674 **Rectangular End Table**
No. 12-4035 **Refreshment Upper Unit**
No. 12-4034 **Refreshment Lower Unit**
No. 12-4006 **Upper Bookcase**
No. 12-4002 **Refrigerator Unit**
No. 50-1011 **19" Color T-V & Cabinet**
No. 15-8661P **Pedestal Cocktail Table**
No. 20-7048 **Three Cushion Tuxedo Sofa**
No. 16-6013 **Flip-Top Table**
No. 13-7110 **Cabriolet Arm Chair**
(Photo-simulated T-V reception)
Upper unit backs are wood-grained balanced hardboard.

For detailed specifications on Antiqued Pine Custom Room Plan—see pages 377-378.

Shown above from left to right:
No. 16-6013 Flip-Top Table
No. 20-7184 Three Cushion Sofa
No. 10-4030 Refreshment Upper Unit
No. 10-4515 Refreshment Cabinet Base
No. 10-4006 Upper Cabinet Bookcase
No. 10-4516 Refrigerator Unit
No. 10-4510 Three Drawer Chest
No. 10-4500 Corner Filler Unit
No. 10-4510 Three Drawer Chest
No. 50-1101 Upper Stereo Unit
No. 50-1010 Color T-V & Cabinet
No. 20-7407 Ottoman
(Photo-simulated T-V reception)

The Heirloom—No. 50-1013 Cabinet: 38¼"x
19"x42½"H. (Plus 3" in back for
tube). Heirloom finish on Solid
Birch and/or Maple and
selected veneers.
Picture area: 25" visible
diagonal (315 sq. in.)
Two 5"x3" oval Dynapower
speakers. GE insta-color®
picture and automatic
tint lock. 100% Solid
State Reliacolor chassis.
Tilt-out controls.
(Photo-simulated
T-V reception).

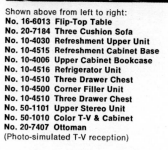

Ethan Allen
AMERICAN TRADITIONAL INTERIORS

For detailed specifications on:
Heirloom Custom Room Plan—see pages 362-363.
Upholstery—see pages 392-406.

265

ETHAN ALLEN BEDDING

The perfect "Good-night" touch for a beautiful bedroom

Do you feel like you're buying a "pig-in-a-poke" when it comes to choosing the right bedding for you and your family?

It doesn't have to be a mystery. We think we can help you —because Ethan Allen offers you superb bedding carefully designed to fill your basic need for dependable *quality*, personal *individuality*, complete *confidence* in performance and restful, healthy *sleep*. The next three pages tell you how. Ethan Allen bedding is scientifically engineered for total support...tested construction assures quality, performance... fabrics are beautiful yet sturdy...and there's a complete range of sizes for your personal selection.

With Ethan Allen bedding, it's easy to add that important hidden asset that makes a beautiful bedroom really live up to its name—a haven of rest and comfort.

ETHAN ALLEN
ELEGANCE CLASSIC

King Size—76"x80"

The incomporable bedding set, exquisitely styled, masterfully constructed with every luxury feature:

TRUE COMFORT—Rest and extra deep support are provided by layers of high density Polyurethane and Dacron, and luxurious ULTRILON cover.

SCIENTIFIC ENGINEERED SUPPORT—Torsion Bar "88" foundation combines with multiple coil spring unit for individual sleeping comfort and luxurious firm support.

SUPERB MATTRESS BEAUTY—with engineered—knit comfort is provided by the Ultrilon fabric with Chemstitch process.

- Knit Comfort
- Enkalure Nylon
- Permanent Quilting
- Easily Cleaned
- No Thread Breakage
- Flame Retardant
- Non Allergenic
- Mildew Resistant

The new excitement in bedding luxury for those who seek the ultimate in night-time comfort, rest and total support... Ethan Allen's finest!

All Elegance Classic Mattresses are also available in Latex Foam Rubber.

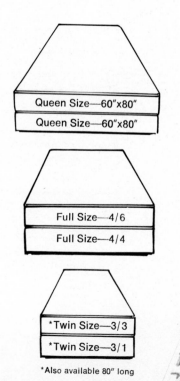

Queen Size—60"x80"
Queen Size—60"x80"

Full Size—4/6
Full Size—4/4

*Twin Size—3/3
*Twin Size—3/1

*Also available 80" long

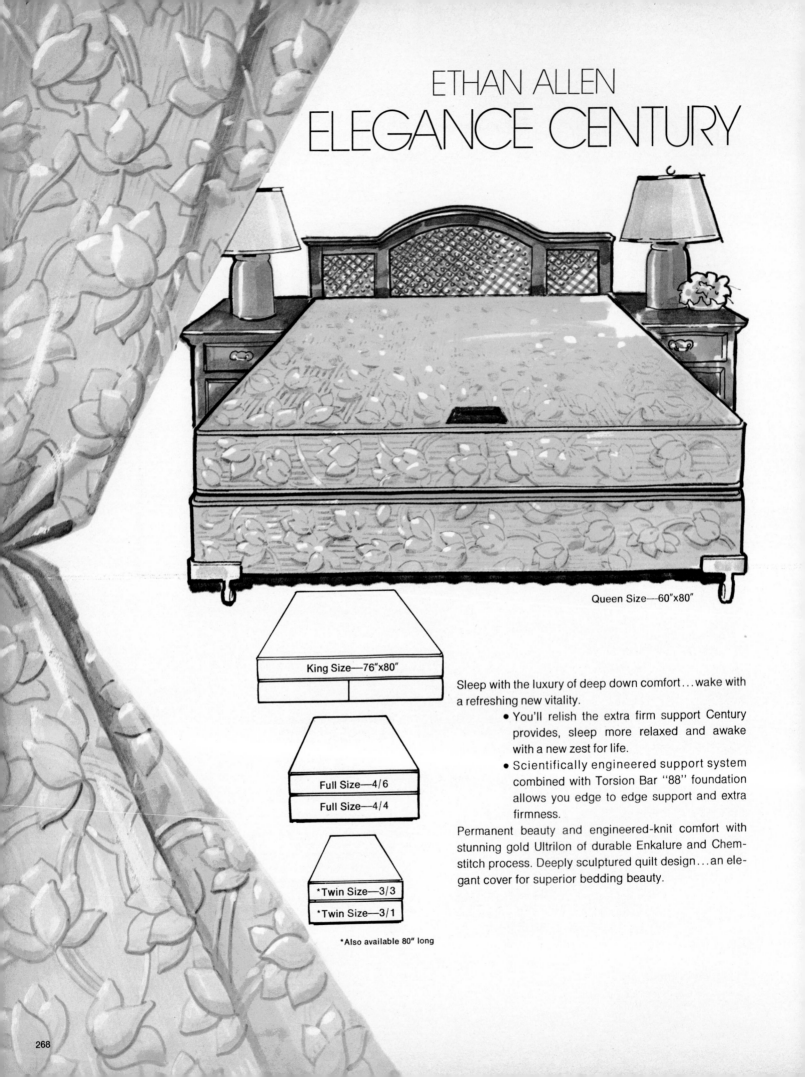

ETHAN ALLEN
ELEGANCE CENTURY

Queen Size—60"x80"

King Size—76"x80"

Full Size—4/6
Full Size—4/4

*Twin Size—3/3
*Twin Size—3/1

*Also available 80" long

Sleep with the luxury of deep down comfort...wake with a refreshing new vitality.

- You'll relish the extra firm support Century provides, sleep more relaxed and awake with a new zest for life.
- Scientifically engineered support system combined with Torsion Bar "88" foundation allows you edge to edge support and extra firmness.

Permanent beauty and engineered-knit comfort with stunning gold Ultrilon of durable Enkalure and Chemstitch process. Deeply sculptured quilt design...an elegant cover for superior bedding beauty.

ETHAN ALLEN
LUXURY

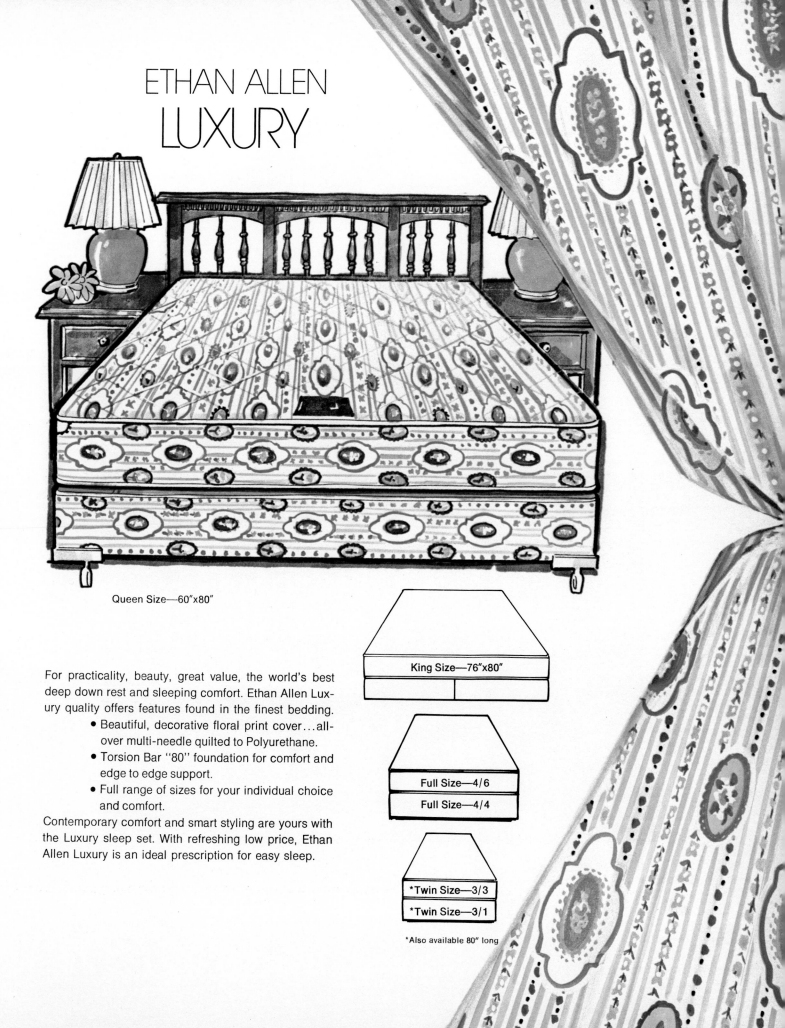

Queen Size—60"x80"

King Size—76"x80"

Full Size—4/6

Full Size—4/4

*Twin Size—3/3

*Twin Size—3/1

*Also available 80" long

For practicality, beauty, great value, the world's best deep down rest and sleeping comfort. Ethan Allen Luxury quality offers features found in the finest bedding.

- Beautiful, decorative floral print cover...all-over multi-needle quilted to Polyurethane.
- Torsion Bar "80" foundation for comfort and edge to edge support.
- Full range of sizes for your individual choice and comfort.

Contemporary comfort and smart styling are yours with the Luxury sleep set. With refreshing low price, Ethan Allen Luxury is an ideal prescription for easy sleep.

269

ETHAN ALLEN
COLLECTORS
CLASSICS

No room is ever complete—nor can it be personal or interesting—without those finishing touches that somehow bring it all together. Lamps, mirrors, clocks, statuary, candlesticks, shelves, chandeliers and wall ornaments are among the many finishing touches in the remarkably comprehensive Ethan Allen Collection. On the following pages are shown only a few of these charming and versatile accessories.

the romantic glow of chandeliers

Recalling the charm of the past when festive occasions in our ancestors' homes were graced by soft candlelight, the Ethan Allen Collection of Chandeliers and hanging fixtures offers a wide range of style to suit every mood and decor. Traditional designs are expressed in brass, pewter, wood, tole and ceramics. A few notable highlights appear on this page.

Shown at left:
No. 09-3104 Pewter Chandelier. 26" x 27"H. 9-light. Two tier. Includes chain.

No. 09-3100 Brass Chandelier. 23" x 19"H. 6-light. Includes chain.

Shown at left:
No. 09-3113 Glass and Brass Foyer Light. 19" x 14". 6-light.

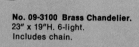

Shown above:
No. 09-3107 Brass and Wood Hurricane Chandelier. 24" x 22". 6-light. Includes chain.

Shown at right:
No. 09-3161 Wood and Brass Hurricane Chandelier. 15" x 22". 3-light. Includes hurricane chimneys decorated shades and chain.

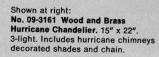

Shown above:
No. 09-3109 Tole Chandelier. 15" x 22". 5-light. Tole shades in choice of 401 Black, 603 White Decorated, 612 Red Decorated or 623 Yellow Decorated.

floor lamps

The Ethan Allen floor lamp collection includes a diverse selection of styles; many have decorative furniture details such as cloverleaf and Queen Anne tray table designs. Some feature rope and bamboo turnings. Shades come in assorted opaque silk and tole designs.

Shown below:
No. 09-2054
Floor Lamp.
54"H.

Shown at right:
No. 09-2041 Brass and Tole
Floor Lamp. 57"H. Available in 401—Black.

Shown below:
No. 09-2039 Cloverleaf Tray
Floor Lamp. 61"H.

Shown above:
No. 09-2035 Bamboo
Design Floor Lamp.
58"H.

Shown at left:
No. 09-2060
Floor Lamp.
56"H.

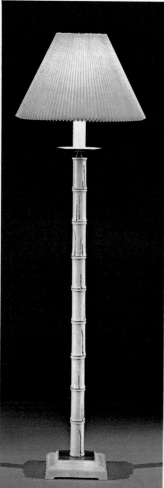

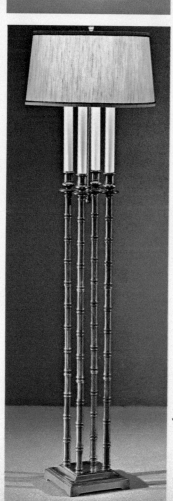

Shown at left from left to right:
No. 09-2038 Tray Floor Lamp. 55"H.

No. 09-2032 Spiral Tray Floor Lamp. 55"H.

Shown at left:
***No. 09-2059 Floor Lamp.** 59"H. Available in 603, 623, 627, or 813.

Shown at right:
No. 09-2033 Tray Floor Lamp. 54"H.

Shown at left:
No. 09-2052 Bamboo Design Floor Lamp. 58"H.

***No. 09-2045 Tole Floor Lamp.** 57"H. Available in 609, 612, 627 or 813.

No. 09-2037 Wood and Brass Floor Lamp. 59"H.

*Description of Finishes:
603—White Decorated; 609—Black Decorated; 612—Red Decorated; 623—Yellow Decorated; 627—Yellow; 813—Weathered Brass

ceramic designs

A.

A. **No. 09-1312 Ginger Jar Lamp.**
Brown Decorated. 28"H.

B. **No. 09-1315 Delft Ginger Jar
Lamp.** 30" H.

C. **No. 09-1301 Bamboo Jar Lamp.**
26"H. Finishes: 902, 903, 911.

D. **No. 09-1319 Oriental Vase Lamp.**
35"H.

E. **No. 09-1321 Large Jar Floral
Design Lamp.** 39"H.

Classically popular
shapes such as ginger jar,
temple jar and urn styles
are featured in imported
and domestic ceramic
lamps. There are also fretwork and smoked glass
designs. These table
lamps range in height
from 24 to 42-inches.

C.

B.

D.

E.

A.

B.

E.

D.

C.

F.

A. No. 09-1317 Fretwork Vase Lamp.
33"H.

B. No. 09-1302 Hexagonal Jar Lamp.
28"H. Finishes: 904, 905, 907.

**C. No. 09-1304 Crackle Finish Vase
Lamp.** 33"H. Finishes: 907, 908, 910.

**D. No. 09-1303 Ginger Jar Lamp. 30"H.
Crackle Finish.** Finishes: 906, 908, 909.

E. No. 09-1310 Smoked Glass Lamp.
24"H.

F. No. 09-1320 Rope Urn Lamp. 32"H.

Ethan Allen
AMERICAN TRADITIONAL INTERIORS

light up with brass & crystal.

Versatile lamps include bouillotte, shield, candlestick, column, vase and font designs, plus crystal imports of hand cut full lead. Shades are of silk, some pleated. Lamps come in both bright and antique brass finishes; brass and wood combinations. There are many more to delight you in the total Ethan Allen collection.

A. **No. 09-4021 Twin Arm Ormolu.** 25"H.
B. **No. 09-4009 Brass Urn.** 39"H.
C. **No. 09-4001 Brass Column.** 36"H.
D. **No. 09-4005 Brass and Black Column.** 35"H.

E. **No. 09-4014 Candlestick.** 24"H.
F. **No. 09-4011 Brass Font.** 40"H.
G. **No. 09-4030 Bethel.** 37"H.
H. **No. 09-4013 Wood and Brass Column.** 39"H.

A.

B.

C.

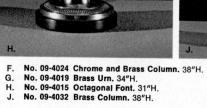

F.

G.

H.

J.

A. No. 09-1378 **Crystal Urn.** 28"H.
B. No. 09-1380 **Crystal Column.** 36"H.
C. No. 09-1375 **Crystal Urn.** 30"H.
D. No. 09-4012 **Brass Front.** 38"H.
E. No. 09-3010 **Brass Swag Lamp.** 18" diameter.

F. No. 09-4024 **Chrome and Brass Column.** 38"H.
G. No. 09-4019 **Brass Urn.** 34"H.
H. No. 09-4015 **Octagonal Font.** 31"H.
J. No. 09-4032 **Brass Column.** 38"H.

tole and glass

Reminiscent of "whale oil" lamp days are adaptations of Colonial glass hurricane designs. On opposite page are more from the Ethan Allen collection including bookstack, eagle, candlestick and balustrade designs in wood, brass, tole or polyester.

A. **No. 09-1401 Glass Hurricane Pin Up Lamp.** 12″ diam.
B. **No. 09-1402 Decorated Glass Hurricane.** 19″H.
C. **No. 09-3155 Tole Swag Lamp.** 15″ diam. Available in 609—Black decorated, 612—Red decorated, 614—Green decorated or 627—Yellow.
D. **No. 09-1503 Tole Column Lamp.** 28″H. Available in 609—Black decorated, 612—Red decorated or 627—Yellow.
E. **No. 09-1408 Decorated Glass Hurricane.** 19″H.
F. **No. 09-1451 Hurricane Desk Lamp.** 24″H.
G. **No. 09-1404 Decorated Glass Hurricane.** 28″H.
H. **No. 09-1415 Ruby Glass Hurricane.** 23″H.

A. **No. 09-1552 Urn.** 31"H. Base of polyester.
B. **No. 09-1697 Eagle Lamp.** 35"H.
C. **No. 09-1501 Tole Column.** 23"H.
   Available in 609—Black decorated,
   612—Red decorated or 627—Yellow.
D. **No. 09-1652 Spiral Turned Column.** 42"H.
E. **No. 09-1550 Bookstack Lamp.** 18" H. Base of polyester.
F. **No. 09-4004 Wood and Brass Candlestick.** 29"H.
G. **No. 09-1672 Turned Post.** 34"H.
H. **No. 09-1120 Stuyvesant Candlestick.** 27"H.
   Available in 408—Green, 409—Blue or 410—Gold.

Ethan Allen
AMERICAN TRADITIONAL INTERIORS

handsome keepers of time

In the proud tradition of the master clock-makers, Ethan Allen presents magnificent clocks for your home. Richly-finished and intricately detailed, many floor-length cases feature precision 8-day movements with polished chimes and pendulums. Charming wall clocks feature stencil decorations on traditional finishes. These pages show representative styles from our collection.

Shown below from left to right:
No. 08-3805. The "Bristol". 84" H. 8-Day weight-driven movement. Westminster chimes with pendulum. Grandfather clock featuring scroll pediment top and Queen Anne arched panel. Georgian Court finish in Cherry solids and veneers.

No. 08-3801. The "Townsend". 73" H. 8-Day weight-driven movement. Westminster chimes with pendulum. Classic Manor finish.

No. 08-3802. The "Willard". 76" H. 8-Day weight-driven movement. Westminster chimes with pendulum. Heirloom Nutmeg finish.

Description of finishes:
211—Nutmeg
212—Old Tavern
402—Sugarbush Red
404—Autumn Gold
405—Holly Green
406—Spruce Blue

Wall clocks shown from left to right:
No. 07-3818 22″ H. x 16″ W. Finish 211.
No. 07-3811 17″ H. x 12″ W. Finish is: 211, 212, 402, 404, 405 or 406.

No. 07-3813 21″ H. x 11″ W. Finish is: 212, 402, 404, 405, 406.
No. 07-3814 20″ H. x 12″ W. Finish is: 212.
No. 07-3812 21″ H. x 11″ W. Finish is: 211 or 212.
No. 07-3816 21″ H. x 13″ W. Finish is: 211 or 212.

Shown below from left to right:
No. 08-3806 Chatham Floor Clock, 74″ H. Full glass panel front and sides. Grandfather clock movement with Westminster Chime and Big Ben strike. Available in mellow fruitwood finish.

No. 08-3800 The "Chandler". 74″ H. 8-Day weight-driven movement. Westminster chimes with pendulum. Old Tavern Finish. Grandmother clock with shaped spindle posts and raised, beveled panel adornments.

No. 08-3804 The "Wheaton". 72″ H. 8-Day weight-driven movement. Westminster chimes with pendulum. Grandmother clock featuring rope turned spindles and linenfold panel. Royal Charter finish.

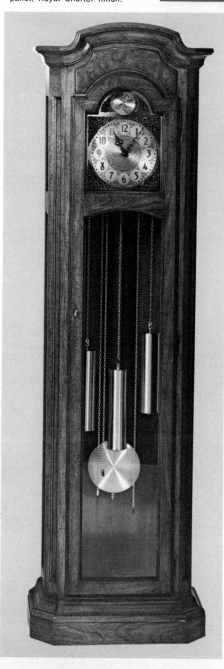

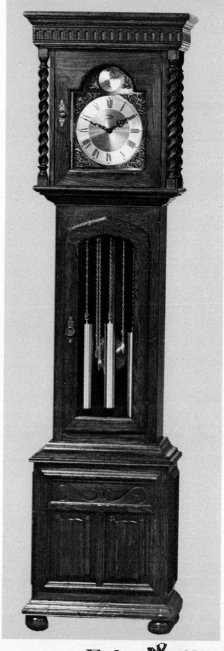

candlesticks

Shown above left to right:
A. No. 06-1009 5 light **Candelabra.** 14½" x 13"H.
B. No. 06-1022 **Faceted Post.** 7½"H.
   No. 06-1048 **Candlestick.** 15"H.
   No. 06-1032 **Faceted Post.** 10½"H.
C. No. 06-1041 **Turned Post.** 10"H.
   No. 06-1011 **Turned Post.** 5"H.
   No. 06-1001 **Turned Post.** 3"H.
   No. 06-1049 **Turned Post.** 10"H.
   No. 06-1021 **Turned Post.** 7"H.
D. No. 06-1007 **Chamberstick.** 6" x 3"H.
   No. 06-1035 **Beehive.** 10"H.

Ethan Allen
AMERICAN TRADITIONAL INTERIORS

Use singly, in pairs, or grouped —for glowing accents on table, mantel, console or wall. Here are saucer, beehive and ship candles, and sconces; only a few from a stunning selection. Candlesticks and candelabras are of bright, solid polished brass.

Shown from left to right:
A. **No. 06-1008**
   3 light Candelabra.
   14½″ x 13″H.
B. **No. 06-1045**
   Fluted Post. 16″H.
C. **No. 07-1030**
   Hurricane Sconce. 16½″H.
D. **No. 07-1040**
   One Arm Sconce. 12½″H.
E. **No. 06-1050**
   Ship's Candle. 7″H.
   Can be hung on wall.
F. **No. 06-1014**
   Turned Post. 5″H.
G. **No. 06-1016**
   Two-Light Hurricane.
   16½″ x 19″H.
H. **No. 06-1515**
   Three-piece
   Candlestick Set.
   Each 5½″H. 7″H. 9″H.

All styles available in bright brass, some offered in antiqued brass or pewter finish.

gleaming accents

From many corners of the world, here are a sampling of Ethan Allen's decorative accents. Your choice includes brass, copper and a combination of them in an exciting selection of accents and accessories — perfect finishing touches

A.

B.

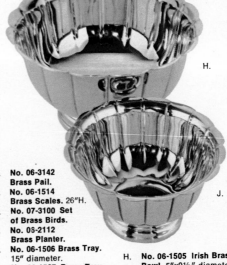

C.

D.

E.

F.

G.

H.

J.

K.

A. **No. 06-3142 Brass Pail.**
B. **No. 06-1514 Brass Scales. 26"H.**
C. **No. 07-3100 Set of Brass Birds.**
D. **No. 05-2112 Brass Planter.**
E. **No. 06-1506 Brass Tray. 15" diameter.**
F. **No. 06-1507 Brass Tray. 12" diameter.**
G. **No. 06-1508 Brass Tray. 10" diameter.**
H. **No. 06-1505 Irish Brass Bowl. 5"x9½" diameter.**
J. **No. 06-1504 Irish Brass Bowl. 3"x6½" diameter.**
K. **No. 07-3101 Brass Bell.**

Ethan Allen
AMERICAN TRADITIONAL INTERIORS

A.

B.

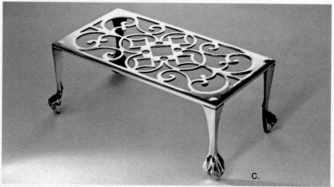

C.

D.

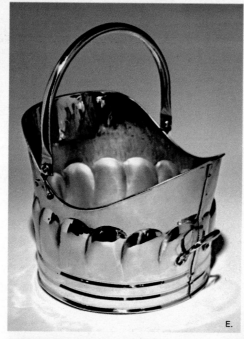

E.

F.

G.

H.

Shown above from left to right:
A. **No. 06-2117 Brass Samovar.** 14"H.
B. **No. 06-3144 Brass Candle Bowl**
C. **No. 06-3155 Brass Hearth Stand**
D. **No. 06-3141 Brass Trivet**
E. **No. 08-3606 Brass Coal Hod**
F. **No. 06-3161 Brass Watering Can**
G. **No. 06-3127 Brass Shell Ashtray**
H. **No. 06-3148 Brass and Copper Jug**
J. **No. 06-3154 Brass Cannon**
K. **No. 06-3150 Brass and Copper Jug**

J.

K.

**No. 06-2116
Copper Porringer**
7½″ Diam. Tin-lined.

Left.
**No. 06-2107
Copper Scuttle.** 8″H.

No. 06-2104 Copper Kettle. 15″H.

Right:
**No. 06-3138
Copper Measure**

copper & brass

**No. 07-3108
Copper Horn**

No. 06-2114 Copper Planter. 12″x8″H.

No. 06-3152 Copper Kettle

No. 08-3602 Copper Hod—Medium

No. 06-3147 Copper Planter. 12″H.
No. 06-3146 Copper Planter. 10″H.
No. 06-3145 Copper Planter. 8″H.

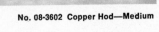

No. 07-3107 Copper Horn

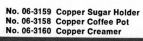

No. 06-3159 Copper Sugar Holder
No. 06-3158 Copper Coffee Pot
No. 06-3160 Copper Creamer

No. 06-3129
Brass Candle
Snuffer

No. 08-3601
Copper Hod—Large

No. 06-2106
Cauldron Copper/Brass. 6"H.

No. 06-3136 Copper Water Can

No. 07-3102
Brass Martingales—Three

No. 07-3103
Brass Martingales. Five

No. 07-3109
Brass Mirror. 12" Diameter.

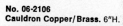

No. 08-3604 Brass Log-Box

No. 08-3609 Brass Planter—Large
No. 08-3608 Brass Planter—Medium
No. 08-3607 Brass Planter—Small

statuary & porcelain

For an old world accent—bisque statuary in hand painted colors. Place them on table tops or group them as a collection on an étagère. A handsome compliment to any home is the hand decorated Lowestoft porcelain eagle pattern.

A.

B.

C.

D.

E.

F.

G.

Shown above from left to right:
A. **No. 06-3206 Goldfinches.** 7½"H.
B. **No. 06-3207 Eagle.** 10½"H.
C. **No. 06-3005 Abraham Lincoln.** 39½"H.
D. **No. 06-3225 Quail.** 8"H. Wood base 1¼"H.
E. **No. 06-3223 Hummingbirds.** 8"H. Wood base 1¼"H.
F. **No. 06-3224 Roosters.** 8"H. Wood base 1¼"H.
G. **No. 06-3218 Porcelain Ashtray.** 6"x6".

A.

B.

C.

D.

E.

F.

G.

H.

J.

K.

Shown below from left to right:
- **A.** No. 06-3211 **Boy and Girl with Lamb.** 8″H.
- **B.** No. 06-3215 **Boy and Girl with Basket.**
- **C.** No. 06-3208 **Doves.** 7″H.
- **D.** No. 06-3222 **Robin.**
  No. 06-3221 **Bluebird.**
  No. 06-3220 **Cardinal.**
  All 8½″H.
- **E.** No. 03-3219 **Porcelain Ashtray.** 4¾″ x 4¾″.
- **F.** No. 03-3217 **Porcelain Dessert Set.** 8″ plate, cup and saucer.
- **G.** No. 06-3228 **Porcelain Cache Pot.** 4½″ diam.
- **H.** No. 06-3227 **Porcelain Temple Jar.** 10″H.
- **J.** No. 03-3226 **Porcelain Bowl.** 4½″H x 10″ Diam.
- **K.** No. 06-3210 **Elephants.** 9″H.

Wood accessories and shelves

These versatile accents also serve a useful purpose. Three panel screen fills a corner or divides two areas. Shelves store and display. Cheval mirror is an authentic Colonial design. Other charming accent ideas include library steps, octagonal waste basket, cigarette table, magazine stand, three tier stand, ships wheel, Winthrop cabinet, spice rack with bottles.

A. **No. 07-1521 Winthrop Cabinet.** 27"x7½"x30"H. Drop-leaf "shutter door" has melamine plastic work surface. Use as an accent piece. Old Tavern finish.

B. **No. 07-1702 Ship's Barometer.** 21" Diameter.

C. **No. 08-3543 Three Panel Screen.** 48"x78"H. Beveled panels. Royal Charter finish.

D. **No. 07-4012 Lexington Mirror.** 18"x26" overall. Old Tavern finish. **No. 07-3020 Lexington Console.** 24"x9"x11"H. Old Tavern finish.

E. **No. 08-3545 Library Steps.** 19"x 19"x42"H. Royal Charter finish.

A.

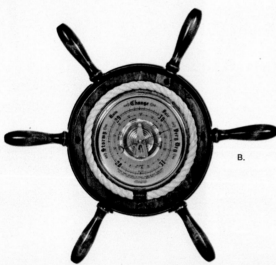

B.

D.

C.

E.

A.

B.

C.

D.

E.

F.

G.

H.

A. **No. 08-3512 Cigarette Table.** 14"x23"H.
Old Tavern finish.
No. 08-3513 Smoking Stand. 24"H.
with 8" amber recessed glass
ashtray. Old Tavern finish.

B. **No. 08-3505 Octagonal Waste Basket.**
11"x12"H. Old Tavern finish.

C. **No. 07-1802 18" Gallery Shelf.** 18"x8"x6"H.
No. 07-1803 24" Gallery Shelf. 24"x8"x6"H.
No. 07-1804 30" Gallery Shelf. 30"x8"x6"H.
Old Tavern finish.

D. **No. 08-3515 Magazine Stand.** 22"x8"x22"H.
Can be hung by recessed keyhole slots
on back. Old Tavern finish.

E. **No. 08-3514 Three Tier Stand.** 12"x27"H.
Old Tavern finish.

F. **No. 06-3506 Cheval Mirror.** 18"x8"x24"H.
Adjustable mirror. One storage drawer.
Old Tavern finish.

G. **No. 07-1526 Bulletin Board.** 14"x5"x24"H.
Blackboard/corkboard combination.
With eraser. Old Tavern finish.

H. **No. 07-1523 Spice Rack with Bottles.**
16"x13"H. Holds sixteen bottles complete
with labels. Old Tavern finish.

lots of service lots of style

These decorative accents include shelf units, curio cabinets, valet and bookstands, barometers and a compact bar. Designs are made of oak, maple or pine.

A. **No. 07-1583 Cup Shelf.** 24" x 6" x 20"H. Old Tavern finish. Includes cup hooks.

B. **No. 06-1700 Horse and Barometer**

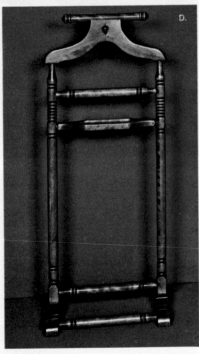

C. **No. 08-3550 Bunching Table.** 22" x 22" x 17"H. Glass top. Royal Charter finish.

D. **No. 08-3510 Gentleman's Dressing Stand.** Old Tavern finish.

E. **No. 08-3551 Curio Cabinet.** 16" x 13" x 72"H. Pewter grill with adjustable glass shelves. Royal Charter finish.

F. **No. 08-3544 Bookstand.** 24" x 12" x 24"H. Storage under lift top. Royal Charter finish.

G. **No. 08-3547 Tray Table.** 28" x 16" x 30"H. Black melamine plastic top. Royal Charter finish.

A. **No. 08-3549**
Folding Bar.
28″ x 18″ x 37″H.
Opens to 14″ x 36″.
Royal Charter finish.

B. **No. 07-1706 Barometer.**

C. **No. 07-1704**
Duck Decoy and Barometer.

D. **No. 07-1550**
Adjustable Shelf.
8″ x 36″ x 25″H.
Royal Charter finish.

E. **No. 08-3542 Etagere.**
14″ x 14″ x 42″H.
Royal Charter finish.

F. **No. 07-1800 Wall Shelf.**
36″ x 5″ x 25″H.
Nutmeg finish.

G. **No. 08-3546**
Book Trough Table.
22″ x 15″ x 23″H.
Royal Charter Finish.

H. **No. 07-1808**
Pier Cabinet.
9″ x 5″ x 21″H.
Nutmeg finish.

THE ETHAN ALLEN GALLERY OF ART

Beautiful pictures are like windows to your favorite world. Ethan Allen offers a massive collection to suit every taste, mood and decor and will help you choose a single subject or arrange a dramatic wall grouping. Shown on these four pages are a few examples from hundreds which include reproductions of museum masterpieces, Renaissance subjects, still life, florals, landscapes, fruit and bird prints, portraits, historical scenes, maps, mini-prints, oils, etchings and water colors.

- **A.** No. 07-5146 "Bird Print"
- **B.** No. 07-5351 Mini oil "Fruit"
  No. 06-3301 Easel
- **C.** No. 07-5371 "Village Setting" etching
- **D.** No. 07-5366 "Girl with Beret"
- **E.** No. 07-5021 "Bird Print"
- **F.** No. 07-5275 "Composition"
- **G.** No. 07-5122 "Homestead"
- **H.** No. 07-5009 "English Scene"
- **J.** No. 07-5312 "Green Winged Teal"
- **K.** No. 07-5065 "Naval Scene"
- **L.** No. 07-5176 "Owl"
- **M.** No. 07-5126 "Pressed Flower"

A.

F.

B.

D.

G.

J.

L.

C.

E.

H.

K.

M.

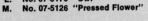

No. 07-5144 Sea View

No. 07-5133 Ships

No. 07-5137 Williamsburg

No. 07-5258 At the Pump (Blish)

No. 07-5376
"Peche Mignon"

No. 07-5684 Woman
with Chrysanthemums (Degas)

No. 07-5171 Carriage

No. 07-5289 Geisha (Hibel)

No. 07-5671 Country Bridge (Rico)

No. 07-5676 Sunday Morning (Durand)

No. 07-5673 Picnic (Gerhart)

Ethan Allen
AMERICAN TRADITIONAL INTERIORS

295

No. 07-5688 "Meet at Blagdon"

No. 07-5203 "Girl Reading"

No. 07-5384 "Bookworm"

No. 07-5394 "Winter in 1610"

No. 07-5225 "Captain Bligh"

No. 07-5685 "Tribute Horse"

No. 07-5291 "Stable of Champions"

THE ETHAN ALLEN GALLERY OF ART

No. 07-5230 "Cottage In Woods", Lorenz

No. 07-5398 "Low Tide At Damariscotta", Hanna

No. 07-5655
"Bowden's Children",
Hoppner

No. 07-5205 "Garden Glory", Dering

No. 07-5369 "Antique Map"

No. 07-5638 "Two Pheasants", Abbett

No. 07-5452
"Jerked Down", Russell

No. 07-5441
"Cheyenne Buck", Remington

No. 07-5421
"Ivy-Cooking"

No. 07-5418
"Boy With Dog"

No. 07-5412
"Elephant"

No. 07-5658
"Bredon on Avon", Parsons

Ethan Allen
AMERICAN TRADITIONAL INTERIORS

297

mirror, mirror...

Pretty reflections for your home in a
wide choice of styles: Chippendale,
Queen Anne, Chinese Chippendale,
sunburst and Federal designs...also
trumeau and brackets.

No. 07-4535
Baroque Mirror. 12"x15"H.
Red finish as shown.

No. 07-4501 Chippendale Mirror.
25½"x34½"H. Crackle finish.

No. 07-4520
Octagon. 12¼"x14¼"H.
Black velvet border.

No. 07-4569
Queen Anne Federal Mirror.
24"x46"H.

No. 07-4522
Diamond Mirror.
8"x13"H.

No. 07-4558 Mirror.
25"x31"H.

No. 07-4521
Florentine Mirror.
9"x15"H.

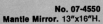

No. 07-4525
Shadowbox Mirror.
7"x11"H.

No. 07-4550
Mantle Mirror. 13"x16"H.

No. 07-1601
Bracket. 6"x8"H.

No. 07-4531
Trumeaux Mirror.
10"x32"H.

No. 07-1602
Bracket. 6"x8"H.

No. 07-4530
Queen Anne Mirror.
24"x53"H.

No. 07-4512
Smoke Mirror. 11"x25"H.

No. 07-4511
Smoke Mirror.
8"x22"H.

No. 07-4561
Bamboo Motif Mirror.
27"x44"H.

No. 07-4549
Shield Mirror.
11"x13"H.

No. 07-4526
Sunburst Mirror.
18" diameter.

Ethan Allen
AMERICAN TRADITIONAL INTERIORS

on the wall

A. **No. 07-4559 Oval Mirror.** 30"x36"H.
B. **No. 07-4505 Federal Mirror.** 22"x38"H.
C. **No. 07-4564 Rectangle.** 30"x42"H.
   No. 07-4565 Rectangle. 36"x52"H.
   No. 07-4566 Rectangle. 38"x62"H.
D. **No. 07-4563 Federal with Eagle.** 18" Glass. 27"x38"H.
E. **No. 07-4555 Octagon Mirror.** Green. 16"x16".
   No. 07-4556 Octagon Mirror. Yellow. 16"x16".
   No. 07-4557 Octagon Mirror. Pine finish. 16"x16".
F. **No. 07-4500 Queen Anne Mirror.** 27"x40"H.
G. **No. 07-1608 Bracket.** 8"x15"H.
H. **No. 07-1607 Bracket.** 8"x15"H.
J. **No. 07-1605 Bracket.** 14"x15"H.

A.

B.

C.

D.

E.

F.

G.

H.

J.

Ethan Allen
AMERICAN TRADITIONAL INTERIORS

floral accents

Brighten your room, accent your table top with these delightful floral arrangements offered in a diversity of containers and flowers—both artificial and dried. They're also wonderful gifts. Shown are but a few beauties from our Ethan Allen "garden"

THE ETHAN ALLEN HOME FASHION CENTER

A New Way to Help You Have the Home You Want.

Let us introduce the Ethan Allen Home Fashion Center—right in the heart of the Ethan Allen Gallery. Here on these next 18 pages you will meet an idea so sensible you wonder why no one ever thought of it before.

Unlike anything you have ever seen before. The Ethan Allen Home Fashion Center brings together in one convenient area for you, complete selections of fabrics and swatches of just about every imaginable pattern and color for just about every imaginable purpose in your home. Without running from store to store, you will find entire selections of: Broadloom carpeting; Oriental designs; Caucasian & American stencil design rugs; Bedspreads; Pillows; Upholstery; Drapery fabrics; Traditional and Contemporary wallpaper.

The Home Fashion Center is also a place with special people—Experienced Home Planners who know many ways to turn the ideas in your head into rooms in your home. Here, you can try out your ideas—in one place. With the help of special displays and one of our talented Home Planners, you will mix and match to your heart's content. In surprisingly short time, you've decorated the home you have been dreaming of for years.

These pages are only a taste of what is in store . . . no where will you find a simpler nor more exciting way to put together the home you have always wanted.

The ETHAN ALLEN Home Fashion Center...

Now you can finish your decorating in the same place you start. No more scurrying from store to store—salesman to salesman—memorizing patterns, styles and colors. And trying to put them all together in your head.

We've put them all together for you, in our Ethan Allen Home Fashion Center. Not only does it add convenience to your decorating—it also helps avoid costly decorating mistakes. Because you could try out your ideas in our Fashion Center instead of in your home.

HERE'S HOW IT WORKS:

The Home Fashion Center, right in the heart of the Ethan Allen Gallery provides fabrics and swatches in just about every imaginable pattern and color for just about every purpose in your home—

> Broadloom carpeting, area rugs in Oriental, Caucasian, American Stencil, Design and Braided rugs, upholstery and drapery fabrics, bedspreads and pillows, and to help pull everything together—a broad selection of traditional and contemporary wall paper.

With the help of our special displays and one of our specially trained decorating experts, you'll mix and match to your heart's content. We'll take your ideas and help you turn them into rooms that express you, not someone else.

Now you can decorate your home from ceiling to floor in one place. The Ethan Allen Gallery. Nowhere will you find a simpler or more exciting way to put together the home you've always wanted.

Ethan Allen
AMERICAN TRADITIONAL INTERIORS

... birthplace of beautiful home decoration

From the moment you enter the Home Fashion Center in an Ethan Allen Gallery, you are in a world of color, pattern and texture, the basic ingredients of beautiful decorating. And of course, the Ethan Allen Home Fashion Center is surrounded by something that will further inspire the decorator in you: the Ethan Allen Gallery—with dozens of beautifully decorated rooms. Every room in the house from the basement to the attic. Completely decorated down to details as small as the last ashtray.

HOW TO WORK MAGIC WITH CARPETS

For a dramatic change in any room: put down a great rug or marvelous broadloom carpet. The Ethan Allen Home Fashion Center has a superb selection of carpets and rugs in a rainbow of colors and patterns. Let our Home Planners help you work your own carpet magic.

BEDSPREADS AND PILLOWS

You'll find pillows and bedspreads in just about every style and color. You will also find advice to help you choose the bedspreads and pillows that are best for your decor.

MIXING PATTERNS CAN BE AS SIMPLE AS MIXING PAINT

Here you'll find an exciting array of upholstery and drapery fabrics to choose from—all color correlated to blend with Ethan Allen carpets and rugs, bedspreads and pillows. Our Ethan Allen Home Fashion Center offers just about every kind of curtain and drapery fabric imaginable—plus exciting ideas on how to use them.

Remember the excitement of your first home? On moving day it was just empty rooms. But it was yours. And you dreamed how it would be the warmest, coziest spot on earth. You've tried for years to make it come true. You've probably shopped at store after store. Trying to guess if that big sofa would fit in the living room. How that chandelier would look in the dining room. How that bedspread would look with a new rug.

There's an easier way—the Home Fashion Center at your Ethan Allen Gallery. Surrounded by beautiful rooms, the Home Fashion Center brings together in one place a carefully and professionally correlated collection of floor coverings, draperies, upholstery fabrics, bedspreads, pillows, wall paper—even paints—to help you put together the rooms you've always wanted. No running from store to store to find the right fabric, the right rug, the righ accessory. No guessing how things look together—here you try out your ideas to your hearts' content.

And best of all, the Home Fashion Center is a place with special people—experienced Home Planners who know many ways to help you turn those ideas in your head into rooms in your home. Their dream is to make your dreams come true.

Ethan Allen
AMERICAN TRADITIONAL INTERIORS

Frame your windows in beauty

Sometimes, window treatments seem to be the most perplexing problem you face during home decorating. Maybe it's because there are so many appealing styles to choose from: formal draperies, casual curtains, practical shades, swags and valances and more. Window treatments need to be styled in complete decorative harmony with the room's total scheme. Ethan Allen offers you not only a vast selection of drapery fabrics, colors and textures but the "know-how" to help you choose the right design. All fabrics are correlated with Ethan Allen floor coverings and upholstery fabrics for complete color harmony . . . Ethan Allen Home Planners are skilled in planning curtains to suit the size and type of window that fully integrate with the decor of your room.

The Ethan Allen Home Fashion Center—where windows become beautiful pictures

from halfway around the world to your home...

There's a ring of decorating excitement for your floors in cherished names like Kerman, Kermanshah, Ming, Bokhara and Sarouk. Ethan Allen brings you Oriental design rugs to flavor your home with a rich legacy—vibrant patterns that date back to ancient Persia and Turkey where they graced the walls of palaces and temples.

the magic and beauty of the Orient

Here's a comprehensive selection of over 50 Oriental-inspired rugs, improved with modern technology and encompassing a wide diversity of styles, a few of which are shown here. These contemporary counterparts inspired by hand-woven antiques are rich accents for today's interiors.

bring drama and color to your floors...
area rugs from Ethan Allen set the stage!

Here are sparkling accents underfoot—area rugs of every style genre that will make your floors glow with vibrant color and exuberant pattern. Your Ethan Allen Home Fashion Center offers you a large collection of rug designs in both traditional and contemporary expression—including American Indian, Caucasian, American Primitive and Wool and Herd Animal area rugs. There are plaids, stripes and traditional braids in stunning contemporary colors, rich, warm and luxurious. All are glamorous accents for any room in the house, each available in a wide choice of colors and room sizes.

from the ETHAN ALLEN Home Fashion Center...

wall-to-wall elegance for your home

Floor covering is the important anchor of a room's decorating scheme, but if all the choices—between colors, fibers, sizes, surface finishes and prices—seem confusing, take heart. In the Ethan Allen Home Fashion Center we'll help you solve the mystery—keep you from making a wall-to-wall mistake. We've assembled a great collection of broadloom carpet offering a rainbow of colors, all correlated to Ethan Allen draperies and upholstery fabrics. You can pick from a complete range of fabric content and surface finishes, including acrylics, nylon, polypropylene and traditionally cherished wool. Surfaces include plush, loop pile, combination of loops and twists. We'll help you choose the right carpet or rug for any room of your home—help you find the style that suits your interior design and your budget.

cover
your beds
with beauty

From Your Ethan Allen Home Fashion Center . . .
Decorative Excitement in Bedspreads,
Canopies, Shams, Ruffles, Valances
and Draperies.

Just as you can alter your mood by slipping on a new dress, you can transform your boudoir or bedroom by giving it a new costume. A change of bedspreads can make all the difference in the world—and in a room. Changing decor can be just as easy as changing a pillowcase when you discover what Ethan Allen has available in ready-mades for the bedroom. The choice is endless: color, texture, pattern in every conceivable style, whether you want lace and frills or a trim, tailored look.

What's your favorite? Your Ethan Allen Home Fashion Center has an array of bedspreads, all with matching drapery fabrics, valances, some with matching wall coverings. There are multi-needled fully quilted patterns, tone on tone damasks, florals, stripes with over-prints, solids, Chinese garden and English bouquet designs. Fabrics include rayon/acetate, cotton, linen, Avril, polyester in various combinations. There are hundreds of colors from which to choose. With Ethan Allen, it's easy to strike the right note for a new bedroom or magically transform an old one.

WALL COVERINGS
from the Ethan Allen Home Fashion Center

It's no longer called *wall paper* (though the term lingers like "ice-box" for refrigerator). Walls today are as apt to be covered with plastic, fabric or wood as they are with paper.

The new coverings do more than just cover a wall—they add texture, architectural interest, reflection—new bright patterns and colors can work decorating wonders in a room.

Ethan Allen has carefully chosen an exciting collection of wall coverings in traditional and contemporary patterns and surfaces, color compatible with drapery fabrics, rugs and upholstery textiles—all to help you choose the right look for your room, conveniently and confidently.

Wall coverings by J. Josephson, Inc.

DECORATIVE PILLOWS
the final touch of comfort and color

Like costume jewelry on a favorite dress, decorative pillows can provide the dramatic touch to complete a decorating plan. Bright accents of color and comfort—they add invitation to a sofa or chair, pattern and color to your bedroom.

The Ethan Allen Collection of decorative pillows offers a score of sizes, styles, colors, patterns, textures all carefully correlated to upholstery fabrics, bedspreads and drapery fabrics. It's fun and it's easy to choose the right ones for your home.

Shown here (and on front cover)
from left to right:
No. 11-8206 **Nest of Tables**
No. 13-7126 **Sheraton Sofa**
No. 11-8201 **Lamp Table**
No. 11-8200 **Cocktail Table**
No. 13-7125 **Sheraton Loveseat**
No. 20-7606 **Queen Anne Wing Chair**

For detailed specifications on
Upholstery—see pages 392-406.

ETHAN ALLEN
TREASURY
DECORATING
GUIDE

40-pages of exciting "how to" ideas

Color Schemes•Room Arranging

Decorating Windows•Table Settings

Apartment Decorating

American Traditional Handcrafts

PLUS

Design History and Glossary

Great Restorations

The Ethan Allen Treasury Bookshelf and

Quality, Care and Use Information

THE GREAT AGE OF FURNITURE DESIGN

The 18th and 19th centuries were a decorative arts era, one of the richest the world has known. People were ready for the comforts of furniture and houses designed to reflect the elaborate social customs of the day. The fashion pendulum swung from the early flamboyant baroque to the exuberant rococo of the mid-1700s and on to the simplicity and discipline of neoclassicism.

Designers and craftsmen came into their own, and four great names, all from England, are widely honored to this day: Thomas Chippendale; the brothers Adam; George Hepplewhite; and Thomas Sheraton. But styles were also named for the monarchs of the period—Anne and the Georges in England and the Regent Louis XV, and Louis XVI in France. For the most part, these styles overlapped or merged gradually into one another. But in the last quarter of the century, the delicate neoclassicism of the English architect-designer Robert Adam, inspired by the discoveries of the ruins at Herculaneum and Pompeii, brought into fashion new vocabulary of design.

The American colonies adopted the styles of the mother country, adapting and refining them, usually simplifying them. In the flourishing seaboard cities were many skilled and talented cabinetmakers such as Duncan Phyfe in New York, William Savery in Philadelphia and the Townsend-Goddard family in Newport.

Since they were first created, these classic furniture designs have endured and are cherished. In America, small city and country cabinetmakers continued to adapt Chippendale, Hepplewhite and Sheraton long after their more fashionable contemporaries in New York and Baltimore had gone on to something new. And many reproductions of 18th-century designs were made for the Philadelphia Centennial Exposition of 1876. Today, some of these "Centennial pieces" are hard for an amateur to distinguish from furniture made a century earlier.

From HOUSE & GARDEN'S COMPLETE GUIDE TO INTERIOR DECORATION; copyright © 1957 by The Conde Nast Publications, Inc.

French Chairs

The most durable accomplishment of the French during this century was the upholstered armchair —the fauteuil with open arms and the bergère with closed arms. Comfortable for both men and women, they were a good deal more graceful and lighter looking than their English counterparts.

1

The *Régence* armchair was comfortable but rather large in scale like its predecessors in the reign of Louis XIV.

2

Louis XV fauteuil retained the cabriole legs, had a broad back, but was not so high.

3

Transitional bergère began to be more restrained. Back was sometimes square; serpentine line of seat disappeared.

4

Popular contemporary version of a comfortable country French chair has many authentic touches: spindle cross stretcher, tapered spindle legs and arched ladderback treatment.

English and American Chairs

English chairs and their American derivatives were more varied in design than the French. But except for some Windsors and the Sheraton styles at the end of the century, the wood —first walnut, later mahogany— was always given a natural finish.

1

Ladder-back rush-seat chair, with or without arms, was probably the most common chair in ordinary houses both in England and the Colonies.

2

Windsor chair with scooped-out plank seat and spindle back was especially popular in modest Colonial houses.

3

Bamboo-turned chair, often linked with Chippendale, reached height of popularity mainly in England at end of century. It was revived with enthusiasm in the 1960s, especially for garden rooms.

4

Corner chair, which had first appeared in previous century, took on vase-shaped splats and cabriole legs of Queen Anne style. Chair was used mostly at desk.

5

Early Chippendale upholstered chair "in French taste" retained cabriole legs. Later version with straight legs was known as "Martha Washington" chair.

6

Chippendale side chairs with openwork back splats were often elaborately carved—especially those made in Philadelphia.

7

Ladder-back chairs with pierced horizontal rails are often called "Chippendale," though none appear in his design books.

8

"Gothic" was a term applied to Chippendale chairs with Gothic arches and quatrefoils worked into design of back splat.

9

Queen Anne chair with splat back and cabriole legs began as a court piece in carved walnut. But in the Colonies many were made of maple and pine.

10

Shield backs enclosing balusters or splats were an earmark of the Hepplewhite style, actually an adaptation of Adam. Legs were usually straight and tapered.

11

Square backs, divided in three by a splat or balusters, were Sheraton's favorites, with the legs turned and reeded.

12

Early wing chairs had cabriole legs, claw-and-ball feet. Arm terminating in vertical roll was typical of New England and New York.

13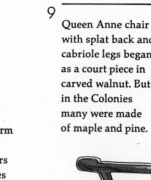

Hepplewhite wing chairs had deeper wings and straight, square legs. Horizontally rolled arms were popular in Philadelphia.

Sofas

As the social customs of the tea table and the salon came to have more importance, the stiff settee grew into the longer, more comfortable sofa.

1

Serpentine-back sofa in the Chippendale style reflects rolled arms of wing chair 13, *above*, and straight legs and stretchers of armchair 8.

2

Curved-back sofa in the Hepplewhite style had exposed wood on back rail and concave front of arms.

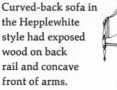

3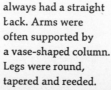

Sheraton sofa almost always had a straight back. Arms were often supported by a vase-shaped column. Legs were round, tapered and reeded.

4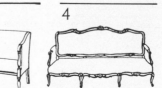

Louis XV sofas were elaborately carved, closely resembled Louis XV chairs such as 2, *opposite page.*

5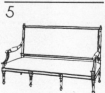

Louis XVI sofas usually had straight, rectangular backs and the same straight, fluted legs.

Tables

During the 18th century, more and more tables were designed for special purposes, such as serving tea when that custom was brought from the Orient. Many had space-saving aspects.

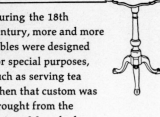

1
The candle stand had a top just large enough to hold a candle, but it was tall enough to keep light at comfortable height.

2
Large drop-leaf tables with cabriole legs in Queen Anne style were used for dining, especially in houses lacking separate dining rooms.

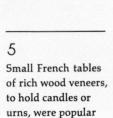

3
Queen Anne tea table often had a dished top with raised molding and, sometimes, pull-out shelves for candles.

4
Card tables, both French and English, had round or square tops hinged in center so one half could fold flat or be raised against wall.

5
Small French tables of rich wood veneers, to hold candles or urns, were popular under Louis XV.

6
Tilt-top tripod table with pie-crust edge was also used for tea, could be pushed against wall when tea was over.

7
Drop-leaf Pembroke table, often used for breakfast, came in with Hepplewhite style. Some versions had rectangular leaves and cross stretchers.

Desks and Secretaries

Furniture designed for writing became elaborately ornamental as well as functional. Chippendale launched the true secretary.

1
Block-front secretary with bonnet top was an elegant American type—specifically Newport—with no English counterpart.

2
Slant-top desk with bracket feet was very popular in the Colonies. Plain ones like this were made in Newport for export to the West Indies.

5
Large writing tables, called *bureaux plats* in France, generally had three drawers, were designed for great house libraries.

3
Hepplewhite tambour desk had fold-over writing surface and upper section of pigeonholes and small drawers hidden by sliding tambour doors.

6
Double pedestal desk, forerunner of our office desks, was popular in both France and England. Tops were usually covered with leather.

4
Venetian secretaries, designed along Queen Anne lines, had intricate inner fittings, were lavishly decorated with lacquer.

7
Fall-front desk or *secrétaire à abattant* was introduced in France under Louis XV. Sometimes it had a marble top, was decorated with marquetry, paint or bronze doré.

Beds

The bed achieved far more importance as decorative furniture, often dominating the room as it does today. Wooden frames replaced rope supports for bedding.

1

High-poster bed came in when houses became easier to heat. Posts supported wood frame for canopy or valance.

3

French alcove bed, with headboard and footboard of equal height, was popular from time of Louis XVI.

2

"Field beds" were so called because they resembled the demountable beds used when traveling.

4

Venetian bed, with luxuriously carved and painted headboard, but no footboard, no hangings, prevailed in the South.

Chests of Drawers

Commodes and chests took on a great variety of shapes and heights. On the whole, they were simpler than those of the previous century.

1

Early chests of drawers were fairly undistinguished, usually stood on bracket feet. Mirror was a separate piece.

2

Philadelphia lowboy, with claw-and-ball feet and richly carved knees, is one case where American design is more ornate.

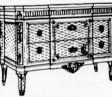

3

Louis XVI commode was marked by straight lines and straight legs, typical of neoclassical period.

4

Block-front chests were similar to Chippendale chests, except for blocking which was unique to Colonies. Carved shell spells Newport.

5

Chest-on-chest of tallboy offered maximum storage in minimum space. Flat top and bracket feet were popular around Charleston, South Carolina.

6

Hepplewhite bowfront chests had feet of flaring, French bracket type and drawers embellished with bands of light satinwood.

7

French provincial armoires furnished closet-shy country châteaus, are popular today to house stereo and bars.

8

French provincial commodes, usually made of fruitwood in natural finish, were simplified adaptations of the Louis XV style.

9

Philadelphia bonnet top highboy was probably the epitome of American Colonial cabinetmaking. It had practically no parallel among English furniture.

Cabinets

As personal and family possessions increased, the need arose for storage designed for special purposes: clothes (there were no built-in closets), china, books.

1

Hudson River Valley *kas* was decorated with painted trompe l'oeil motifs, to simulate carving on 17th-century Dutch clothes cupboards.

2

Corner cupboards, usually intended for china, made use of space that would otherwise have gone to waste.

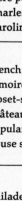

3

Flattop or Queen Anne highboy was earlier type and the one most popular in New England, where it was often made of maple or cherry.

4

Breakfront bookcase got its name because projecting center section "broke" line of facade. Some included a writing compartment.

A BASIC TRADITIONAL FURNITURE VOCABULARY

PERIOD DEFINITIONS

Colonial: The American period extending from the time of the earliest 17th Century settlements to the Revolution. (The term is frequently but improperly applied to most American furniture up to 1850.) The more primitive styles were developed in New England and the Pennsylvania Dutch area. The more elegant styles, in large cities north and south, were greatly influenced by English cabinet makers, but American designers adapted and embellished with great success on their own.

Federal: The American period coincidental with early years of the Republic, 1780 to 1830. Duncan Phyfe was the outstanding designer.

BEDS

Bonnet: Has a short extended canopy on tall headboard posts.

Bunk: Single bed with matching bed fitted on top (with ladder). ONE ETHAN ALLEN type can be rearranged into a trundle or twins.

Cannonball: Large balls cap each of its four low posts.

Canopy (or Tester): Tall four-poster with fabric-covered wood frame over it. Originally had vertical hangings to keep out drafts.

Poster: Has four tall posts, decoratively turned.

Spindle: Has decorative turnings, like some chair backs. (Right)

Spool: Its turnings are shaped like thread spools.

Trundle: Low bed on rollers which fits under a single bed.

STORAGE PIECES

Apothecary Chest: Chest with many small (or simulated) drawers adapted from early American druggists' chests.

Bachelor's Chest: Small-scale chest of drawers.

Chest-on-Chest: Two-sectioned chest; one mounted on top is usually slightly smaller.

Cheval Mirror: Mirror that swings between posts and is adjustable. Small versions, often with drawers in base, are used on chests or tables.

Commode: Originally an enclosed bedroom "chamber box," later combined with a wash stand. Now the term means night stand or console chest.

Credenza: Buffet-like storage cabinet, usually with doors.

Dry Sink: Originally water was added for washing dishes. Today's version: cupboard with open well in top, often lined with copper tray.

Highboy: Tall chest of drawers on legs (usually cabriole legs).

Hutch: Open-shelved storage piece on a base with cupboards and/or drawers.

Secretary: Desk with drawers below, open or closed bookshelves above.

CHAIRS

Captain's Chair: Type of Windsor, with saddle seat; often with low bentwood back and arms. Once used on ships, later in taverns. (Right)

Comb-back: Type of Windsor with spindles resembling an old-fashioned high comb.

Duxbury: See Windsor.

Hitchcock: Named for early Connecticut chair maker. Derives from a Sheraton design called "fancy chair"; usually has an oval top rail. Many are painted and decorated with stencils.

Ladder-Back: Popular design from 1750 to 1800. Back is ladder-shaped, with horizontal slats.

Lawson: Upholstered. Low-backed; arm is often set back at the front to accommodate a 'T" cushion (seating cushion that extends forward and across front of arm). (Right)

Mate's Chair: Smaller than a Captain's style, with shorter arms.

Saddle Seat: Scooped away to side and back from central ridge, for more comfort. Resembles the pommel of a saddle.

Settle: All wood, often of Windsor design. In reality, a bench with arms, sometimes called a Deacon's bench."

Tub: Upholstered. Small circular chair, rather like half a barrel.

Tuxedo: Upholstered. Arms are same height as back.

Windsor: Characterized by slender turned spindles, wooden saddle seat and turned, splayed or raked legs usually joined by stretcher at bottom. Also referred to as "Duxbury." (Right)

Wing: Upholstered. High side pieces (once used to ward off drafts).

TABLES

Butterfly: Has rounded drop leaves supported by wing brackets. (Right)

Candlestand: Small tripod, pedestal, or four legged table, used to hold candles and their drippings.

Cobbler's Bench: Originally a shoemaker's work seat with drawer for tools. Copied for cocktail and coffee tables.

Doughbox: Deep slopesided box, once used for "raising" bread, adapted for occasional table with roomy storage compartment.

Drum: Round library or lamp table. Deep open or closed top (that suggests a drum) sometimes revolves on a pedestal base.

Gateleg: Has two drop leaves. Legs swing out like a gate to support the leaves when extended.

Harvest: Very long drop leaf table, usually with narrow leaves running entire length. Originally used for feeding harvest "hands."

Lazy Susan: Round, revolving wood tray for center of dining table.

Pedestal: Single turned center pedestal supports table, or pedestal may have tripod base. Extension tables often have two pedestals for firm support when extended.

Pembroke: Small rectangular table with two drop leaves, shallow drawer.

Step: Originally made to reach high bookshelves. Adapted today, keeping the steps, as two or three-level end table.

Trestle: Long rectangular top on two vertical supports. Informal.

DESIGN ELEMENTS

Apron. Structural support placed at right angles to underside of table or chair for decorative trim and to increase support.

Broken Pediment: A triangular top, from classical architecture, sometimes used on headboard, mirrors, tall chests or cabinets. Its sloping lines stop short of the peak, leaving a gap for an ornamental finial such as a turned knob or urn shape. (Right)

Cabriole Leg: Shape has a graceful "S" curve. (Right)

Cornice: A projecting molding used to give an architectural finish to the top edge of a chest, dresser or cabinet.

Dental: A small rectangular block. Used in a row projecting like teeth under a cornice. A classic Greek form of ornamentation. (Right)

Fiddleback: Chair or bed back whose splat resembles a violin.

Fluting: Vertical channels carved into columns, as seen in ancient Greek architecture.

Gallery: Decorative railing around edge of table, shelf or tray.

Grill: Can be metal or wood, combined with glass for some cabinet doors.

Louvers: Fixed, shutter-like slats used for decorative door panels.

Mullion: Slender moulding dividing the panes of glass of doors.

Ogee Bracket Foot: Shaped like a bracket, with a double curve. (Above)

Spoonfoot: Simple flattish end of a cabriole or turned leg.

Stenciling: Pattern applied to furniture by painting over thin metal or heavy paper cut-outs.

Stretcher: Support connecting legs of any piece of furniture; frequently turned for decorative interest.

FINISH

Antiquing and/or Distressing: Method of treating wood to lend an old appearance or "patina." This may be done with chemicals, paint or stain. It adds a worn-away look to the color and reduces the brilliance of the surface. Specking adds a soft look instead of continuous color.

CONSTRUCTION

Center Drawer Guide: Channel under center of the drawer rides over a guide on the case frame to prevent jamming and insure smooth operation.

Dovetail: Joint made by flared tongues of wood that interlock with shaped pieces of wood to hold front and back drawer corners securely. (Right)

Dowel: Round peg of wood that fits into corresponding hole to form a strong joint. Used originally instead of nails.

Floating Construction: Used for furniture made of solid woods; it permtis top and side panels to expand or contract with changes of temperature and humidity, thus avoiding warping or cracking.

Mortise and Tenon: A Tongue or projecting part of wood that fits into a corresponding rectangular hole or mortise (one of the most important joints in woodworking).

HARDWARE

Back Plate: A metal mount or escutcheon, on which the drawer handle or pull is mounted.

Bail Handle: Made of metal in the form of a half-loop.

Drop Handle: Pear or tier-shaped pull, usually brass.

H and L Hinge: An early design, resembling the letters H and a connecting L, made originally of iron or brass.

From the past for the present

Handsome 17th Century furniture in the Buttolph-Williams House, a Connecticut landmark, are American versions of Jacobean, Tudor and William & Mary designs. Substantial Ethan Allen Royal Charter offers the same decorative details such as rope trim, shape of high back chair, intricate carving, robust turnings.

For complete Royal Charter Collection, see pages 120-133.

Ethan Allen Designs Shown:
No. 16-6013 Flip Top Table
No. 16-6011A Arm Chair
No. 16-9001 Mirror
No. 16-7439 Tufted Bench

JACOBEAN-TUDOR ROYAL CHARTER

Built in 1638, the Whipple House is one of the earliest Colonial homes still standing. Furniture design is understated as in master bedroom with its lacy canopy and simple cupboards. A contemporary counterpart: Ethan Allen Heirloom.

Ethan Allen Designs Shown:
No. 10-5304 Six Drawer Chest
No. 10-5631/5993 Spindle Bed and Canopy
No. 11-8008 Wine Stand
No. 10-6020 Duxbury Chair

For complete Heirloom Collection, see pages 134-177.

EARLY AMERICAN HEIRLOOM

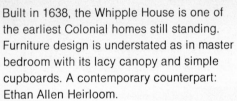

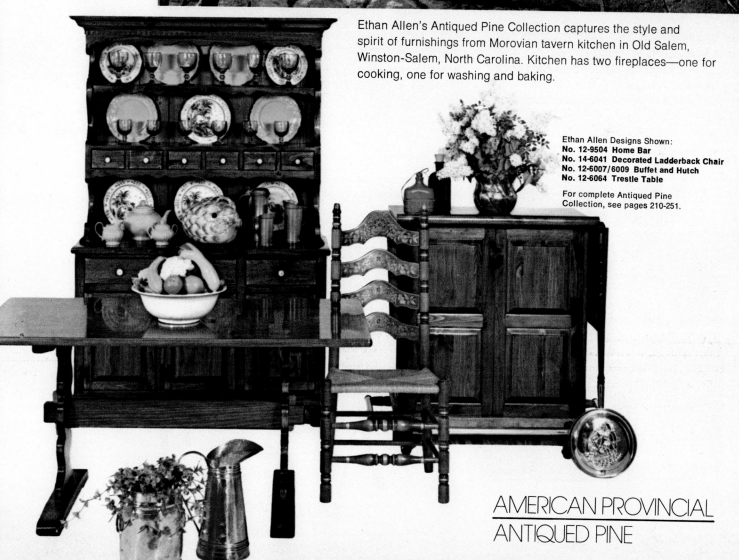

Ethan Allen's Antiqued Pine Collection captures the style and spirit of furnishings from Morovian tavern kitchen in Old Salem, Winston-Salem, North Carolina. Kitchen has two fireplaces—one for cooking, one for washing and baking.

Ethan Allen Designs Shown:
No. 12-9504 Home Bar
No. 14-6041 Decorated Ladderback Chair
No. 12-6007/6009 Buffet and Hutch
No. 12-6064 Trestle Table

For complete Antiqued Pine Collection, see pages 210-251.

AMERICAN PROVINCIAL
ANTIQUED PINE

Stressing simplicity, Shaker craftsmen designed furniture to be purely utilitarian, as seen in room from Shaker Village, Hancock, Mass. Ethan Allen Custom Room Plan units achieve the same harmony of proportion and unadorned beauty of design.

Ethan Allen Designs Shown:
No. 10-4553P Three Drawer Chest
No. 10-4511P Two Door Cabinet
No. 10-4018 Upper Cabinet Bookcase
No. 08-3507 Treat Table
No. 12-6002 Ladderback Side Chair

For complete Heirloom Custom Room Plan Collection, see pages 180-209.

SHAKER
CUSTOM ROOM PLAN

Meticulously detailed Queen Anne and Chippendale furniture grace the drawing room of The Lindens, built in the middle of the 18th Century. Ethan Allen Georgian Court faithfully adapts the fine lines of great cabinetmakers' designs.

Ethan Allen Designs Shown:
No. 11-9201 **Lowboy**
No. 11-9202 **Chippendale Looking Glass**
No. 11-6201A **Duncan Phyfe Arm Chair**
No. 20-7122 **Chippendale Love Seat**
No. 11-8204 **Tea Table**
No. 04-1400 **Oriental Design Rug**

For complete Georgian Court Collection, see pages 74-95.

18th CENTURY ENGLISH GEORGIAN COURT

Resplendent and dignified, this early 19th Century dining room is from the Spite House in Maine, built out of the competitive spite of a family feud. A fine match for its regal elegance is Ethan Allen Classic Manor, designed in the highest tradition of the cabinetmaker's craft.

FEDERAL
CLASSIC MANOR

Ethan Allen Designs Shown:
No. 15-9506/9507 Secretary and Top
No. 15-6001A Queen Anne Chair
No. 15-6002 Dining Table
No. 07-4000 Federal Mirror

For complete Classic Manor Collection, see pages 96-119.

making color count

Color is so much a part of our world that we take it for granted, failing to really 'see' all the glorious hues around us. But the colors that tint a room have head-on impact; contained within rigid limits they force themselves upon the senses and we are aware of color scheme and color combinations before we see furniture, fabrics or anything else. And because color is such a powerful decorating tool it must be employed with skill, imagination, and both freedom and restraint, especially now that all the old hat color rules have been thrown out the window. Since we are no longer restricted to using pastels in the bedroom, yellow in the kitchen, or told to avoid the mix of blue with green or orange with red, we can create more interesting and personal schemes. But individual preferences should be followed and an overall color look should be planned at the onset. Once these are established the color scheme can be developed.

cool color

Certain tones glow with warmth, others are a cooling tonic. But warmly colored rooms can be expressed in a broad range of hues, although rich yellows, soft oranges and golds, and mellow browns are often favored for such a mood. Blue can be cool; it can also generate excitement and a delighting liveliness. In concert with green blue emulates the appealing accord fashioned by nature itself.

Color can animate or soothe, add hearthside warmth or subtle sophistication—evoke any mood we wish. Color can also camouflage — disguising awkward proportions or dreary architecture. One of the most popular color looks around are bright-and-light schemes, seen on preceding page. Lifting the spirit of smaller rooms they create the illusion of space and add the verve of vibrant colors.

warm
color

The drama of dark walls is an added element in today's richly colored rooms. Lacquered paints or gleaming wallpapers introduce such hues as sepia, nutria, or tobacco brown—tones that make a room warmer and more intimate. In setting top left, sepia walls are set off by the stark white of tufted velvet sofa. The only other color in the room is old rose. A more zestful interpretation of the same look is seen left center, with vivid scarlet entering in oriental rug and printed draperies. Golden orange walls in tandem with chocolate brown carpeting, opposite page, offers still a third way to approach this color look. Again a white sofa and a few light accents relieve the rich intensity of deep and vibrant hues.

Cool rooms that are also fresh and satisfying come from the harmonious mingling of blues and greens. Green imparts the leafy hues of the landscape, blue the myriad tones of the changing sky and sea. Its a combine that can be applied in settings of formal sophistication or used equally well in rooms of casual charm. Two examples are seen bottom on this and opposite page. In living room, blues and greens are literally pulled out of the print to color the rest of the setting. Furniture itself contributes color in blue and green dining room, underscored by vivid plaid carpeting.

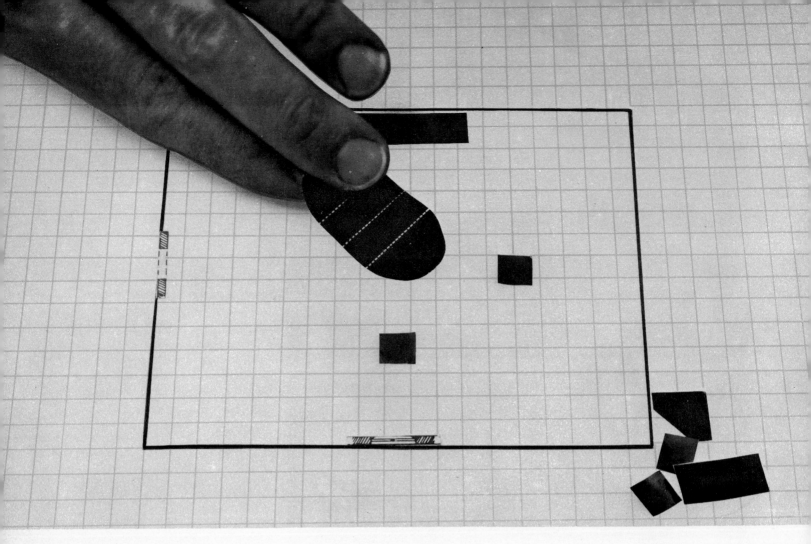

Arrange your furniture on paper first...

AND MOVE IT AROUND WITH A FINGER

Professional decorators push paper patterns around a floor plan until they find the ideal arrangement. It's a sure way to arrive at the best solution with the least effort. You can easily follow this system by using the graph paper and templates on the following pages.

MEASURE YOUR ROOM

Do it carefully. Include the exact positions and dimensions of all architectural features such as openings, wall breaks, chimney breast or alcove. Measure the width of each door and window from the outer edges of its frame. Then draw an accurate room plan on the graph paper, pages 338-340. Each square represents 1 foot. Indicate important details such as radiators, the swing of doors, electric outlets and so on. (Use the symbols given on the next page; you'll also find them helpful when reading blueprints.)

CUT OUT THE TEMPLATES (FURNITURE PLANS)

There are templates for every room in the house, on the next page. All types of furniture are represented, and many sizes. Select the templates that approximate the pieces you want, and place them on your floor plan.

EXPERIMENT THE EASY WAY

Arrange and re-arrange the cut-outs until you're satisfied. Consider comfort and function first. Allow space for doors that swing into the room, for furniture, cupboard doors and drawers to be opened without crowding, for convenient traffic lanes. Take advantage of built-in focal points such as big windows, a long wall or a fireplace. Distribute large pieces to maintain a balance.

WORK OUT YOUR CUSTOM ROOM PLAN GROUPS

Use the cut-outs of the bases on the opposite page. Select the ones that total the overall length you want for your storage wall; you'll probably find several combinations that fit. Then refer back to the small photographs of the Custom Room Plan group you prefer; Nutmeg finished Maple and Birch; Hand-Decorated finishes, pages 362-363; Antiqued Pine, pages 377-378. See which base units come in the sizes you need. Take your time, shifting until you're completely satisfied. Select tops to match your base, always remembering that the right *kind* of storage is important as its exterior design.

...mplates and symbols to plan ...ooms. Cut out the templates ...nd fit them into your room plan on the graph on the following pages. Move them around to achieve the decorative and storage results you need.

Single Bed 3/3

Double Bed 4/6

Queen Size (5/0)

Hollywood Bed 6/6

40" Chest

38" Chest

34" Chest

24" Night Table

22" Night Table

20" Night Table

CUSTOM ROOM PLAN

24" x 18"

24" x 18"

30" x 18"

30" x 18"

30" x 18"

34" x 18" Corner Unit

30" x 18"

34" x 18"

34" x 18"

40" x 18"

40" x 18"

48" x 18"

48" x 30" Corner Desk

60" x 18"

24" x 14"

30" x 14"

30" x 14"

34" x 14"

DINING ROOM

72" Buffet

66" Buffet

56" Buffet

48" Buffet

Chair

Chair

Chair

40" Buffet

24" Corner Unit

78" x 48"

(48" Round Table with 2 leaves)

72" x 42"

(42" Round Table with 2 leaves)

66" x 44" Table

60" x 40" Table

56" x 38" Table

48" Round Table

42" Round Table

LIVING ROOM

55" Loveseat

70" Sofa

77" Sofa

83"

Piano 54" x 60"

89" Sofa

99"

Chair 30"

Chair 30"

Chair

Chair

Desk 50" x 25"

Desk 30" x 18"

Cocktail Table 50" x 20"

Bookcase 35" x 12"

Step-End Table 18" x 28"

25" Square End Table

25" Round End Table

35" Round Cocktail Table

Dough box Table 18" x 26"

Chair 33" x 32"

Piano 20" x 50"

TYPICAL SYMBOLS Here are some typical symbols to use on the graph when you are planning your rooms. They will help you achieve practical results.

BASE OUTLET

WALL OUTLET

CEILING LIGHT

TELEPHONE

RADIATOR

DOOR, SWING IN OR OUT

DOUBLE-HUNG WINDOW

WINDOW, OPEN IN OR OUT

ARCHED OPENING

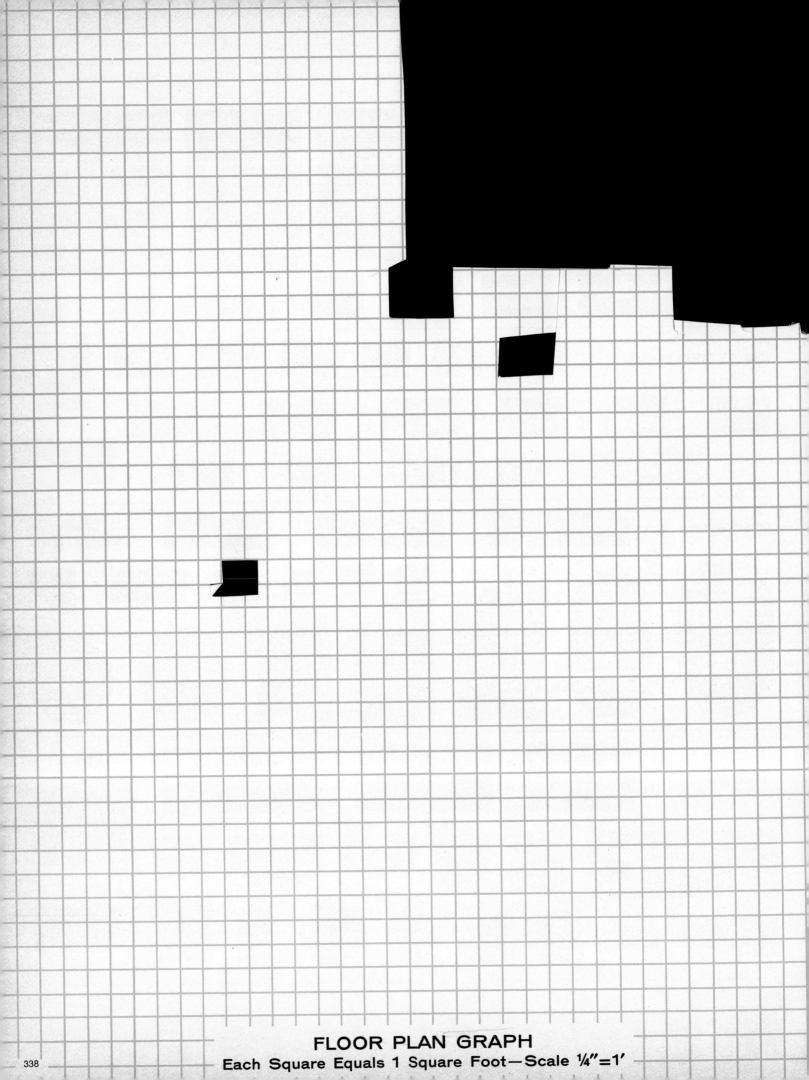

FLOOR PLAN GRAPH
Each Square Equals 1 Square Foot—Scale ¼"=1'

beautiful window design

Make the most of your windows. When skillfully handled, windows become dramatic focal points, rich architectural ornaments, or simply eye-pleasing compositions of color and pattern. Never a mere afterthought, window dressing should be planned in concert with the decoration of the room as a whole. Then it can never be a thing unto itself, but rather an interesting and coordinated part of the décor—as well as suitable dressing for the shape and size of the window. And windows are never to be taken too literally; clever camouflage can widen skinny windows, enlarge tiny ones, make two separate windows appear to be one. Apply this art in tandem with the right window treatment for the most effective background design. Happily there are many possible treatments to choose from; often two or more can be combined for the same window design. So give windows the consideration they deserve, while being careful not to overdo a good thing.

Ethan Allen
AMERICAN TRADITIONAL INTERIORS

winning windows

To the amateur designer, choosing a window treatment is like being offered an embarrassment of riches. The possibilities are almost infinite: formal draperies with various trimmings, curtains in an broad assortment of styles, Roman shades, window shades, valances, swags, jabots, shutters are only some of the many choices available. In bedroom, opposite page left top, tie-back draperies and valance reiterate the patchwork print used for wall alcove and ceiling treatment. The tailored and subtle background design of a home office, opposite page left bottom, teams soft hangings with louvred shutters. French doors take a simple yet decorative treatment in room, opposite page right. Deep cornice, framing draperies tied high, were an excellent choice for a bedroom with a high ceiling, left. Shades gives fine light control, so they were used in tandem with louvred shutters for sunny dining room, below.

festive tables
flavor the menu

Embellished with splendor or set with Spartan restraint, the skillfully decorated table imparts the flavor of a meal even before it is served. And table setting is a continuing art; each dining event provides a fresh challenge. Why play it safe? It's more fun to mix than match, use unexpected color themes and centerpieces.

2

3

Colorful country supper is served in rustic mood Ethan Allen Antiqued Pine dining room, top right. Table above is set with pewter for Colonial spirit New England lunch. The goose that laid a scarlet table, right, garnished with holly, pine boughs and fresh fruit.

Oneida Silver 2, 4
Royal Copenhagen 3, 6
Gorham Company 5

For a children's party, right, what could be more fun than limited edition plates by Norman Rockwell, a blue denim cloth and red bandana napkins? An antique horse and wagon accompanies the floral centerpiece. Patriotic red, white and blue theme sets an inviting family supper, below. Fringed placemats let the pretty Ethan Allen Heirloom table top show through. Other furniture are also Heirloom or Decorated designs. Indian-style table for two, below right, is keyed to an Indian dinner. Shimmering brown silk cloth, delicately colored napkins and brass ornaments compose the elegant yet intimate table design. Gold rimmed porcelain mixes with beautifully wrought silver flatware.

the first apartment

When today's bride is carried over the threshold, that threshold is usually the entrance to a small apartment—often short on charm and never long on space. Yet a tight budget or dreary floor plan seldom dampens the spirits of the young-in-heart. This is their moment to sweep aside middle-aged notions and trot out a free-wheeling style that takes the do's and don'ts out of decorating and puts youthful pizzazz into that first home.

In our young bride's new apartment we've assembled a lively mix of Ethan Allen designs, in a strategy of color excitement and easy do-it-yourself touches. Such touches are seen in stencilled floor and add-on beams of foyer, above. Writing table flips open for buffets. For living room, right, sapphire blue of floor and walls begins a spirited scheme. Tall étagères create niche for sleep-loveseat, striped in an explosion of colors. Adding to the fun are large Chippendale chairs and ottomans, in easy-care white glove-leather vinyl. Fluffy fur rugs, a felt table cover and voilà— a room that delights and refreshes.

Shown above:
No. 16-6013 **Flip-Top Table**
No. 16-6001 **Ladderback Side Chair**
No. 24-9009 **Framed Oval Mirror**

Shown opposite page from left to right:
No. 20-7403 **Wing Chairs**
No. 11-9206 **Etageres**
No. 21-7043 **Sleeper Sofa**
No. 24-8081 **Square Cocktail Table**
No. 20-7404 **Ottomans**

For detailed specifications on:
Royal Charted Dining Room—see pages 389-390
American Foliage Colors—see pages 379-383
Georgian Court Accent Pieces—see page 376
Upholstery—see pages 392-406

Ethan Allen
AMERICAN TRADITIONAL INTERIORS

What looks great in that first dining area might be mini-size for that next, hopefully larger dining room. So we've solved the problem with white Custom Room Plan units, offering ample storage and serving surface now, yet ideal for a child's room eventually. Drop leaf table, which just fits here, is a versatile Heirloom design.

Tiny rooms can have big style...done with understatement and overstatement, opposite. Canopy bed, further dramatized by scarlet panel, distracts from room's meager proportions. Lightly scaled Heirloom dresser and nightstands do not crowd. Giving it all marvelous zing—the play of checks in floor, bedspread and canopy.

Shown above from left to right:
No. 14-4026 Upper Bookcases
No. 14-4521 Apothecary Chests
No. 10-6074P Drop Leaf Harvest Table
No. 12-6002 Ladderback Side Chairs

Shown opposite from left to right:
No. 10-5026 Night Tables
No. 10-5631 Tall Poster Bed with Canopy frame
No. 10-5302 Seven Drawer Double Dresser
No. 14-9703 Boston Rocker
No. 08-3507 Treat Table

For detailed specifications on:
Heirloom Bedroom—see pages 364-366.
Decorated Furniture—see pages 384-385.
Heirloom Custom Room Plan—see pages 362-363.
Heirloom Dining Room—see pages 366-369.
Antiqued Pine Dining Room—see pages 379-381.

Ethan Allen
AMERICAN TRADITIONAL INTERIORS

GREAT AMERICAN RESTORATIONS

Among our cherished historical monuments are the fine old homes of those who founded and nurtured our country. Dramatic reminders of our past, these homes document the aspirations, tastes and customs of their day. Here are brief sketches of but a few of the historic houses and villages that symbolize our heritage. A visit to them will provide a rich and rewarding experience.

COLONIAL WILLIAMSBURG—
Williamsburg, Virginia
This world famous restoration at Williamsburg is a fascinating chapter of history that has attracted thousands yearly since 1932. It recreates accurately the environment of the men and women of Colonial Williamsburg, bringing about an understanding of their lives and times.

The exhibition buildings house a distinguished collection of Seventeenth and Eighteenth century antiques—furniture, silver, paintings and textiles of England and Colonial America. Craftsmen can be seen working, using the authentic tools of 200 years ago.

OLD STURBRIDGE VILLAGE—Sturbridge, Massachusetts
A community out of the past, Old Sturbridge is a recreation of a New England community of 150 years ago. Its 200 acres of rolling meadow and woodland nestle serenely on the banks of the Quinebaug River, unperturbed by the hustle of the outside world.

Old Sturbridge Village is a collection of more than 36 exhibit buildings: homes, meetinghouses, shops, farm house, sheds and mills, brought together from throughout New England to give a true picture of what life in a typical Yankee community was like during the early 1800's. Even the early crafts are practiced as they were then.

MYSTIC SEAPORT—Mystic, Connecticut
Mystic Seaport, located along the Mystic River, ten miles east of New London, Connecticut, is a restored whaling town with an unexcelled collection of old ships and exhibits of actual crafts, a remarkable art gallery which contains different items all relating to Nineteenth Century American maritime history.

GREENFIELD VILLAGE—Dearborn, Michigan

Greenfield Village presents a panorama of American life from Colonial times to the dawn of this century. Its 100 historic buildings represent a variety of architectural styles and literally all walks of life.

Most of the buildings, carefully transplanted from their original locations, are included because they illustrate the progress of this country's industrialization and commerce.

A short distance away are the humble birthplaces of Henry Ford and George Washington Carver.

THE FARMERS MUSEUM—Cooperstown, New York

In the lobby of the Farmers Museum there stands a great log with an old ax sunk deep into the wood, a symbol of the story this museum of history is trying to tell...of the plain people of yesterday, in doing their daily work, building a great nation where only a forest had stood. The story is bound up with the farmer; his wife and family; the community with its craftsmen, professional men, and tradesmen and their tools and implements; the buildings in which they lived and labored. Nearby is Fennimore House, a museum of American history and folk art.

THE HENRY F. DU PONT WINTERTHUR MUSEUM—
Winterthur, Delaware

The house at Winterthur, from which the museum has grown, was built in 1839 by James Antoine Bidermann who had married the great-aunt of Henry Francis duPont in 1814. On inheriting the Winterthur estate in 1927, Mr. duPont began installing interior woodwork collected from houses from New Hampshire to North Carolina.

Over 100 period rooms, covering the American domestic scene between the Seventeenth and early Nineteenth centuries, reflect the skill of those who fashioned useful products of refinement and beauty for the early Colonist and his home. Winterthur represents the largest and richest assemblage of American decorative arts.

OLD DEERFIELD—Deerfield, Massachusetts

When you walk down Old Deerfield Street, you may actually feel that you are in the 18th Century. Old Deerfield, not a formal organized historic site, having retained its village life relatively unchanged from its 18th Century way, stands as a living monument to the early Americans.

Having the means for it, the Deerfield citizens built beautifully designed houses and furnished them with the finest materials available. You can see these houses and furnishings essentially as they were in the late 1700's.

hand crafts personalize your home

It is both pleasurable and productive to make things with our hands, working in whatever medium suits our special talents. The fruit of our labors—hand crafts—adds a personal touch and a warm and unique flavor when used in our own homes. This need to personalize our environment is especially strong today, living in an age where so much has been mechanized and mass-produced. Hence the enormous growth of interest in hand crafts —seen in the blossoming of stores and boutiques devoted to a particular craft, and in the scores of books being written on the subject. Originally crafts were learned out of necessity; today they are an enjoyable and fulfilling hobby that can enrich our leisure hours and our homes. The mediums are many: weaving, needlework, découpage, quilting, candlemaking, macramé, leatherwork and pottery are but a few of the crafts that offer a creative way to make things of enduring usefulness and personal sentiment.

Reading clockwise from top, illustrations are: candles from *The Complete Book Of Candlemaking* by Webster and McMullen, Doubleday; rug from *Handmade Rugs from Practically Anything* by Laury and Aiken, Doubleday; needlepoint designs from the Betty Crocker Home Library *Pleasures of Needlepoint* by Inman Cook and Daren Pierce, Western Publishing Co., Inc.; rug from *Handmade Rugs From Practically Anything*; address oval and lap desk from *Decoupage* by Leslie Linsley, Doubleday.

Left: quilts from *Polly Prindle's Book of American Patchwork Quilts* by Alice I. Gammell, Grosset & Dunlap.
Below: afghan and rug from *Good Housekeeping Needlecraft Magazine*.

Shown above: embroidered placemats, *Good Housekeeping Magazine*.
Top right: appliqued picture, *Good Housekeeping Magazine*;
Right: hanging candles from *The Complete Book Of Candlemaking* by Webster & McMullen, Doubleday.

353

the Ethan Allen Treasury Bookshelf

Great books with classic editorial content and beautiful format devoted to our cherished American Traditional arts and culture. Be a collector! Start your own expert's library. Keyed to today's all time high interest in American Traditional, here are 20 authoritative books dedicated to the preservation of America's cultural beauty...books by authors who share your enthusiasm and offer you variety, detailed information and superb quality.

To order, use handy order blank inside rear cover.

TREASURY OF AMERICAN DESIGN (Two Volumes)
A pictorial survey of popular folk arts based on the index of American Design, at the National Gallery of Art. Over 846 pages, lavishly illustrated in color covering every aspect of American Design heritage. The most authoritative work of its kind. By Clarence P. Hornung. 49.95

THE HERITAGE OF EARLY AMERICAN HOUSES
Takes its readers on a unique house tour—encompassing 65 houses whose architectural and decorating styles reflect the life of early America. More than 250 black and white photographs and more than 40 full-color photographs plus a narrative that unfolds the intriguing histories of these houses and their inhabitants. Introduction by a noted actor and collector, Vincent Price. By John Drury. ...12.50

AMERICA'S FOLK ART
One of the most complete offered on America's folk art, this book is a lavishly illustrated compendium of the wide range of arts and crafts which flourished in this country before 1900. More than 250 photographs, 63 in full color record handiwork of every description. A classic reference, great fun to look at and read. By the Editors of Country Beautiful. 8.50

THE AMERICAN HERITAGE HISTORY OF AMERICAN ANTIQUES
A combination of intriguing social history and authoritative guidebook to the changing modes of living between the Revolution and the Civil War, this book presents the largest collection of artifacts ever assembled from that remarkably inventive period. The narrative of American antiques puts each successive style in the context with the way of life that developed it. By Marshall B. Davidson. 13.95

AMERICA'S HISTORIC HOUSES
Mt. Vernon. Hyde Park. Walt Whitman's humble abode. The Carrie Nation house. The sumptuous. The simple. The famous. These are America's historic houses, representing 200 years of American history and taste—shown in over 96 photographs of which 32 are in full color. Includes fascinating background information on each of the 96 homes described. By the Editors of Country Beautiful. 8.50

THE INDEX OF AMERICAN DESIGN
Here is everything—figureheads, merry-go-round horses, cigar store indians, Shaker furniture, Silver, glassware, pottery, toys, hitching posts, woven coverlets, quilts, ironwork, old-fashioned dresses. 378 pictures (117 in full color). By Erwin O. Christenson. 11.95

AMERICAN GLASS
A comprehensive work on glass and glassmakers of America. The McKearins are consulted by almost all of the great museums and collectors. Here is a detailed history of glassmaking. Every type— hand blown, blown-molded, presses, sandwich and others— is described. There are over 3,000 illustrations, a glossary of terms, bibliography and index. By George S. and Helen McKearin. 14.95

AMERICAN NEEDLEWORK
An absorbing text on needlework in America. Over 200 pages of needlework treasures in color. Step-by-step instructions teach techniques of embroidery, crewel, cross stitch, needlepoint, patchwork, applique, quilting, hooking, crochet, knitting, candlewicking and rug making. It shows what American women have done to bring beauty into their homes, and how you can do it. By Rose Wilder Lane. 15.00

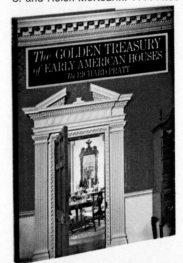

THE GOLDEN TREASURY OF EARLY AMERICAN HOUSES
A magnificent presentation of America's great and gracious houses built from 1650 to 1850. Hundreds of magnificent color photographs the Golden Treasury is an antique lover's dream and a delight to architecture buffs. It gives an insight into how Americans lived and a fascinating picture of Traditional decorating at its best. By architectural historian Richard Pratt. 29.95

NUTTING'S FURNITURE TREASURY

Most famous work on American antiques published. All periods of American furniture with some foreign examples in America plus American hardware and household utensils. Over 5,000 illustrations with descriptions. By Wallace Nutting. 18.50

FINE POINTS OF FURNITURE— EARLY AMERICAN

A new kind of handbook for the collector. Over 300 pages with 800 photographs. An analysis of the elements of design, decoration and craftsmanship of American furniture. Showing with each type discussed, three examples — comparing their relative merits. An outstanding guide. By Albert Sack. 3.95

THE PINE FURNITURE OF EARLY NEW ENGLAND

Virtually every aspect of Colonial pine furniture is covered. Over 200 illustrations with descriptive captions and 55 working plans make this an indispensable handbook for the collector or the craftsman. By Russel H. Kettell. 10.00

AMERICAN FOLK PAINTING

For all interested in American folk art. The folk artist has been important in the history of American art. His role as a social historian can be seen in the lavishly illustrated text. . .146 black/white reproductions, 86 full-color plates. By Mary Black and Jean Lipman. 7.95

POLLY PRINDLE'S BOOK OF AMERICAN PATCHWORK QUILTS

One of America's favorite crafts and pastimes is lovingly chronicled and explained by an authentic practitioner of the art. Simple, step-by-step instructions for putting a quilt together and 50 American patterns with full size pattern pieces are included along with yardage requirements for each. By Alice I. Gamell. 12.95

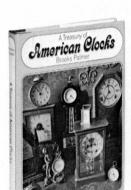

A TREASURY OF AMERICAN CLOCKS

A new volume. Over 360 pages and 500 photographs, with descriptive captions, covering Grandfather, banjo, lyre, gallery, pillar and scroll, shelf, steeple, novelty, and alarm. Pictures show the makes of clocks and timepieces in America from early to recent times. By Brooks Palmer. 12.95

AMERICAN COUNTRY FURNITURE 1780-1875

Here's an indispensable handbook for collectors of 19th century American country furniture. More than 700 closeup photos with detailed captions provide the expertise you need to identify, buy authentic country furniture. Style, construction, woods, finishes, are pointed out. By Ralph and Terry Kovel. 7.95

THE AMERICAN HERITAGE COOKBOOK

More than 500 great traditional recipes, old and new, are gathered together in this new larger-size version of a perennial best seller. It includes all-American dishes, like Indian pudding, succotash, apple pie and Kentucky burgoo. 40 historic menus are included. 6.95

CRAFTS FOR FUN AND PROFIT

18 exciting crafts to do in your home with easy step-by-step instructions in full color. A no-nonsense, easy-to-follow guide to a wide range of craft skills, prepared for the woman with no previous experience and requiring a minimum of special equipment. Color photographs and texts cover hooked rugs, candle making, batik, flower pressing, decoupage, picture framing, ideas for Christmas, and others. By Eleanor Van Zandt. . . .6.95

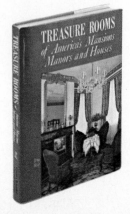

TREASURE ROOMS OF AMERICA'S MANSIONS, MANORS AND HOUSES

Exceptionally appealing to women and written by a noted New York Times reporter of homes, furnishings and antiques. Mrs. Reif takes you on a tour of rooms in 54 American homes embodying over 200 years of American decorating. More than 275 photos. 100 in full color. By Rita Rief. . . .15.00

THE ANTIQUES TREASURY OF FURNITURE AND OTHER DECORATIVE ARTS

Antiques lovers can take a breathtaking tour of 7 "living" American museums in the pages of this book. 840 illustrations, 16 pages of full-color photos trace American furniture in all its periods. Unique 8 page Chronology of Crafts gives over-all picture of most significant styles, crafts in history of country. By Alice Winchester. 15.00

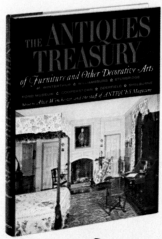

YOUR GUIDE TO UPHOLSTERED FURNITURE

1. CHOOSING UPHOLSTERED FURNITURE. Skilled craftsmanship and fine materials are the key items to look for when purchasing upholstered furniture. Since chairs and sofas represent a sizeable investment, it's well worth spending the extra time examining and studying before you buy. Here are some hints to help you make a better selection.

The best time to discover faulty workmanship or materials is before you buy. Knowing the contents of cushions and backs on sofas and chairs will insure a better purchase. Frame and spring construction are also important. You'll want to know that they will stand up against wear and tear.

Tailoring is also important. If the fabric has a design, the pattern should be matched. Seams and stitches should be straight and neat. Skirts which are lined will hang better and look neater. Rough edges and loose ends have no place on fine furniture.

2. PROTECTIVE FINISHES AND WHAT THEY DO. The advent of stain-repellent finishes has increased the life-span of upholstered furniture by keeping surfaces relatively dirt and spot-free. Most fabrics sold today are thus finished with a stain-repellent coating. The best known are ZePel® by DuPont and Scotchgard® by Minnesota Mining. Since these offer resistance to everyday soiling, most spills will sponge off easily. Stains should always be removed while they are still fresh. Never allow them to set. When you are shopping for fabrics, be sure to ask for those with stain-repellent finishes.

3. THE FIBERS IN UPHOLSTERED FURNITURE. Combining synthetics and natural fibers creates fabrics with higher tensile strength, stronger abrasive resistance, easier cleanability and more decorative interest. Cotton, a widely-used fiber in upholstery, can be given added style by blending it with acetate, rayon or nylon. These fibers are sometimes used alone. Here is a guide to the most commonly-used synthetic fibers:

ACETATE is the generic name for a man-made compound of cellulose. It can take an unlimited range of dyes. When woven with cotton, nylon or rayon, acetate can take one color and the other fiber another for interesting decorative effects. (Cross-dyeing.)

NYLON is one of the most durable upholstery fibers, having high-abrasion resistance and excellent cleanability. It may be used alone, or can be mixed with other fibers. Nylon fabrics can have a luxurious wool hand.

OLEFIN (Polypropylene) is a fiber of extremely high abrasion-resistance and strength. This fiber has outstanding resistance to staining and unusually good soil-release qualities which guarantee easy cleanability.

RAYON is the oldest man-made fiber and the most widely used of the synthetics. It may be dyed any color and can have the hand and appearance of fabrics ranging from silk to wool.

POLYESTER is the newest of the synthetic fibers and one of the most highly resistant to abrasion, stretching and shrinking. Easy to dye and when used in a blend with cotton, prints beautifully and cleans easily.

4. HOW TO CLEAN UPHOLSTERED FURNITURE. If properly cared for, your upholstered furniture will last longer and keep its original bright colors. It is important to clean it regularly with a vacuum cleaner or a brush. Clean under the cushions and in the seams. Cushions should be fluffed up and turned to preserve their shape. Upholstery fabrics generally respond well to the many cleaning agents sold in stores.

Always test any cleaning method first on a pleat or cushion back to see how the fabric reacts. Zippers on cushions are not an indication that covers can be removed and washed or dry-cleaned. To guard against shrinkage, it is recommended that covers *never* be removed, but that they be cleaned in the same manner as the rest of the upholstery. If you are hesitant about cleaning your furniture, we suggest you call a professional cleaner. With just a reasonable amount of care, your upholstered furniture will beautify your home for many years.

FINE FURNITURE FINISHES

Furniture finishes today provide two important benefits...they beautify wood and protect it.

The creation of a furniture finish, rich in luster and beautiful detail begins deep in the forest when trees are selected by a keen judge of those which will provide beautiful cabinet woods. Eyes trained by years of experience can select those trees which promise interesting grain configuration, free from distortion, mineral streaks or other natural defects.

Enhancing the natural beauty of wood continues with careful hand matching of wood grains followed by meticulous sanding. Staining is next used to enrich, deepen and clarify the natural beauty of the wood. This is followed by artistic hand shading of stains to highlight and dramatize interesting grain structure and smoothly blend lighter and darker areas.

On Ethan Allen furniture, certain finishes such as Old Tavern on Antiqued Pine, Classic Manor on Maple and Birch or Georgian Court on Cherry reflect the artistry and craftsmanship of hand distressing, highlighting, hand-padding to achieve an authentic traditional effect harmonious with the form and mood of the design.

Protection begins with a sealer coat to stabilize the staining and continues with the application of various 'top coats' each punctuated by careful sanding and rubbing to bring the final finish to the desired degree of uniformity, depth and sheen. Lacquer, shellac or varnish usually provide these final top coats, following which the luster and uniformity of the finish is enhanced by hand rubbing with oil and pumice.

Modern production methods provide time-saving techniques and chemistry has provided more durable, table finishes...but the essence of a fine furniture finish is still a painstaking step-by-step creation blended with careful attention to craftsmanship and detail.

THE CARE OF
FINE FURNITURE SURFACES

Elementary as it sounds, regular dusting and polishing are the best guardians of the beauty of a fine furniture finish. Grandma with her featherduster understood the secret of preventing the accumulation of surface soil, often abrasive and harmful to a carefully rubbed finish. Today you have a choice of excellent waxes and polishes which if used regularly deepen the luster and clarity of fine finishes as they maintain an important protective film. Accidents will occur and for the care and treatment of these we present the suggestions below. First aid for minor scratches, blemishes, burns and stains might include:

FOR MINOR SCRATCHES:

Use a wax stick in a matching color to fill the scratch. These are inexpensive, usually available at paint, hardware or furniture stores. Rub in well. Wipe with a soft, dry cloth and apply your preferred polish.

WHITE SPOTS—CAUSE UNKNOWN

Rub blemish with cigar or cigarette ashes, using cloth dipped in wax, lubricating oil, vegetable shortening, lard or salad oil. Wipe off immediately and rewax with your preferred polish.

ALCOHOL SPOTS:

Method A—Rub with finger dipped in paste wax, silver polish, linseed oil or moistened cigar ash. Rewax with your preferred polish. Method B—On some finishes a quick application of ammonia will do the trick. Put a few drops on a damp cloth and rub the spot. Follow immediately with an application of polish.

WATER MARKS:

Marks or rings from wet glasses are common on tables, especially if these surfaces have not been waxed. Wax cannot prevent damage when liquids are allowed to stand on the finish indefinitely. However, it will keep them from being absorbed immediately, thus giving you time to wipe up liquid before it damages the finish. If water marks appear, here are some tips to try:
Method A—Apply preferred wax or polish with fine 3/0 steel wool, rubbing lightly.
Method B—Place a clean thick blotter over the ring and press with a warm (not hot) iron. Repeat until ring disappears.

CANDLE WAX:

Hold an ice cube on the wax for a few seconds to harden it but wipe up melted ice immediately. Crumble off as much wax as can be removed with the fingers and then scrape gently with a dull knife. Rub briskly with clean cloth saturated with liquid wax, wiping dry with a clean cloth. Repeat until mark disappears.

MILK SPOTS:

When milk, or foods containing milk or cream are allowed to remain on furniture, the effect of the lactic acid is like that of a mild paint or varnish remover. Wipe up the spilled food as quickly as possible. If spots show, clean with wax. Then follow the tips under alcohol spots.

THE CARE OF RUGS, SILVER, PEWTER, BRASS AND COPPER

RUGS

The amount of cleaning necessary for a rug or carpet usually depends upon its color, texture, fiber, and the amount of use to which it is exposed. It is a good practice to go over carpets and rugs lightly each day with a carpet sweeper or vacuum cleaner. A thorough cleaning requires at least five to seven strokes—be sure the vacuum cleaner is in good working condition. Carpet colors may become dulled after a period of time, and home cleaning methods can be used to improve the carpet appearance, though they cannot equal a thorough professional cleaning job. The two suggested types of home cleaning are: wet method, using a water and detergent solution; the dry method, using an absorbent powder-type cleaner. Many area and accent rugs will have cleaning instructions affixed to back of rug. Frequent maintenance of carpet and rugs will maintain their look of elegance and give them added years of wear.

SILVER

Silver tarnish can be removed with paste cleaners, rouge cloths or common household solutions. Polish should be applied with a soft, damp cloth or sponge, rubbed lightly and then rinsed thoroughly. To prevent tarnish: store covered with silver cloth or plastic wrap.

PEWTER

Dullness is its virtue. One advantage of Pewter is easy care. To clean, wash in hot soapsuds, rinse in clean warm water. Important—leave no trace of soap, wipe thoroughly dry with soft cloth.

BRASS

An elegant alloy of copper, with its tradition and richness of the ages, brass fits the decor of nearly every home. To clean and preserve: rub surface with a piece of lemon dipped in salt or smooth on thick creamy mixture of rottenstone powder and linseed oil. Rub into surface until tarnish disappears. Rinse under hot water, dry with soft cloth. For a lasting finish, spray or paint on a clear lacquer.

COPPER

Copper resembles silver in that it is sensitive to sulphur which causes it to tarnish. To care for and clean, use the same method as brass except for cooking ware. Wash in hot soapsuds, rinse thoroughly, wipe dry. To restore lustre, spread scouring powder on flannel cloth, wet and wash thoroughly with hot soapy water, rinse and dry with soft cloth.

WHAT TO LOOK FOR WHEN YOU SHOP FOR FURNITURE

Fine furniture is a long-term investment. It should therefore be careful one. Several factors should be carefully considered before you make your final selection.

Choose pieces which are functional as well as beautiful. The furniture should suit your purpose and fit your space. Eye appeal alone is not enough.

Pick a style which you like, but be certain it is a style which will last. A current craze or fad is never a safe investment. American traditional design is a gracious and perennial favorite, having a foundation solidly grounded in our history and heritage.

Examine the quality and craftsmanship of the styling. Fine woods such as maple, birch, cherry and pine combine both warmth and beauty in richly finished furniture.

Some of the features which insure quality are illustrated below:

(1). The best drawers are hand-fitted and can be closed with a "test" finger at one corner.

(2). The insides are smoothly sanded and sealed against snags to protect delicate fabrics.

(3). The finish is hand-sanded to satin smoothness and protected by a double-coat lacquer.

(4). The lacquered finish is hand-rubbed to bring out the beauty of the grain and the rich patina of the wood. Look for a clear sheen, rather than a hard gloss.

(5). Check these construction features in illustration #5:

A. Sturdy top and side panels that won't warp or split.

B. Floating top construction on case pieces and tables.

C. Recessed back for rigidity and smoothness.

D. Dust panels between drawers.

E. Carefully-fitted drawer guides, waxed for smooth action.

F. Smoothly interlocking dovetail fingers on all drawer corners.

G. Solid drawer sides.

H. Three-ply, non-warp drawer bottoms held firmly in place in grooves.

If you're working on a budget, you may want to complete your decorating plans by making purchases gradually. The continuity of Ethan Allen styles over a long period of time provides you the opportunity to make future purchases with designs and finishes compatible with the pieces you acquire today.

A reliable brand name in a dependable store is your best guarantee of quality. ETHAN ALLEN is such a name. Look for it. It's trustworthy.

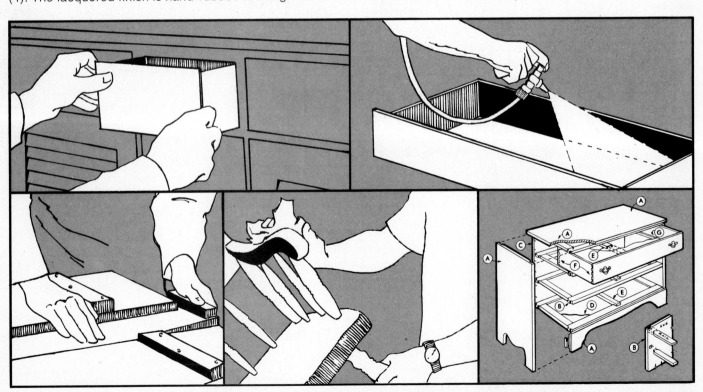

How to solve almost any decorating problem with Ethan Allen Custom Room Plan

You can use these units to key a rooms' mood, alter its proportion, increase its usefulness and make the most of its good points. Properly arranged, they will perform all kinds of visual tricks and even turn faulty architecture into an asset! Study the sketches on these two pages and the rooms on pages 178-209. Copy or adapt the ideas you like—or simply look at them for inspiration and dream up your own decorative solution to your own problem.

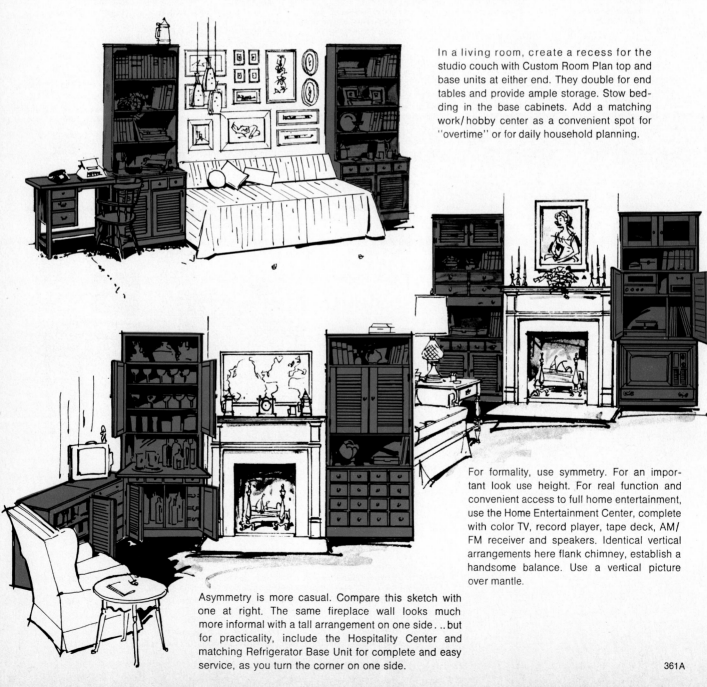

In a living room, create a recess for the studio couch with Custom Room Plan top and base units at either end. They double for end tables and provide ample storage. Stow bedding in the base cabinets. Add a matching work/hobby center as a convenient spot for "overtime" or for daily household planning.

For formality, use symmetry. For an important look use height. For real function and convenient access to full home entertainment, use the Home Entertainment Center, complete with color TV, record player, tape deck, AM/FM receiver and speakers. Identical vertical arrangements here flank chimney, establish a handsome balance. Use a vertical picture over mantle.

Asymmetry is more casual. Compare this sketch with one at right. The same fireplace wall looks much more informal with a tall arrangement on one side...but for practicality, include the Hospitality Center and matching Refrigerator Base Unit for complete and easy service, as you turn the corner on one side.

Custom Room Planning

← 24" →

***No. 10-4006**
Upper Cabinet Bookcase.
Adjustable shelf and mirror
behind doors.

← 24" →

***No. 10-4007**
Upper Bookcase

← 30" →

***No. 10-4017**
Upper Cabinet Bookcase.
Adjustable shelf and vertical
partitions behind drop lid.

← 30" →

***No. 10-4018**
**Three Drawer Upper Cabinet
Bookcase.** Permanent
compartment top 2 drawers.

← 30" →

***No. 10-4019**
Upper Bookcase

← 24" →

#No. 10-4501P
3 Drawer Chest

← 24" →

#No. 10-4503P
Two Door Cabinet.
Adjustable shelf behind
doors. One drawer.

← 30" →

#No. 10-4510P
3 Drawer Chest

← 30" →

#No. 10-4511P
Shutter Door Cabinet.
Adjustable shelf behind
doors. One drawer.

← 30" →

#No. 10-4521P
Four Drawer Apothecary Chest.
Permanent compartments in
top drawer.

←18½"→

#No. 10-4500P
Corner Filler Unit

← 18½" →
(Along wall)

#No. 10-4505P
Corner Bookcase.
One adjustable shelf.

← 30" →

#No. 10-4512P
Bookcase. One adjustable
shelf. One drawer.

← 30" →

#No. 10-4514P
4 Drawer Chest. 40"H.

← 30" →

#No. 10-4523P
Fitted Vanity. Seven permanent
compartments lined with white
laminate. Mirror and plastic
vanity tray.

All Base Units are 18½" deep and 30" high except where otherwise noted.

All Upper Units with prefix "10—" have backs of wood-grained balanced hardboard; those
with prefix "14—" have backs of lacquered balanced hardboard.

All Upper Units are 48" high; Cabinet Units are 13" deep; Bookcase Units are 10" deep.
All shelves except bottom shelf of unit are adjustable and removable. Each
shelf is grooved to display standing dishes attractively.

All shutter doors have back panels to protect storage area from dust.

All Base and Upper Units have end panels with selected veneer face.

Ethan Allen
AMERICAN TRADITIONAL INTERIORS

362A

is easy with Ethan Allen...

*No. 10-4086
T-V Upper Unit. Revolving sliding shelf behind doors. Will accept TV chassis weighing up to 70 lbs.

*No. 10-4088
Record Utility Cabinet Upper Unit. Vertical removable partition.

No. 50-1101
Upper Stereo Unit. 15½" deep. Two doors, G.E. components; 4-speed turn table, AM/FM stereo tuner, 8-track stereo cartridge tape player, jack pack, 40-watt amplifier, two removable speakers. Available only in Nutmeg finish (211).

*No. 10-4036
Upper Bookcase.

(Along wall)
*No. 10-4037
Upper Corner Bookcase.

#No. 10-4522P
Music Cabinet. Vertical partitions behind doors.

No. 50-1010
Color T-V. G.E. 100% solid state chassis, 19" diagonal screen. Cabinet available only in Nutmeg finish (211).

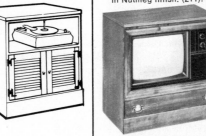

#No. 10-4531P
Console Extension Table. Opens to 54½" with three 12" filler leaves.

(Along wall)
#No. 10-4532P
Three Drawer Corner Chest.

(Along wall)
#No. 10-4530P
Corner Desk. One drawer.

*No. 10-4030
Refreshment Upper Unit. 15½" deep. Two adjustable glass shelves behind shutter doors. Melamine plastic work surface. Mirrored interior. Recessed electric light.

#No. 10-4516P
Refrigerator Unit. Four tray ice cube unit. Sliding shelf. Ample space for bottles and snacks.

#No. 10-4515
Refreshment Cabinet Base. One felt lined drawer with removable partitions. Four glass racks, wine rack.

We have assembled on these four pages all the individual "building blocks" that compose our fabulous Custom Room Plan series. From this great choice of units you can create a combination that will solve all your storage problems, suit your wall, your room and living requirements.

The Custom Room Plan series include upper and lower cabinet units in a variety of widths—ranging fom 18½" to 48". In addition to the many dressers, general storage pieces and bookcase cabinets, you will find a variety of desks, television cabinets, a complete Hi-Fi Stereo/TV/Tape Deck home entertainment center, record cabinets, a Hi-Fi cabinet, a Hi-Fi speaker unit, hospitality center with matching refrigerator, work center, hobby center, sewing center and fitted vanity. There are units designed to fit into corners and a corner bookcase designed to go around corner so that you can continue, from one wall to another, uninterrupted flow of Custom Room Plan units.

PICTORIAL INDEX

On the following 46 pages, you will find detailed specifications including sizes, choice of finishes and many construction features of Ethan Allen furniture. Most of the designs in the vast Ethan Allen collection have been shown in the preceding color pages . . . the pictorial index will give you additional detailed information that will be helpful. Any design can be located by referring to its series number in the numerical list below and turning to the pages indicated.

HOW IT WORKS:

Typical information available from the pictorial index is shown at the right.

Series Number.

Description including alternate sizes available.

Series Number and alternate finish available.

For color photo.

No. 10-5631
Tall Poster Bed. Overall 66" H. Available in 3'3" and 4'6" sizes. Available with Canopy Frame.

*No. 14-5631 Same item in Decorated Finishes 400, 409, 411.
see page 176

Even a dining ell, with just one un-broken wall can grow—with Custom Room Plan. The floor plan shows a bay window occupying one wall. A door centered on the second, and storage units making the most of the third (see sketch). For easy circulation, choose a round table.

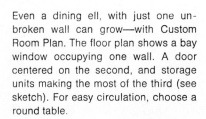

Two windows, whether balanced or not, can be incorporated into a made-to-order look . . . with Custom Room Plan. Here bases lined from corner to corner with top units between windows, include a Custom Room Plan Study Center complete with typewriter pull-out and filing features . . . the entire wall a convenient "office-at-home". Short curtains cover remaining wall when open and the windows as well, when closed. This arrangement can conceal innumerable architectural defects.

A window wall: an awkwardly placed off-center window can be effectively balanced by an L-shaped arrangement. Custom Room Plan units sketched at right include a Sewing Center, and an extension table for handy accessible use. Upper units provide easy storage—balance window with height.

A bed wall: create an alcove for your bed with Custom Room Plan. This is an excellent solution for the bedroom with little wall space. The one long wall is utilized both for storage and the bed.

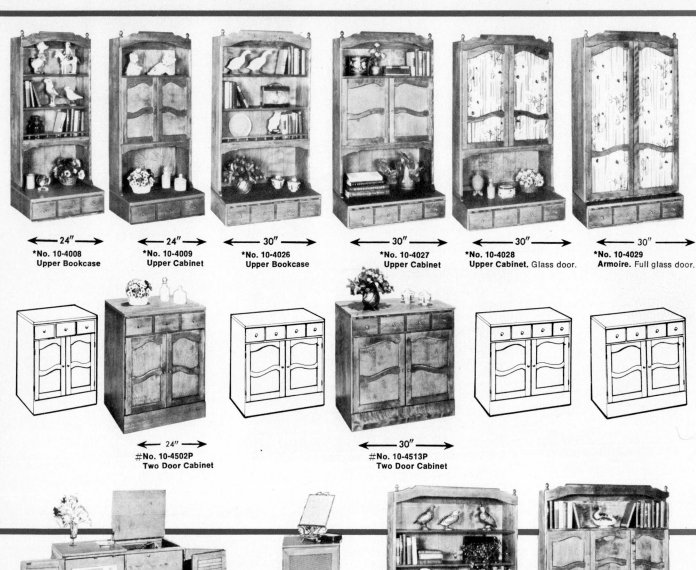

←— 24″ —→
*No. 10-4008
Upper Bookcase

←— 24″ —→
*No. 10-4009
Upper Cabinet

←— 30″ —→
*No. 10-4026
Upper Bookcase

←— 30″ —→
*No. 10-4027
Upper Cabinet

←— 30″ —→
*No. 10-4028
Upper Cabinet. Glass door.

←— 30″ —→
*No. 10-4029
Armoire. Full glass door.

←— 24″ —→
#No. 10-4502P
Two Door Cabinet

←— 30″ —→
#No. 10-4513P
Two Door Cabinet

←— 40″ —→
#No. 10-4525P
Hi-Fi Cabinet.

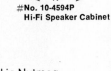

←19″→
#No. 10-4594P
Hi-Fi Speaker Cabinet

←— 40″ —→
*No. 10-4066
Upper Bookcase

←— 40″ —→
*No. 10-4067
Upper Cabinet

Custom Room Plan designs are offered in Nutmeg finish or in American Traditional colors: Alabaster White, Antiqued Blue or Daffodil Yellow, except where otherwise noted.

Base units come with matching wood-grain Formica® plastic tops. By substituting prefix "14-", units may be ordered in the following decorated finishes:
400—Alabaster White 409—Antiqued Blue 411—Daffodil Yellow.

Note: Base units are offered in solid color only with matching Formica® plastic top (except No. 10-4558 Hobby Center). No. 50-1010 Color TV available only in Nutmeg finish (211).

* Upper units may be ordered in the above solid colors, and may also be ordered in the following combination of Decorated Finishes:
608—White with Blue 619—White with Yellow
617—Blue with White 620—Yellow with White

All items with prefix "10—" are offered in a warm brown Nutmeg finish (211).

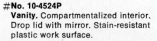

←— 40″ —→
#No. 10-4524P
Vanity. Compartmentalized interior. Drop lid with mirror. Stain-resistant plastic work surface.

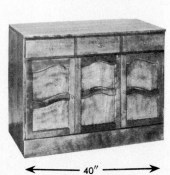

←— 40″ —→
#No. 10-4552P
Three Door Cabinet

*No. 10-4059
Photography Center Upper Unit.
Two tray drawers, one adjustable
shelf behind door, cork-surfaced
display area with adjustable
shelf. Partition and adjustable
shelf behind drop lid. Engineered
for efficient storage of slides,
lenses, photography equipment.

*No. 10-4056
Upper Cabinet Bookcase.
Adjustable shelves behind doors
and an open center.
(Center shelf not shown above.)

*No. 10-4058
*Upper Bookcase

*No. 10-4076
Upper Bookcase

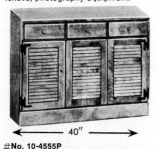

#No. 10-4555P
Photography Center Base Unit.
One partitioned drawer and five
compartments behind three doors.

#No. 10-4553P
Three Door Cabinet.
Permanent compart-
ment in top drawer.
Adjustable shelf
behind doors
which open and
accordion fold.

#No. 10-4551P
Three Drawer Dresser

#No. 10-4550
**Four Drawer Student's
Desk.** Pencil tray
in drawer.

#No. 10-4570P
Six Drawer Double Dresser
#No. 10-4571P
Four Drawer Dresser Desk.
Pencil tray in drawer.

Interior details of
units shown above.

#No. 10-4558
Hobby Center. Features
solid maple butcher block
top with removable back
gallery. Two drawers
for storage.

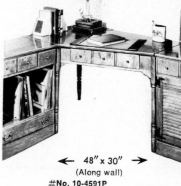

48″ x 30″
(Along wall)
#No. 10-4591P
Corner Desk. One drawer.

#No. 10-4556P
Study Center. Typewriter storage area.
Pull out typewriter tray. Removable
vertical dividers tailored for storage.
File drawer with metal racks; drawer
slotted for letter rack; pencil tray;
pull out writing slide. Sketch below
shows unit closed.

#No. 10-4557P
Sewing Center. Storage space
for sewing machine plus a
large flip tray to place
machine on while operating
it. Shutter doors, three
drawers with dividers, velvet-
lined tray for storage,
spool rack on inside of door.
Sketch shows unit with
doors closed.

HEIRLOOM COLLECTION

Ethan Allen AMERICAN TRADITIONAL INTERIORS

No. 10-5000
Tall Pediment Mirror. 23" x 36" H. Use over single dressers and items shorter than 50".
see page 174

No. 10-5013
Ten Drawer Fitted Dresser. 63" x 20" x 35" H. Interior storage custom engineered for a lady's wardrobe.
see page 168

No. 10-5050
Framed Mirror. 48" x 32" H. Use over pieces 54" to 64" long.
see page 171

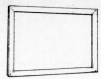

No. 10-5001
Five Drawer Dresser. 42" x 19" x 35" H. Permanent compartment in top drawer.
see page 174

No. 10-5014
Six Drawer Chest. 33" X 19" X 46" H.
see page 171

No. 10-5060
Cheval Floor Mirror. 21" x 63" H.
*No. 14-5060
Same item in Decorated Finishes 400, 409 or 411.
see page 174

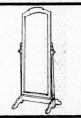

No. 10-5002
Six Drawer Double Dresser. 50" x 19" x 32" H. Permanent compartment in top left drawer.
see page 171

No. 10-5020
Scalloped Mirror. 46" x 30" H.
*No. 14-5020
Same item in Decorated Finishes 400, 409 or 411.
see page 170

No. 10-5100
Pediment Mirror. 50" x 39" H. Use over pieces 53" to 63" long.
No. 15-5220 Same item 54" x 41" H in Classic Manor finish.
see page 166

No. 10-5004
Five Drawer Chest. 32" x 19" x 41" H.
see page 174

No. 10-5026
Night Table. 16" x 14" x 26" H. One drawer.
No. 10-5026P
Same item with Formica® plastic top.
*No. 14-5026P
Same item in Decorated Finishes 400, 409 or 411.
see page 174

No. 10-5210
Framed Mirror. 55" X 35" H. for pieces 61" to 71" long.
No. 15-5210. Same item in Classic Manor finish.
see page 165

No. 10-5005
Seven Drawer Chest on Chest. 34" x 19" x 51" H. Permanent compartments in third and fifth row drawers.
see page 168

No. 10-5030
Cheval Mirror. 19" x 8" x 21" H. One drawer.
see page 170

No. 10-5302
Seven Drawer Double Dresser. 54" x 20" x 33" H. Removable partitions in middle row drawers.
see page 167

No. 10-5006
Cabinet Night Table. 20" X 16" X 28" H. One drawer. Back is selected veneer.

No. 10-5036
Night Table. 22" x 18" x 26" H. One Drawer.
see page 168

No. 10-5303
Eight Drawer Triple Dresser. 60" x 20" x 33" H. Removable partitions in top outer and middle center drawers. Felt-lined compartments in top outer drawers.
see page 166

No. 10-5010
Scalloped Mirror. 38" x 26" H.
*No. 14-5010
Same item in Decorated Finishes 400, 409, 411.
see page 170

No. 10-5040
Framed Mirror. 42" X 30" H. Use over pieces 48" to 58" long.
see page 171

No. 10-5304
Six Drawer Chest. 35" x 19" x 47" H. Removable partitions in third and fourth row drawers.
see page 167

No. 10-5012
Nine Drawer Double Dresser. 52" x 19" x 35" H.
see page 170

No. 10-5046
Cabinet Night Table. 18" X 14" X 28" H. One drawer. Back is selected vaneer.
No. 10-5046P Same item with Formica® plastic top.
*No. 14-5046P Decorated Finishes 400, 409 or 411.
see page 177

No. 10-5305
Seven Drawer Chest on Chest. 36" x 19" x 51" H. Removable partitions in third and fourth row drawers.
see page 166

Also available in Classic Manor finish as noted.
All doors are equipped with magnetic catches.

Dressers and chests of No. 10-5300 Series feature swivel casters as standard equipment.

BEDROOM, DINING ROOM, OCCASIONAL TABLES AND DECORATIVE ACCENTS

No. 10-5306
One Drawer Cabinet Night Table. 22" x 16" x 26" H. Adjustable shelf. Back and bottom shelf are selected veneer.

see page 167

No. 10-5315
Eight Drawer Chest on Chest. 40" x 20" x 55" H. Removable partitions in third, fourth and fifth row drawers.

see page 165

No. 10-5316
One Drawer Commode Night Table. 22" x 16" x 26" H. Adjustable and removable shelf behind doors.

see page 165

No. 10-5323
Ten Drawer Triple Dresser. 66" x 20" x 34" H. Removable partitions in top middle and third row drawers. Felt-lined compartments in top middle drawer.

see page 165

No. 10-5600-3
Tri-Way Bed with Side Rails and Slats. Overall 61" H.; headboard 37" H.
***No. 14-5600-3**
Same item in Decorated Finishes 400, 409 or 411.

see page 172

No. 10-5604
Fiddleback Bed. 39" H. Available in 3'3" and 4'6" sizes.
see page 168

No. 10-5607
Fiddleback Headboard. 39" H. Available in 6'6" size only.

No. 10-5605
Bunk and/or Twin Bed. Overall 64" H.; headboard 37" H. Complete with rails, slats, guard rail and ladder.

see page 173

No. 10-5606
Panel Headboard. 33" H. Available in 3'3" and 4'6" sizes.

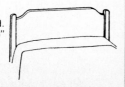

No. 10-5609
Spindle Headboard. 41" H. 3'3" and 4'6" sizes.

***No. 14-5609**
Same item in Decorated Finishes 400, 409, or 411.

see page 177

No. 10-5610
Spindle Panel Bed. 33" H. Available in 3'3" and 4'6" sizes.

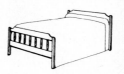

No. 10-5611
Spindle Bed. 41" H. Available in 3'3" and 4'6" sizes.
***No. 14-5611**
Same item in Decorated Finishes 400, 409 or 411.

see page 171

No. 10-5612
Pediment Bed. Overall 53" H. Available in 4'6" and 5' sizes.
No. 15-5612
Same item in Classic Manor finish.

see page 167

No. 10-5614
Panel Bed. 35" H. Available in 3'3" and 4'6" sizes.
***No. 14-5614**
Same item in Decorated Finishes 400, 409 or 411.

see page 174

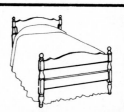

No. 10-5621
Cannonball Bed. 44" H. Available in 3'3", 4'6" and 5' sizes.

see page 177

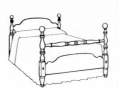

✔**No. 10-5622**
Tall Poster Bed. Overall 69" H. Available in 4'6" and 5' sizes. Available with Canopy Frame.

see page 166

No. 10-5624
Crib. 55" X 31" X 43" H. Non-toxic safety finish and transparent safety-plastic teething surface for top of rails. End panels only, selected Maple veneer.
***No. 14-5624** Decorated Finishes 400 or 411.

see page 175

No. 10-5626
Sliding Door Bookcase Headboard. 39" H. Available in 3'3" (single door in center), 4'6" and 5' sizes. Back is selected veneer.
***No. 14-5626.** Same item in Decorated Finishes 400, 409 or 411. 3'3" size only.

No. 10-5627
Sliding Door Bookcase Headboard. 38" H. Available in 6'6" size only. Back is selected veneer.

see page 176

No. 15-5627 Same item in Classic Manor finish.

No. 10-5628
Spindle Headboard. 41" H. Available in 5' and 6'6" sizes.

see page 177

No. 10-5630
Spindle Bed. 41" H. 5' Queen sizes only.

see page 177

✔**No. 10-5631**
Tall Poster Bed. Overall 66" H. Available in 3'3" and 4'6" sizes. Available with Canopy Frame.

***No. 14-5631** Same item in Decorated Finishes 400, 409, 411.

see page 176

No. 10-5633
Captain's Trundle Bed. Overall 34" H X 84" L. Lower drawer rolls out on casters to be used as an extra bed (39" X 75" mattress) or as storage bin. Use a 39" X 80" mattress for upper bed.

see page 173

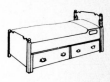

No. 10-5637
Cornice Headboard. 42" H. Available in 5' and 6'6" sizes.

see page 177

No. 15-5637 Same item in Classic Manor finish.

If you wish to order extra length bed rails, please specify **No. 10-5999 81" Extra Length Rails,** along with the number of your bed.

✔**No. 10-5993 Regular Length 76" Canopy Frame.** 3'3" and 4'6" sizes.

No. 10-5994 Extra Length 81" Canopy Frame. 5' (Queen size). 81" rails shipped automatically with 5' beds.

---

*Description of Decorated Finishes: 400—Alabaster White;   409—Antiqued Blue;   411—Daffodil Yellow;

No. 10-5638
Ladderback Headboard. Available in 3'3'' and 4'6'' sizes.
*No. 14-5638
Same item in Decorated Finishes 400, 409 or 411.
see page 170

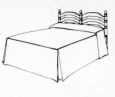

No. 10-5660
Cradle. 43'' X 22¼'' X 36''H. Safety locking pin to put in "non-rocking" position if desired.
see page 175

No. 10-6005P
Revolving Lazy Susan. Formica® plastic top is 20'' in diameter.
see page 143

No. 10-5641
Hi-Rise Trundle Bed. Overall 37'' H. Available in 3'3'' only.
*No. 14-5641
Same item in Decorated Finishes 400, 409 or 411.
see page 173

**HEIRLOOM
DINING ROOM**

No. 10-6006
Two Drawer Server. 38'' x 18'' x 33'' H. Adjustable shelf behind doors. Removable partitions and felt-lined compartments in top left drawer.
see page 145

No. 10-5644
Panel Headboard. 33'' H. Available in 3'3'' and 4'6'' sizes.

No. 10-6000
Squire's Chair. 33½'' H.
see page 150

No. 10-6009
Grilled China Cabinet. Two adjustable shelves behind doors. For use with No. 10-6006.
see page 149

No. 10-5645
Scroll Spindle Headboard. 42'' H. Available in 3'3'' and 4'6'' sizes.

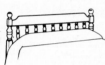

No. 10-6002
Concord Chair. 34'' H.
see page 149

No. 10-6011
Thumb Back Chair. 35'' H.
* No. 14-6011
Same item in Decorated Finishes 400, 409, 411, 604 or 610.
see page 151

No. 10-5646
Arrow Headboard. 42'' H. Available in 4'6'' and 5' sizes.

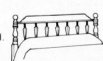

No. 10-6003
Round Spoonfoot Drop Leaf Extension Table. Extra-heavy top. Shown without leaves.

No. 10-6013
Round Spoonfoot Extension Table. 48'' diameter; opens to 78'' with two 15'' aproned filler leaves. Extra-heavy top. Seats 8-10. Shown without leaves.
No. 10-6013P Same item with Formica® plastic top.
see page 146

No. 10-5653
Scroll Spindle Bed. Overall 42'' H. Available in 3'3'', 4'6'' and 5' sizes.

No. 10-6003
Same item, 26'' x 48'' x 78'' with two aproned filler leaves. Seats 8-10. Shown with leaves.

No. 10-6014P
Round Drop Leaf Extension Table. Formica® plastic top. Shown without leaves.
see page 152

No. 10-5654
Arrow Bed. Overall 42'' H. Available in 4'6'' and 5' sizes.
see page 164

No. 10-6004
Spoonfoot Extension Table. Center leg for added support. Seats 8-10. Shown without leaves.
see page 151

No. 10-6014P
Same item, 26'' x 48'' x 78'' with two 15'' filler leaves. Seats 8-10. Shown with leaves.

No. 10-5655
Ladderback Bed. Available in 3'3'' and 4'6'' sizes.
*No. 14-5655
Same item in Decorated Finishes 400, 409 or 411.
see page 177

No. 10-6004
Same item, 40'' x 60'' x 84'' with two 12'' aproned leaves. Seats 8-10. Shown with leaves.
No. 10-6004P
Same item with Formica® plastic top.

No. 10-6016
Six Drawer Buffet. 54'' x 18'' x 33'' H. Adjustable, removable shelves behind left folding doors and three tray drawers behind right folding doors. Solid partition divides area between doors. Silver tray in top left drawer.
see page 138

---

366   To order extra length bed rails, please specify **No. 10-5999**
81'' Extra Length Rails, along with number of bed.

*Description of Decorated Finishes: 400 — Alabaster White; 409 — Antiqued Blue; 411 — Daffodil Yellow; 604 — White Decorated with Nutmeg; 610 — Black Decorated with Nutmeg.

No. 10-6017
Two Drawer Buffet. 48" x 18" x 32" H. Stationary shelf behind doors. Removable partitions and felt-lined compartments in top drawer.

see page 147

No. 10-6030 Side Chair
No. 10-6030A Arm Chair
Duncan Phyfe Chairs. 34" H. Upholstered seat.

see page 138

No. 10-6044P
Same item. 36" x 54" x 84" with two 15" filler leaves. Seats 8-10. Shown with leaves.

No. 10-6018
China Cabinet. 38" H., 48" W. Adjustable shelf in area behind right doors and also in separate area behind left door. For use with No. 10-6017 and No. 10-6036.

see page 147

No. 10-6031
Captain's Chair. 30" H.

see page 147

No. 10-6046
Grilled Corner Hutch. 39" x 23" x 75" H. Adjustable shelf behind cabinet and grilled glass doors. Upper shelves grooved for display of dishes.

see page 143

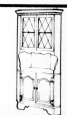

No. 10-6020 Side Chair.
No. 10-6020A Arm Chair.
Fiddleback Duxbury Chairs. 35" H.

see page 139

No. 10-6034P
Round Extension Table. 48" diameter. Opens to 78" with two 15" filler leaves. Seats 8-10. Formica" plastic top. Shown without leaves.

see page 147

No. 10-6048
China Cabinet. 34" H. Two glass doors. For use with No. 10-6027.

see page 148

No. 10-6023P
Round Extension Table. 42" diameter. Opens to 72" with two 15" filler leaves. Seats 6-8. Formica" plastic top. Shown without leaves.

No. 10-6035
Deacon's Bench. 60" x 21" x 33" H.

No. 10-6049
Hutch Cabinet. 28" H. For use with No. 10-6027.

see page 147

No. 10-6024P
Round Extension Table. Formica" plastic top 42" diameter opens to 52" with single 10" filler leaf. Shown without leaf.

see page 143

No. 10-6036
One Drawer Buffet. 48" x 17" x 31" H. Stationary shelf behind doors. Removable partitions and felt-lined compartments in top drawer.

see page 151

No. 10-6050 Side Chair.
No. 10-6050A Arm Chair.
Ladderback Chairs. 41" H. Fiber seat.

see page 140

No. 10-6025
Deacon's Bench. 46" x 20" x 34" H. Nutmeg finish.

see page 151

No. 10-6039
Hutch Top. 38" H. 48" W. For use with No. 10-6017 or 10-6036.

see page 148

No. 10-6051
Comb Back Swivel Mate's Chair. 30" H. Similar to 10-6040 with swivel seat.

see page 152

No. 10-6027
Server. 34" x 18" x 32" H. One drawer with stationary shelf behind doors. Removable partition and felt-lined compartment in top drawer.

see page 143

No. 10-6040
Comb Back Mate's Chair. 30" H.
*No. 14-6040**
Same item, available in Decorated Finishes 400, 409, 411, 604 or 610.

see page 143

No. 10-6052
Tavern Chair. 30" H.

see page 146

No. 10-6028
Grilled China Cabinet. 40" H., 54" W. For use with No. 10-6016.

see page 146

No. 10-6044P
Spoonfoot Extension Table. Formica" plastic top. Shown without leaves.

see page 148

No. 10-6053P
Spoonfoot Drop Leaf Table. Formica® plastic top. 24" x 38". With leaves extended 58".

see page 151

Hutch and China Cabinet backs are selected veneers. All shelves are grooved to display dishes attractively.

Hutch cabinets include base plate rail which is also grooved for display of dishes.

Cabinet doors have magnetic catches; shutter doors have solid back panel to protect interior from dust; finished interiors.

No. 10-6056
Three Drawer Buffet. 72" x 17" x 27" H. Adjustable, removable shelves behind each set of doors. Silver tray in top drawer. Fifth leg for added support.

see page 136

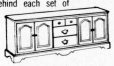

No. 10-6072 **Side Chair**
No. 10-6072A **Arm Chair**
Duxbury Chairs. 39" H.
*★No. 14-6072**
*★No. 14-6072A**
Same item in Decorated Finishes 601, 604 or 610.

see page 144

No. 10-6090
Comb Back Mate's Chair. 35" H.

see page 151

No. 10-6058
Crown Glass China Cabinet. 55" H. Two drawers. Two adjustable, removable shelves behind wooden mullion decorated doors. For use with No. 10-6056.

see page 136

No. 10-6073
Drop Leaf Extension Table. 42" x 28"; opens to 72" with leaves extended. Shown without leaves.
No. 10-6073P Same item with Formica® plastic top.

see page 140

No. 10-6093
Spoonfoot Oval Extension Table. Shown without leaves.
No. 10-6093P Same item with Formica® plastic top.

see page 147

No. 10-6059
China Cabinet. 40" H. Adjustable, removable shelves behind three doors. Doors decorated with wooden mullions. For use with No. 10-6016.

see page 138

No. 10-6073
Same item. Opens to 42" x 92" with two 10" filler leaves. Seats 10. Shown with leaves.
No. 10-6073P
Same item with Formica® plastic top.

No. 10-6093
Same item. Opens to 38" X 55" X 86" with two 15" filler leaves. Seats 8-10. Shown with leaves.
No. 10-6093P
Same item with Formica® plastic top.

No. 10-6060 Side Chair.
No. 10-6060A Arm Chair.
Tall Arrowback Chairs. 39" H.

see page 136

No. 10-6074P
Drop Leaf Harvest Table. Formica® plastic top. 22" x 42" x 48".

see page 150

No. 10-6094P
Round Pedestal Extension Table. 48" diameter. Extra-heavy Formica® plastic top. Shown without leaves.

see page 144

No. 10-6063
Spoonfoot Harvest Drop Leaf Table. 22" x 66"
No. 10-6063P
Same item with Formica® plastic top.

see page 142

No. 10-6083P
Center Extension Table. 30" x 40" x 48" with one filler leaf. Seats 6. Formica® plastic top. Shown without leaf.

see page 149

No. 10-6094P
Same item. Opens to 78" with two 15" aproned filler leaves. Seats 8-10. Shown with leaves.

No. 10-6063
Same item. Opens to 45" x 66" with leaves extended. Seats 8-10.
No. 10-6063P
Same item with Formica® plastic top.

No. 10-6084
End Extension Trestle Table. 38" X 70". Shown without leaves. Extra heavy top.

see page 136

No. 10-6095
Swivel Bar Stool. 21" x 20" x 42" H. Height may be shortened at any of three places marked by rings. Tubular steel footrest with brushed brass finish. Nutmeg finish.

see page 154

No. 10-6067
Three Drawer Buffet. 56" x 20" x 30" H. Adjustable, removable shelves behind doors. Center drawer custom-fitted with Pacific cloth inserts for silver storage. Tarnish resistant.

see page 139

No. 10-6084
Same item. Opens to 100" with two 15" filler leaves. Seats 10-12.

No. 10-6100 Side Chair.
No. 10-6100A Arm Chair.
Spindleback Formal Chairs. 37" H. Upholstered seat padded with Urethane foam.

see page 141

No. 10-6069
China Cabinet. 48" H. Adjustable, removable shelves of wood-framed glass behind doors. Lighted interior. For use with No. 10-6067.

see page 139

No. 10-6085
Drop Leaf Tea Wagon. 19" X 32" X 29" H. Opens to 42" X 32" with leaves. Large artillery wheels and swivel casters. Handle swings under cart. Matching plastic wheels.
*★No. 14-6085** Same in Decorated Finishes 604 or 610. see page 140

No. 10-6101
Mate's Chair. 29" H.

see page 148

Hutch and China Cabinet backs are selected veneers. All shelves are grooved to display dishes attractively.   Hutch cabinets include base plate rail which is also grooved for display of dishes.   Cabinet doors are equipped with magnetic catches; shutter doors have solid back panel to protect interior from dust; finished interiors.

BEDROOM, DINING ROOM, OCCASIONAL TABLES AND DECORATIVE ACCENTS

No. 10-6102 Side Chair.
No. 10-6102A Arm Chair.
Governor Bradford Chairs.
33'' H., 34'' H.

see page 148

No. 10-6111
Button Back Hitchcock Chair.
33'' H. Fiber seat.
*No. 14-6111 Same item. Available in Decorated Finishes 601, 603, 604, 609, 612, 614 or 616.

see page 149

No. 10-6126
Two Drawer Buffet. 50'' x 20'' x 30'' H. Top left hand drawer fitted with Pacific cloth. Inserts for silver storage. Tarnish resistant.

see page 140

No. 10-6103P
Drop Leaf Extension Table. Formica® plastic top. Shown without leaves.

see page 150

No. 10-6112
Ladderback Chair. 20'' x 15'' x 41'' H. Fiber seat.

see page 151

No. 10-6128
China Cabinet. 44'' H. Three doors, adjustable shelf behind doors. For use with No. 10-6126.

see page 140

No. 10-6103P
Same item. Opens to 23'' x 42'' x 66'' with two 12'' filler leaves. Seats 6-8. Shown with leaves.

No. 10-6113P
Round Pedestal Extension Table. 44'' diameter. Extra-heavy Formica® plastic top with equalizer slide. Shown without leaves.

see page 139

No. 10-6133P
Round Extension Table. 48'' diameter. Extra-heavy top. Center leg. Formica® plastic top. Shown without leaves.

see page 152

No. 10-6104P
Round Extension Table. 36'' diameter. Formica® plastic top. Shown without leaf.

see page 149

No. 10-6113P
Same item. Opens to 74'' with two aproned filler leaves. Seats 8-10. Shown with leaves.

No. 10-6133P
Same item. Opens to 102'' with three 18'' aproned filler leaves. Seat 10-12. Shown with leaves.

No. 10-6104P
Same item. Opens to 48'' with 12'' filler leaf. Shown with leaf.

No. 10-6114
Spoonfoot Oval Extension Table. 44'' X 66''. Shown without leaves.

see page 141

No. 10-6180
Child's Thumback Chair. 25'' H.

see page 196

No. 10-6105
Four Drawer Dry Sink. 40'' x 20'' x 35'' H. Felt-lined compartments. Adjustable shelf behind doors. Matching wood-grained plastic top. Removable copper tray. Swivel casters.

see page 140

No. 10-6114
Same item. Opens to 102'' with two 18'' aproned filler leaves. Serves 10. Shown with leaves.

No. 10-6183P
Child's Table. 32'' x 24'' x 22'' H. Formica® plastic top.

see page 196

No. 10-6106
Dry Sink. 34'' x 18'' x 40'' H. One drawer. Adjustable shelf behind doors; felt-lined compartments. Door panel is selected veneer.
*No. 14-6106 Same item in Decorated Finishes 604, 610.

see page 138

No. 10-6123P
Trestle Table. 35'' x 60'' x 29'' H. Matching extra-heavy Formica® plastic top.

see page 151

No. 10-6301
Farmhouse Chair. 21'' X 14'' X 33½'' H.
No. 14-6301 Same item. Available in Decorated Finishes 601, 603, 604, 609, 610, 612, 614 or 616.

see page 150

No. 10-6110 Side Chair
No. 10-6110A Arm Chair
Hitchcock Chairs. 33'' H. Fiber seat.
*No. 14-6110
*No. 14-6110A
Same item in Decorated Finishes 601, 603 or 609.
see page 142

No. 10-6124P
Round Pedestal Table. 42'' diameter. Extra-heavy Formica® plastic top. Non-extension.

see page 148

No. 10-6315
Trestle Bench. 62'' x 14'' x 17'' H. Nutmeg finish.

see page 136

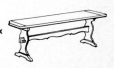

---

*Description of Decorated Finishes: 601 — Nutmeg Decorated; 603 — White Decorated; 604 — White Decorated with Nutmeg; 609 — Black Decorated; 610 — Black Decorated with Nutmeg; 612 — Red Decorated; 614 — Green Decorated; 616 — Blue Decorated; 618 — Old Tavern Decorated.

HEIRLOOM OCCASIONAL TABLES

No. 10-8355
Spoonfoot Cloverleaf Lamp Table. Opens to 27" in diameter with leaves extended. 24" H.

No. 14-8355 Same item in Decorated Finish 610.
see page 163

No. 10-8584
Magazine End Table. 18" x 28" x 24" H. Deep storage area under lid.
see page 163

No. 10-8302
Bookcase Table. 27" x 13" x 23" H.
see page 158

No. 10-8440P
Cocktail Table. 44" X 20" X 15" H. One drawer.
see page 162

No. 10-8586
Revolving Drum Table. 28" diameter x 26" H.
see page 163

No. 10-8303
Nest of Tables. Top table is 25" x 17" x 23" H. Three tables in all.
see page 162

No. 10-8442P
Step End Table. 19" x 27" x 25" H. One drawer. Formica® plastic top.
see page 162

No. 10-8587
Two Drawer Commode Table. 20" x 25" x 23" H.
see page 163

No. 10-8340
Spoonfoot Cocktail Table. 42" x 20" x 15" H.

No. 14-8340 Same item in Decorated Finish 610.
see page 163

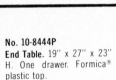

No. 10-8444P
End Table. 19" x 27" x 23" H. One drawer. Formica® plastic top.
see page 162

No. 10-8620
Octagonal Cocktail Table. 60" X 23" X 16" H.
see page 159

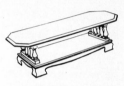

No. 10-8344
Spoonfoot Drop Leaf End Table. 18" x 25" x 24" H. Opens to 36" x 25" with leaves extended.

No. 14-8344 Same item in Decorated Finish 610.
see page 163

No. 10-8445P
Lamp Table. 23" square x 27" H. One drawer. Formica® plastic top.
see page 162

No. 10-8625
Square Lamp Table. 26" x 26" x 20" H. One drawer.
see page 159

No. 10-8346
Spoonfoot Doughbox End Table. 18" x 24" x 24" H. Deep storage area under lid.
see page 163

No. 10-8580
Cocktail Table. 42" x 18" x 18" H. Storage area under both lids.
see page 161

No. 10-8626
Hexagonal Pedestal Table. 29" x 25" x 20" H. One drawer.
see page 159

No. 10-8350
Spoonfoot Harvest Drop Leaf Cocktail Table. 44" x 18" x 15" H. Opens to 44" x 32" with leaves extended.

No. 14-8350 Same item in Decorated Finish 610.
see page 163

No. 10-8581
Clover Leaf Cocktail Table. 36" diameter x 16" H.
see page 161

No. 10-8627
Hexagonal Commode Table. 29" x 25" x 20" H. Large storage area behind doors. Door panels are selected veneer.
see page 159

No. 10-8354
Spoonfoot Two Drawer Commode Table. 18" x 23" x 23" H.
see page 161

No. 10-8582
Step End Table. 18" x 28" x 24" H. Storage area under lid.
see page 161

No. 10-8635
Square Commode Table. 27" x 27" x 20" H. Large storage area behind doors. Door panels are selected veneer.
see page 159

All doors are equipped with magnetic catches.

All items are Solid Maple and/or Birch and selected veneers (or wood-grained balanced hardboard where noted) in a warm brown Nutmeg finish. Available with matching Formica® plastic tops as noted.

No. 10-8640
Rectangular Cocktail Table. 50" x 21" x 16" H.
No. 10-8640P
Same item with Formica® plastic top.
see page 160

HEIRLOOM DECORATIVE ACCENTS

No. 10-9040P
Drop Leaf Cellarette. 30" x 17" x 33" H. Opens to 53" x 17". Selected veneer on top, sides and door panels. Set of matched glasses for side compartments.
see page 155

No. 10-8642
Square Pedestal Cocktail Table. 20" square x 16" H.
No. 10-8642P
Same item with Formica® plastic top.
see page 160

No. 10-9003
Governor's Cabinet. 26" X 15" X 28" H. Finished back. Two drawers; adjustable shelf behind doors.
see page 155

No. 10-9040P
Drop Leaf Cellarette.
Shown with doors open.

No. 10-8644
Two Drawer Drop Leaf End Table. 19" X 25" X 21" H. Opens to 35" X 25" with leaves extended.
No. 10-8644P Same item with Formica® plastic top.
see page 160

No. 10-9007
Tall Mirror. 20" x 38" H.
No. 15-9007
Tall Mirror. Same item in Classic Manor finish.
see page 154

No. 10-9042
Cigarette Pedestal Table. 15" diameter x 21" H.
***No. 14-9042**
Same item. Available in Decorated Finishes 601, 603, 609.
see page 161

No. 10-8645
Hexagonal Lamp Table. 27" x 24" x 20" H.
No. 10-8645P
Same item with Formica® plastic top.
see page 160

No. 10-9012
Bookcase with Grilled Glass Doors. 36" x 12" x 48" H. Two adjustable shelves behind doors. Back is wood-grained balanced hardboard.
see page 158

No. 10-9500
Seven Drawer Library Desk. 56" X 26" X 30" H. Two file drawers with metal file racks; pencil tray in center drawer. Finished back. Bookcase backs are selected veneer.
No. 15-9500 Same item in Classic Manor finish.
see page 157

No. 10-8646
Commode Table. 23" square X 21" H. Two removable interior partitions for use as record cabinet.
No. 10-8646P Same item with Formica® plastic top.
see page 160

No. 10-9019
Cloverleaf Magazine Rack. 18" x 12" x 15" H.
***No. 14-9019**
Same item. Available in Decorated Finishes 601, 603, 609.
see page 163

No. 10-9506
Nine Drawer Secretary Desk. 36" x 19" x 41" H. Four letter compartments. Lock and key for drop lid. Drop lid is veneer.
No. 15-9506 Same item in Classic Manor finish.
see page 156

No. 10-8654
End Table. 20" x 27" x 21" H. One drawer.
No. 10-8654P
Same item with Formica® plastic top.
see page 160

No. 10-9022
Gossip Bench. 33" x 16" x 29" H.
***No. 14-9022**
Same item. Available in Decorated Finishes 604 or 610.
see page 163

No. 10-9507
Grilled Secretary Top. Overall 76" H. Adjustable shelves behind doors.
No. 15-9507
Same item in Classic Manor finish.
see page 156

No. 10-9026
Bookstack. 30" x 14" x 80" H. Adjustable shelves behind doors. End panels are selected veneer. Back is wood-grained balanced hardboard.
***No. 14-9026** Same in Decorated Finishes 604 or 610.
see page 158

No. 10-9508
Six Drawer Secretary Desk. 33" x 17" x 40" H. Four drawers in base and two behind drop lid. Three letter compartments. Drop lid is selected veneer.
see page 156

No. 10-9035
Two Door Console Cabinet. 39" x 14" x 28" H. Door panels only, selected veneer.
No. 15-9035
Same item in Classic Manor finish.
see page 154

No. 10-9509
Secretary Top. Overall 73" H. Cabinet back is wood-grained balanced hardboard.
see page 156

*Description of Decorated Finishes: 601 — Nutmeg Decorated; 603 — White Decorated; 604 — White Decorated with Nutmeg; 609 — Black Decorated; 610 — Black Decorated with Nutmeg.

Cabinet doors are equipped with magnetic catches; shutter doors have solid back panel to protect interior from dust; finished interiors.

Also available in Classic Manor finish as noted.

Ethan Allen
AMERICAN TRADITIONAL INTERIORS
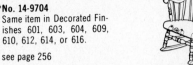

HEIRLOOM COLLECTION

All items are Solid Maple and/or Birch and selected veneers (or wood-grained balanced hardboard where noted) in a warm brown Nutmeg finish. Available with matching Formica* plastic tops as noted.

No. 10-9510
Bookcase. 32" x 11" x 51" H. Back is wood-grained balanced hardboard.

***No. 14-9510** Same item in Decorated Finishes 604 or 610. Back panel in Nutmeg.

see page 158

No. 10-9704
Salem Rocker. 24" X 28" X 42" H.

***No. 14-9704**
Same item in Decorated Finishes 601, 603, 604, 609, 610, 612, 614, or 616.

see page 256

No. 10-9512
Sliding Door Bookcase. 36" x 9" x 37" H. One adjustable shelf. Back is wood-grained balanced hardboard.

see page 158

No. 10-9705
Child's Rocker. 17" X 21" X 29" H.

***No. 14-9705**
Same item in Decorated Finishes 601, 603, or 609.

see page 257

No. 10-9513
Bookcase. 36" x 8" x 36" H. Back is wood-grained balanced hardboard.

see page 158

No. 10-9706
Homestead Rocker. 25" X 28" X 40" H.

***No. 14-9706**
Same item in Decorated Finishes 601, 603, 604, 609, 610, 612, 614, or 616.

see page 258

No. 10-9520P
Eight Drawer Double Pedestal Desk. 43" x 21" x 30" H. File drawer lower right. End panels are selected veneer. Formica® plastic top.

see page 156

No. 10-9709
Gloucester Rocker. 29" X 19" X 42" H.

***No. 14-9709**
Same item in Decorated Finishes 601, 603, 604, 609, 610.

see page 254

No. 10-9521
Four Drawer Single Pedestal Desk. 40" x 21" x 30" H. One file drawer. End panels are selected veneer. Formica® plastic top.

see page 157

No. 10-9710
Litchfield Rocker. 23½" X 19" X 45" H.

***No. 14-9710**
Same item in Decorated Finishes 601, 609, 610.

see page 256

No. 10-9522
Double Pedestal Desk. 46" x 23" x 30" H. Eight drawers. Lower left drawer has metal file racks.

see page 157

No. 10-9702
Cape Cod Rocker. 23" X 28" X 40" H.

***No. 14-9702**
Same item in Decorated Finishes 601, 603 or 609.

see page 254

No. 10-9703
Boston Rocker. 24" X 28" X 40" H.

***No. 14-9703**
Same item in Decorated Finishes 601, 603, 604, 609, 610, 612, 614, or 616.

see page 255

---

*Description of Decorated Finishes: 601 — Nutmeg Decorated; 603 — White Decorated; 604 — White Decorated with Nutmeg; 609 — Black Decorated; 610 — Black Decorated with Nutmeg; 612 — Red Decorated; 614 — Green Decorated; 616 — Blue Decorated.

All items are Solid Cherry with selected veneers wherever noted in an artistically distressed warm brown Georgian Court finish.
All bedrails are metal with matching wood-grain finish.

BEDROOM

No. 11-5110
Queen Anne Mirror. Overall 32" x 48" H.
No. 11-5120
Same item. Overall 23" x 48" H.
see page 91

No. 11-5213
Ten Drawer Triple Dresser. 66" x 20" x 34" H.
see page 92

No. 11-5641
Pediment Headboard. Overall 56" H. Available in 4'6" and 5' sizes.
see page 92

No. 11-5200
Oval Mirror. Overall 40" x 26" H.
see page 89

No. 11-5214
Pier Chest. 24" x 17" x 52" H. Fully compartmentalized jewelry shelf in top drawer. Storage area behind doors.
see page 91

*No. 11-5650
Chairback Bed. Overall 41" H. Available in 3'3", 4'6" or 5'0" sizes.
see page 93

No. 11-5202
Eight Drawer Double Dresser. Overall 56" x 20" x 34" H.
see page 93

No. 11-5215
Armoire. 40" x 20" x 64" H. Two tray drawers behind doors with vertical partitions.
see page 91

No. 11-5651
Chairback Headboard. Overall 41" H. Available in 3'3" size as shown. See below for 5'0" and 6'6" sizes.

No. 11-5203
Nine Drawer Triple Dresser. 74" x 20" x 34" H. Two tray drawer behind doors.
see page 91

No. 11-5216
Commode Night Table. 27" x 16" x 26" H. One drawer and two doors.
see page 94

No. 11-5651
Chairback Headboard. Overall 41" H. Available in 5'0" or 6'6" sizes.
see page 94

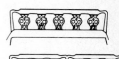

No. 11-5204
Six Drawer Chest. 38" x 20" x 47" H. Four removable partitions.
see page 93

No. 11-5220
Pediment Mirror. Overall 34" x 50" H.
see page 93

No. 11-5652
Panel Headboard. Overall 46" H. Available in 5'0" or 6'6" sizes. Similar to 10-5653.
see page 95

No. 11-5205
Eleven Drawer Bonnet Top Highboy. 38" x 21" x 79" H.
see page 85

No. 11-5225
Seven Drawer Chest on Chest. 40" x 20" x 55" H. Two partitions in drawers above and below waist.
see page 92

No. 11-5653
Upholstered Headboard. Overall 46" H. Available in 5'0" or 6'6" sizes.

No. 11-5206
Night Stand. 28" x 18" x 26" H. Two drawers.
see page 91

No. 11-5226
Cabinet Night Table. 27" x 16" x 26" H. One drawer.
see page 93

*No. 11-5654
Pediment Poster Bed. Overall 56" H. Available in 4'6" or 5'0" sizes.
see page 92

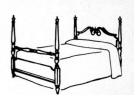

No. 11-5210
Rectangular Mirror. Overall 52" x 34" H.
see page 92

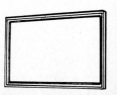

*No. 11-5632
Tall Poster Bed. Overall 84" H. Available in 4'6" and 5'0" sizes.
see page 91
No. 11-5989 Extra Length 81"
Canopy Frame. In 5'0" size only. Shipped with 81" long rails.

No. 11-6047
Five Drawer Buffet. 56" x 20" x 34" H. Felt-lined compartments, removable partitions in top outer drawers. Adjustable shelves behind doors.

Cabinet doors are equipped with magnetic catches, finished interiors.
Casters are standard equipment.

*If you wish to order extra length rails, please specify **No. 11-5999 81" Extra Length Rails** along with the number of your bed.

No. 11-6056
Four Drawer Buffet. 66" x 20" x 34" H. Felt-lined compartments, removable partitions in top outer drawers. Adjustable shelves behind doors.

No. 11-6099
China Cabinet. 66" x 11" x 45" H. Two adjustable shelves behind crowned glass doors. Back is selected veneer. For use with No. 11-6056.

No. 11-6206
Breakfront Buffet. 66" x 19" x 30" H. Two doors and three drawers.

see page 77

No. 11-6084
Cabriole Oval Extension Table. 44" x 66". Shown without leaves.

No. 11-6200 Side Chair
No. 11-6200A Arm Chair
Cane Back Chairs. 40" H. Upholstered seat.

see page 79

No. 11-6207
Queen Anne Sideboard. 66" x 20" x 34" H. Left drawer has Pacific cloth insert to protect silver. Right drawer has flat tray for silver storage.

see page 78

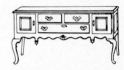

No. 11-6084
Extends to 102" with two 18" aproned filler leaves. Seats 10-12. Shown with leaves.

No. 11-6201 Side Chair.
No. 11-6201A Arm Chair.
Marleborough Chairs. 40" H. Upholstered pad back.

see page 79

No. 11-6208
China Cabinet. 66" x 19" x 50" H. Four crowned glass doors. Two adjustable shelves. Lighted interior. Back is selected veneer. For use with No. 11-6206.

see page 77

No. 11-6093
Double Pedestal Extension Table. 66" x 42". Shown without leaves.

see page 77

No. 11-6202 Side Chair.
No. 11-6202A Arm Chair.
Shield Back Chairs. 39" H. Upholstered seat.

see page 78

No. 11-6209
China Cabinet. 66" x 11" x 46" H. Beveled glass doors. Two adjustable shelves behind each door. Back is selected veneer. For use with No. 11-6207.

see page 78

No. 11-6093
Opens to 102" with two 18" aproned filler leaves. Top extends while base remains stationary. Seats 10-12. Shown with leaves.

No. 11-6203
Drop Leaf Extension Table. 42" x 30". Shown without leaves.

see page 79

No. 11-6210 Side Chair.
No. 11-6210A Arm Chair.
Duncan Phyfe Chairs. 35" H. Upholstered seat.

see page 81

No. 11-6094
Cabriole Oval Extension Table. 40" x 60". Shown without leaves.

No. 11-6203
Opens to 92" with two 10" filler leaves. Seats 10. Shown with leaves.

No. 11-6211 Side Chair.
No. 11-6211A Arm Chair.
Queen Anne Chairs. 40" H. Upholstered seat.

see page 79

No. 11-6094
Opens to 96" with two 18" aproned filler leaves. Seats 10. Shown with leaves.

No. 11-6204
Round Extension Table. 44" diameter. Shown without leaves.

see page 82

No. 11-6212 Side Chair.
No. 11-6212A Arm Chair.
Chippendale Ladderback Chairs. 38" H. Upholstered seat.

see page 77

No. 11-6098
China Cabinet. 56" x 11" x 45" H. Adjustable shelves behind glass doors. Back is selected veneer. For use with No. 11-6047.

No. 11-6204
Opens to 80" x 44" with two 18" aproned filler leaves. Seats 8-10. Shown with leaves.

No. 11-6213
Pembroke Drop Leaf Table. 42" x 22". Shown without leaves.

see page 80

Cabinet doors are equipped with magnetic catches; finished interiors.

Hutch and China Cabinet backs are selected veneers. All shelves are grooved to display dishes attractively.

Hutch cabinets include base plate rail which is also grooved for display of dishes.

BEDROOM, DINING ROOM, OCCASIONAL TABLES AND DECORATIVE ACCENTS

No. 11-6213
Pembroke Drop Leaf Table. Opens to 85" with three 16" aproned filler leaves. Seats 8-10. Shown with leaves.

No. 11-6214
Oval Extension Table. 44" x 66". Shown without leaves.

see page 78

No. 11-6214
Same item. Opens to 102" with two 18" aproned filler leaves. Seats 10-12. Shown with leaves.

No. 11-6216
Three Drawer Buffet. 54" x 20" x 34" H. One adjustable shelf behind doors. Center drawer has Pacific cloth insert to protect silver.

see page 79

No. 11-6217
Two Drawer Buffet 44" x 20" x 30" H. Three pull-out drawers. Top drawer has tarnish resistant tray for silver storage. Cabinet with adjustable shelf behind one door.

see page 82

No. 11-6218
China Cabinet. 54" x 11" x 45" H. Three doors with glass mullions. One adjustable shelf. Back only is selected veneer. For use with No. 11-6216.

see page 79

No. 11-6219
China Cabinet. 44" x 12" x 46" H. Two adjustable shelves behind crowned glass doors are grooved for China display. Back panel only is selected veneer. For use with No. 11-6217.

see page 82

No. 11-6226
Corner China Cabinet. 42" x 22" x 76" H. 32" on each wall. Two adjustable shelves behind doors with glass mullions. Lighted interior. Base has adjustable shelf behind doors. Back only is selected veneer. see page 78

No. 11-6227
Serving Cabinet. 40" x 20" x 37" H. With leaves extended—64" x 20" x 37" H. Two pull-out panels surfaced with black melamine plastic. Two drawers for silver and linen storage. Finished on all sides. Casters for easy mobility.

see page 78

No. 11-6228
Silver Chest. 21½" x 16" x 41" H. Interior covered with Pacific cloth. Holds 8 or more place settings.

see page 84

GEORGIAN COURT OCCASIONAL TABLES AND DECORATIVE ACCENTS.

No. 11-8008
Queen Anne Wine Stand Table. 15" diameter x 21" H.

see page 87

No. 11-8009
Butler's Tray Table. 42" x 30" x 17" H. with leaves down. 35" x 23" x 21" with leaves up.

see page 89

No. 11-8066
Octagonal Book Table. 26" x 26" x 22" H.

see page 88

No. 11-8067
Square Commode Table. 26" x 26" x 22" H. One drawer and large storage area behind doors.

see page 88

No. 11-8070
Hexagonal Pedestal Snack Table. 20" x 23" x 17" H.

see page 88

No. 11-8071
Octagonal Pedestal Cocktail Table. 36" x 36" x 16" H.

see page 88

No. 11-8075
Hexagonal Commode Table. 24" x 24" x 22" H. Large storage area behind doors.

see page 88

No. 11-8160
Rectangular Cocktail Table. 49" x 21" x 15" H. Two drawers.

see page 87

No. 11-8161
Cabriole Drop Leaf Cocktail Table. 50" x 20" x 16" H. Opens to 50" x 38" with leaves extended.

see page 87

No. 11-8164
Drop Leaf Pembroke Table. 21" x 27" x 22" H. Opens to 36" with leaves extended. One drawer.

see page 87

No. 11-8165
Commode Lamp Table. 23" x 23" x 22" H. Large storage area behind doors.

see page 87

No. 11-8200
Rectangular Cocktail Table. 46" x 21" x 18" H. Top is selected veneer.

see page 86

No. 11-8201
Lamp Table. 24" x 24" x 22" H. Two drawers. Top is selected veneer.

see page 86

Cabinet doors are equipped with magnetic catches; finished interiors.

No. 11-8202
Pembroke Table. 18" x 28" x 25" H. Opens to 35" with leaves extended.
see page 86

No. 11-9003
Curio Cabinet Top. 26" x 11" x 42" H. Adjustable glass shelves behind grilled doors. Lighted interior. Back is selected veneer. For use with No. 11-9002.
see page 81

No. 11-9200
Goddard Block Front Chest. 36" x 20" x 31" H. Four drawers.
see page 85

No. 11-8203
Tripod Tea Table. 30" diameter x 28" H. Top revolves and tilts to full vertical position.
see page 86

No. 11-9004
Commode Cabinet. 30" x 16" x 26" H. One adjustable shelf.
see page 89

No. 11-9201
Lowboy. 32" x 17" x 30" H. Four drawers.
see page 85

No. 11-8204
Tea Table. 30" x 19" x 26" H. Two pull-out slides. Top is selected veneer.
see page 86

No. 11-9005
Library Bookstack. 30" x 9" x 52" H. Stationary shelves decorated with long wooden mullions. Backs are selected veneer. For use with No. 11-9004 or No. 11-9009.
see page 89

No. 11-9202
Chippendale Mirror. Overall 19" x 36" H. Fretwork border is selected veneer.
see page 77

No. 11-9207. Same as above. Overall 25" x 44" H.
see page 85

No. 11-8205
Curio Table. 24" x 22" x 21" H. Clear glass top and sides. Brass plated ferrules on feet.
see page 86

No. 11-9006
Seven Drawer Ladies' Writing Desk. 34" x 18" x 40" H. Extends to 25" deep with fold-in lid extended and resting on pull-out supports. Five letter compartments.
see page 89

No. 11-9203
Drop Front Secretary. 27" x 15" x 40" H. Four drawers. Compartmentalized interior behind slide-operated dropfront. Top drawer and dropfront are fitted with locks. Drop-front is selected veneer.
see page 85

No. 11-8206
Nest of Tables. Top table is 23" x 15" x 22" H.
see page 86

No. 11-9007
Tall Framed Mirror. Overall 17" x 46" H.
see page 89

No. 11-9204
Secretary Top. 28" x 19" x 39" H. Bevelled glass doors. Three adjustable shelves are grooved for China display. Back is selected veneer. For use with No. 11-9203.
see page 85

No. 11-9000
Credenza. 50" x 15" x 26" H. One adjustable shelf behind each set of doors separated by a solid wood panel.

No. 11-9008
Framed Oval Mirror. Overall 22" x 32".
see page 85

No. 11-9205
Lowboy. 38" x 21" x 32" Four drawers.
see page 77

No. 11-9001
Five Sided Console. 36" x 12" x 30" H. One adjustable shelf behind doors.
see page 89

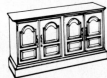

No. 11-9009
Three Drawer Chest. 30" x 16" x 26" H.
see page 89

No. 11-9206
Etagere. 37" x 13" x 81" H. One drawer. Shelves are selected veneer.
see page 79

No. 11-9002
Lowboy Base. 26" x 12" x 25" H. Adjustable shelf behind doors. Doors have magnetic catches.
see page 81

No. 11-9010
Upper Cabinet Bookstack. 30" x 9" x 52" H. Adjustable shelf behind doors. Backs are selected veneer. For use with No. 11-9004 or No. 11-9009.
see page 89

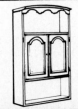

No. 11-9208
Double Pedestal Desk. 52" x 26" x 29½" H. Genuine leather inlays in top. Metal file racks in lower left drawer.
see page 84

All items are Solid Cherry with selected veneers where noted in an artistically distressed warm brown Georgian Court finish. Cabinet doors are equipped with magnetic catches, finished interiors.

ANTIQUED PINE COLLECTION

All items are Solid Pine with selected veneers and inlays where noted. All items are Antiqued Pine in Old Tavern finish — skillfully shaded and hand-distressed to achieve an authentic "aged" look.

Crafted in solid pine and selected veneers.

ANTIQUED PINE CUSTOM ROOM PLAN

No. 12-4021
18" Speaker Cabinet. Speaker area: 15" x 22" H.
see page 244

No. 12-4038
Framed Mirror. Overall 48" x 32" H.

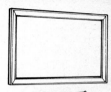

No. 12-4000
24" Three Drawer Chest.
see page 243

No. 12-4030
32" Three Drawer Chest.
see page 243

No. 12-4047
T-V Upper Unit. 32"   17" x 48" H. One rotating pull-out shelf behind doors. Will hold T-V up to 70 lbs.
see page 244

No. 12-4001
35" Corner Cabinet. One drawer. One adjustable, removable shelf behind doors. 35" along each wall.
see page 240

No. 12-4031
32" Shutter Door Cabinet. One drawer, one adjustable, removable shelf behind doors.
see page 244

No. 12-4050
40" Three Drawer Dresser.
see page 247

No. 12-4002
Refrigerator Base Unit. 24" x 18½" x 30" H. Contains Refrigerator with 4 tray ice service.
see page 240

No. 12-4032
35" Corner Desk. One drawer. 35" along each wall.
see page 243

No. 12-4051
40" Three Drawer Dresser. Adjustable, removable shelf behind door.
see page 241

No. 12-4006
24" Upper Bookcase. One center adjustable, removable shelf.
see page 240

No. 12-4034
Refreshment Base Unit. 32" x 18" x 30" H. Felt lined drawer with removable partition. Glass rack, wine rack, adjustable shelf.
see page 240

No. 12-4052
40" Four Drawer Dresser Desk.
see page 246

No. 12-4007
35" Upper Corner Bookcase. 35" along each wall.
see page 240

No. 12-4035
Refreshment Upper Unit. 32" x 17" x 48" H. Three adjustable glass shelves. Interior light. Melamine plastic work surface.
see page 240

No. 12-4056
40" Upper Bookcase. Two center adjustable, removable shelves.
see page 247

No. 12-4008
48" Upper Cabinet Bookcase. Adjustable, removable shelves behind doors.
see page 242

No. 12-4036
32" Upper Bookcase. One center adjustable, removable shelf.

No. 12-4057
40" Upper Cabinet Bookcase. Adjustable, removable shelves behind both doors and one between doors.
see page 246

No. 12-4020
40" Stereo Cabinet. Top only, selected Pine veneer.
see page 244

No. 12-4037
32" Upper Cabinet Bookcase. Adjustable, removable shelves behind doors.
see page 240

No. 12-4070
48" Seven Drawer Double Dresser.
see page 248

Cabinet doors are equipped with magnetic catches; shutter doors have solid back panel to protect interior from dust; finished interiors.

All bases are 18" deep and 30" H. All upper units are 11" deep and 48" H.

All Upper Cabinets, Upper Bookcase and Base Cabinets with exposed backs feature back panels of wood-grained balanced hardboard, white ceramic pulls.

No. 12-4071
48" Four Drawer Dresser Desk.

see page 246

No. 12-5006
Two Drawer Cabinet Night Table. 23" x 17" x 27" H.

see page 238

✓**No. 12-5025**
Five Drawer Chest on Chest. 42" x 20" x 56" H. Two divided trays and three shirt compartments behind doors.

see page 235

No. 12-4072
48" x 32" Corner Study Desk. One drawer.

No. 12-5010
Framed Mirror. Overall 57" x 36" H.

see page 238

No. 12-5026
Cabinet Night Table. 26" x 16" x 28" H. Two doors. One drawer.

see page 236

ANTIQUED PINE BEDROOM

✓**No. 12-5013**
Thirteen Drawer Triple Dresser. 72" x 21" x 34" H. Two tray drawers behind door, horizontal divider in top end drawers.

see page 234

No. 12-5030
Hutch Mirror. 71" x 11½" x 45" H. Six drawers. For use with No. 12-5013 Dresser.

see page 236

No. 12-5000
Framed Mirror. Overall 45" x 34" H.

see page 237

✓**No. 12-5015**
Armoire. 45" x 21" x 76" H. Four pull-out trays behind doors. Three drawers in lower section; molded "Bonnet Top." Massive scale antiqued hinges and hardware.

see page 234

No. 12-5600
Cannonball Bed. Overall 45" H. Available in 3'3", 4'6" and 5' sizes.

see page 237

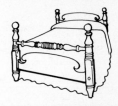

No. 12-5002
Ten Drawer Double Dresser. 54" x 21" x 34" H. Dividers in both third row drawers.

see page 238

No. 12-5016
Four Drawer Commode Night Table. 24" x 17" x 28" H.

see page 237

No. 12-5601
Panel/Spindle Bed. Overall 41" H. Available in 3'3", 4'6" and 5' sizes. Single bed has one panel in headboard.

see page 238

No. 12-5003
Eleven Drawer Triple Dresser. 66" x 21" x 34" H. Removable partitions in top right and third row drawers. Two tray drawers behind right door and adjustable shelf behind left door. Self-leveling fifth center.

see page 237

No. 12-5020
Bonnet Top Mirror. Overall 30" x 50" H.

see page 234

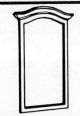

✱ **No. 12-5602**
Dual-Height Poster Bed. Overall 68" H. Can be extended to 80" H. with extension posts which are shipped with every bed. In 4'6" or 5'0" sizes only.

see page 234

No. 12-5004
Seven Drawer Chest. 36" x 21" x 50" H. Dividers in third row drawer.

see page 238

✓**No. 12-5023**
Eight Drawer Triple Dresser. 66" x 21" x 33" H. Removable partition in center and bottom drawers.

see page 237

No. 12-5604
Spindle Bed. Overall 41" H. Available in 3'3", 4'6" and 5' sizes.

see page 238

No. 12-5005
Eight Drawer Chest on Chest. 38" x 21" x 54" H. Dividers in fourth row drawer.

see page 237

✓**No. 12-5024**
Lingerie Chest. 25" x 17" x 52" H. Three drawers, adjustable shelf. Top is selected matching veneer.

see page 235

No. 12-5605
Panel/Spindle Headboard. 41" H. Available in 5' and 6'6" sizes.

see page 238

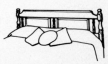

If you wish extra length rails, specify **No. 12-5999 81" Extra Length Rails** along with your bed number.
✱ **No. 12-5993 Regular Length 76" Canopy Frame.** To convert No. 12-5602 to canopy bed. **No. 12-5994 Extra Length 81" Canopy Frame.** For extra long canopy bed. Shipped automatically with 81" long rails.

Crafted in solid pine and selected veneers.
CUSTOM ROOM PLAN, BEDROOM, DINING ROOM
OCCASIONAL TABLES AND DECORATIVE ACCENTS

All items are solid Antiqued Pine and selected veneers in Old Tavern finish — skillfully shaded and subtly distressed to achieve authentic "aged" look. Some designs have veneered components.

All bedrails are metal with matching wood-grain finish.

No. 12-5606
Bookcase Headboard. Overall 40" H. Available in 3'3" size only.

see page 247

No. 12-6000
Captain's Chair. 30" H.

*No. 24-6000
Same item in American Foliage Colors.

see page 214

No. 12-6007
Three Drawer Buffet. 50" x 18" x 33" H. Removable partition and felt-lined compartment in left drawer. One shelf behind all three doors.

*No. 24-6007 Same item in American Foliage Colors.

see page 217

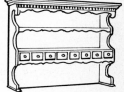

No. 12-5607
Captain's Trundle Bed. Overall 36" H. Lower drawer rolls out on casters as an extra bed (39" x 75" mattress). Use a 39" x 80" mattress for upper bed. Available in 3'3" (Twin) size only.

see page 246

No. 12-6001
Mate's Chair. 30" H.

*No. 24-6001
Same item in American Foliage Colors.

see page 217

No. 12-6008
Hutch Top. 63" x 43" H. Four drawers.

*No. 24-6008 Same item in American Foliage Colors. For use with No. 12-6006.

see page 216

No. 12-5611
Bonnet Top Spindle Headboard. 45" H. Available in 4'6"-5' combination size and 6'6" size.

see page 236

No. 12-6002 Side Chair
No. 12-6002A Arm Chair
Ladderback Chairs. 41" H. Fiber seat.

*No. 24-6002, No. 24-6002A
Same items in American Foliage Colors.

see page 220

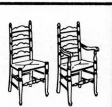

No. 12-6009
Hutch Top. 52" x 43" H. Three drawers.

*No. 24-6009 Same item in American Foliage Colors. For use with No. 12-6007.

see page 217

No. 12-5614
Tri-Way Trundle Bed. Overall 56" H. Headboard 37" H. Available in 3'3" size only.

see page 239

No. 12-5615
Guard Rail and Ladder.

No. 12-6003
Trestle Table. 72" x 35". Seats 6-8. Extra-heavy top.

#*No. 24-6003 Same item in American Foliage Colors. Pine Cone color top.

see page 216

No. 12-6010 Side Chair
No. 12-6010A Arm Chair
Scroll Back Duxbury Chairs. 36" H.

see page 215

No. 12-5620
Cannonball Headboard. Overall 45" H. Available in 4'6", 5'0" and 6'6" sizes.

see page 237

No. 12-6004
48" Round Spoonfoot Extension Table. Extra-heavy top. Shown without leaves.
No. 12-6004P Same item with Formica® plastic top.
#*No. 24-6004 Same item in American Foliage Colors. Pine Cone color top.

No. 12-6011 Side Chair
No. 12-6011A Arm Chair
High Back Catkin Chairs. 39" H.

*No. 24-6011 No. 24-6011A
Same items in American Foliage Colors.

see page 219

No. 12-5622
Spindle Headboard. Overall 41" H. Available in 3'3" size.

see page 238

No. 12-6004
Same as above. Opens to 72" with two 12" filler leaves. Seats 8-10. Shown with leaves.

No. 12-6013
42" Round Center Pedestal Table. Seats 4-6. Extra-heavy top.
No. 12-6013P Same item with Formica® plastic top.
#*No. 24-6013 Same item in American Foliage Colors. Pine Cone color top.

see page 218

No. 12-5660
Cradle. 36" H. x 43" L. x 22¼" H. Safety locking pin to put in non-rocking position if desired. See No. 10-5660 on page 175.

No. 12-6005
Trestle Bench. 66" x 15" x 17" H.

*No. 24-6005
Same item in American Foliage Colors.

see page 216

No. 12-6016
Corner Hutch Base. 27" (along wall). Adjustable shelf behind doors.

*No. 24-6016
Same item in American Foliage Colors.

see page 218

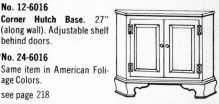

No. 12-6006
Four Drawer Buffet. 60" x 18" x 33" H. Removable partitions and felt-lined compartments in left drawer. One adjustable shelf.

*No. 24-6006 Same item in American Foliage Colors.

see page 215

No. 12-6017
Five Drawer Buffet. 72" x 20" x 33" H. Removable partitions and felt-lined compartments in outer drawers. Adjustable shelves behind bottom outer doors.

see page 213

Wood seats of all pieces, except fiber seat chairs are extra heavy pine, deeply saddled. Remaining wood parts of chairs are Maple and/or Birch (for extra strength) with appropriate Old Tavern finish. All hutch backs are selected veneer. White ceramic pulls.

#Top available in Pine Cone only. Base in choice of American Foliage Colors.

No. 12-6018
Corner Hutch Top. 29"
(along wall).

*No. 24-6018
Same item in American Foliage Colors.

see page 218

No. 12-6026
Three Drawer Buffet. 56" x 20" x 33" H. Removable partition and felt-lined compartment in left drawer. One adjustable shelf behind all three doors.

see page 214

No. 12-6044
End Extension Trestle Table. 70" x 38". Extra-heavy top. Shown without leaves.

see page 219

No. 12-6019
China Cabinet. 63" x 35" H. For use with No. 12-6006.

see page 215

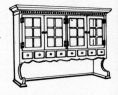

No. 12-6028
Hutch Cabinet. 72" W., 47" H. For use with No. 12-6017.

see page 212

No. 12-6044
Same as above. Opens to 100" with two 15" filler leaves. Seats 10. Extension leaves and top section only, selected Pine veneer. Shown with leaves.

No. 12-6020
Swivel Mate's Chair. 30" H. Extra-heavy back rail.

*No. 24-6020
Same item in American Foliage Colors.

see page 222

No. 12-6029
Hutch Cabinet. 56" W., 47" H. For use with No. 12-6026.

see page 214

No. 12-6050
General's Chair. 30" H.

see page 258

No. 12-6023
42" Round Spoonfoot Extension Table. Extra-heavy top. Shown without leaves.

No. 12-6023P
Same item with Formica® plastic top.

see page 217

No. 12-6031
Country Chair. 34" H.

*No. 24-6031
Same item in American Foliage Colors.

see page 221

No. 12-6053
48" Round Pedestal Extension Table. Equalizer slide allows for easy opening by one person. Shown without leaves.

#*No. 24-6053 Same item in American Foliage Colors. Pine Cone color top.

see page 212

No. 12-6023
Same as above. Opens to 54" with one 12" filler leaf. Seats 6. Shown with leaves.

No. 12-6033
48" Round Center Pedestal Table. Seats 4-6. Extra-heavy top.

#*No. 24-6033
Same item in American Foliage Colors. Pine Cone color top.

see page 214

No. 12-6053
Same as above. Opens to 78" with two 15" aproned filler leaves. Shown with leaves. Seats 10.

No. 12-6024
Spoonfoot Oval Extension Table. 40" x 60". Shown without leaves.

see page 215

No. 12-6040
Mate's Chair. 30" H.

*No. 24-6040
Same item in American Foliage Colors.

see page 218

No. 12-6055
Stereo Dry Sink. 38" x 20" x 39" H. Integrated unit for stereo components and record storage.

*No. 24-6055 Same item in American Foliage Colors.

see page 215

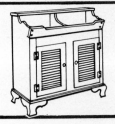

No. 12-6024
Same as above. Opens to 96" with three 12" filler leaves. Seats 10. Shown with leaves.

No. 12-6041 Side Chair
No. 12-6041A Arm Chair
Ladderback Chairs. 44" H. Fiber seat.

No. 14-6041 No. 14-6041A
Same item in Decorated Finishes 601, 603, 609.

see page 216

No. 12-6063
Harvest Trestle Table. 23" x 66" x 44" with leaves extended. Seats 6-8.

see page 224

No. 12-6025
Deacon's Bench. 64" x 20" x 34" H. Scoop Seat.

*No. 24-6025
Same item in American Foliage Colors.

see page 212

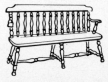

No. 12-6042 Side Chair.
No. 12-6042A Arm Chair.
Arrowback Chairs. 40" H.

see page 212

No. 12-6064
Trestle Table. 60" x 34" x 29" Non-extension

No. 12-6064P Same item with Formica® plastic top.

#*No. 24-6064 Same item in American Foliage Colors. Pine Cone color top.

see page 220

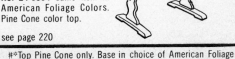

Wood seats of all pieces, except fiber seat chairs are extra heavy pine, deeply saddled. Remaining wood parts of chairs are Maple and/or Birch (for extra strength) with appropriate Old Tavern finish. All hutch backs are selected veneer. White ceramic pulls.

#*Top Pine Cone only. Base in choice of American Foliage Colors.

Crafted in solid pine and selected veneers.
BEDROOM, DINING ROOM, OCCASIONAL TABLES AND DECORATIVE ACCENTS

No. 12-6065
Revolving Lazy Susan. 20" diameter.

*No. 24-6065
Same item in American Foliage Colors.

see page 218

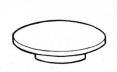

No. 12-8007
Revolving Octagonal Table. 26" x 26" x 22" H. Table sits on swivel base.

*No. 24-8007 Same item in American Foliage Colors.

see page 234

No. 12-8032
Two Drawer Step End Table. 20" x 30" x 24" H.

*No. 24-8032
Same item in American Foliage Colors.

see page 231

No. 12-6120
Hitchcock Chair. 16" x 16" x 34" H.
No. 14-6120
Same item in Decorated Finishes 601 and 611.

see page 259

No. 12-8010
Pedestal Candlestand. 18" diameter x 21" H.
*No. 24-8010 Same item in American Foliage Colors.

see page 250

No. 12-8034
Butterfly Drop Leaf End Table. 20" x 27" x 24" H. Opens to 37" x 27" with leaves extended. One drawer.

*No. 24-8034 Same item in American Foliage Colors.

see page 230

No. 12-6170
High Chair.

see page 259

No. 12-8020
Rectangular Cocktail Table. 54" x 22" x 17" H.

*No. 24-8020 Same item in American Foliage Colors.

see page 230

No. 12-8036
Revolving Drum Table. 28" diameter x 27" H.

*No. 24-8036
Same item in American Foliage Colors.

see page 231

ANTIQUED PINE
OCCASIONAL TABLES
AND
DECORATIVE ACCENTS

No. 12-8021
Drop Leaf Harvest Cocktail Table. 54" x 20" x 17" H. Opens to 54" x 36" with leaves extended.

*No. 24-8021 Same item in American Foliage Colors.

see page 230

No. 12-8037
Commode Table. 25" square x 24" H. Two drawers.

*No. 24-8037
Same item in American Foliage Colors.

see page 230

No. 12-8000
Trestle Cocktail Table. 54" x 22" x 17" H.

*No. 24-8000 Same item in American Foliage Colors.

see page 232

No. 12-8024
End Table. 21½" x 29" x 24" H.

*No. 24-8024
Same item in American Foliage Colors.

see page 230

No. 12-8050
Hearth Stool. 14" diameter x 17" H. Extra-heavy seat.

*No. 24-8050 Same item in American Foliage Colors.

No. 14-8200 Same item in Decorated finishes 604 or 610.

see page 250

No. 12-8001
Square Pedestal Cocktail Table. 23" square x 18" H. Use as an end table or in groups as cocktail table.

*No. 24-8001 Same item in American Foliage Colors.

see page 233

No. 12-8026
Dough Box Magazine End Table. 20" x 30" x 25" H. Deep storage area under drop lid.

*No. 24-8026 Same item in American Foliage Colors.

see page 231

No. 12-8053
Record Cabinet. 26" x 15" x 22" H. Vertical removable partitions behind doors.

see page 232

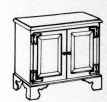

No. 12-8005
Bookstand Table. 16" x 14" x 27" H. One drawer. Ideal as a telephone table.

*No. 24-8005 Same item in American Foliage Colors.

see page 251

No. 12-8030
Double Pedestal Oval Cocktail Table. 58" x 23" x 16" H. Extra-heavy top.

see page 231

No. 12-8054
Square Pedestal Cocktail Table. 19" square x 16" H.

*No. 24-8054 Same item in American Foliage Colors.

No. 14-9218 Same item in Decorated finishes 604 or 610.

see page 234

No. 12-8006
Rudder Drop Leaf Table. 28" x 13" x 23" H. Opens to 28" x 32" with leaves extended. One drawer.

*No. 24-8006 Same item in American Foliage Colors.

see page 231

No. 12-8031
Round Pedestal Cocktail Table. 38" diameter x 16" H. Extra-heavy top.

*No. 24-8031
Same item in American Foliage Colors.

see page 230

No. 12-8058
Revolving Cogwheel Table. 38" diameter x 17" H.

*No. 24-8058
Same item in American Foliage Colors.

see page 229

*Description of American Foliage Colors:
402—Sugarbush Red; 403—Pine Cone; 404—Autumn Gold; 405—Holly Green; 406—Spruce Blue.

Description of Decorated Finishes: 601—Nutmeg Decorated; 609—Black Decorated; 610—Black Decorated with Nutmeg; 603—White Decorated; 604—White Decorated with Nutmeg; 611—Black Decorated with Old Tavern.

No. 12-8059
Pedestal Cocktail Table. 56" x 22" x 22" H. One drop-lid compartment. Similar to 12-9506.

*No. 24-8059 Same item in American Foliage Colors.

see page 229

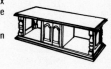

No. 12-8070
Cabinet Cocktail Table. 56" x 22" x 17" H. Large storage area behind doors.

*No. 24-8070 Same item in American Foliage Colors.

see page 229

No. 12-8074
Hexagonal Lamp Table. 29" x 25" x 22" H. Large storage area behind doors.

*No. 24-8074 Same item in American Foliage Colors.

see page 229

No. 12-8075
Square Commode Lamp Table. 26" x 26" x 22" H. Large storage area behind doors.

*No. 24-8075 Same item in American Foliage Colors.

see page 229

No. 12-8080
Rectangular Cocktail Table. 56" x 26" x 18" H.

*No. 24-8080 Same item in American Foliage Colors.

see page 222

No. 12-8081
Square Cocktail Table. 40" x 40" x 18" H.

*No. 24-8081 Same item in American Foliage Colors.

see page 228

No. 12-8082
Hexagonal Lamp Table. 31" across points.

*No. 24-8082 Same item in American Foliage Colors.

see page 228

No. 12-8083
Rectangular End Table. 27" x 22" x 22" H.

*No. 24-8083 Same item in American Foliage Colors.

see page 228

No. 12-9003
Sugar Bin End Table. 28" x 27" x 25" H. One drawer. Large storage bin behind retractable lift-lid.

*No. 24-9003 Same item in American Foliage Colors.

see page 232

No. 12-9004
Two Drawer Dry Sink. 38" x 19" x 37" H. Removable drawer, adjustable shelf behind doors. Matching wood-grained Formica® plastic top.

*No. 24-9004 Same item in American Foliage Colors with black Formica® plastic work surface.

see page 43

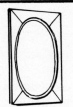

No. 12-9008
Console Cabinet. 30" x 13" x 30" H. One drawer, one adjustable shelf.

*No. 24-9008 Same item in American Foliage Colors.

see page 225

No. 12-9009
Framed Oval Mirror. Overall: 24" x 36" H.

*No. 24-9009 Same item in American Foliage Colors.

see page 225

No. 12-9010
Drop Leaf Serving Tea Cart. 20" x 32" x 29" H. Opens to 40" x 32" with both leaves extended. One drawer. Plastic wheels finished to match.

*No. 24-9010 Same item in American Foliage Colors.

see page 250

No. 12-9012 Spoonfoot Game Table. 34" sq. x 30" H. Inlaid chessboard, four ½"-deep wells for ashtrays, glasses. Center top only, selected Pine veneer with Maple and Walnut Inlay.

#*No. 24-9012 Same item in American Foliage Colors. Pine Cone color top.

see page 223

No. 12-9013
Gun Cabinet. 28" x 15" x 75" H. Structural parts are selected veneer. Back is wood-grained balanced hardboard.

see page 224

No. 12-9014 Library Wall Unit. 34" x 14" x 80" H. Center shelves in upper section are adjustable. One adjustable shelf behind two paneled doors. Back is wood-grained hardboard.

*No. 24-9014 Same item in American Foliage Colors.

see page 225

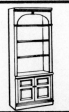

No. 12-9015
Bookstacks. 28" x 13" x 80" H. Center shelves in upper section are adjustable. One adjustable shelf behind two paneled doors. Back is wood-grained balanced hardboard.

*No. 24-9015 Same item in American Foliage Colors.

see page 224

No. 12-9019
Pine Rocker. 26" x 45" H. Deep-saddle seat of Solid Pine. Balance of chair Solid Maple.

see page 258

No. 12-9503
Four Drawer Pedestal Desk. 32" x 25" x 35" H.

*No. 24-9503 Same item in American Foliage Colors.

see page 227

No. 12-9504
Home Folding Bar. 40" x 22" x 42" H. Opens to 72" x 22" with two 16" side units. Matching woodgrained Formica® plastic top.

*No. 24-9504 American Foliage Colors. Formica® top is Old Tavern finish.

see page 222

No. 12-9505
Swivel Bar Stool. 20" x 20" x 42" H. Height may be shortened at any of three places marked by rings. Tubular steel footrest with brushed brass finish.

*No. 24-9505 Same item in American Foliage Colors.   see page 222

No. 12-9506
Drop Lid Four Drawer Pedestal Desk. 54" x 24" x 36" H. Removable partitions, deep storage area under top lid. Four letter compartments.

*No. 24-9506 Same item in American Foliage Colors.

see page 227

No. 12-9509
Seven Drawer Double Pedestal Desk. 54" x 24" x 30" H. Two deep file drawers with metal file supports in bottom left drawer. Center drawer has pencil tray.

see page 227

No. 12-9511
Three Drawer Secretary Base. 24" x 16" x 39" H. Drop lid front with two pull-out slides for support. Deep file drawer at bottom.

*No. 24-9511 Same item in American Foliage Colors.

see page 227

*Description of American Foliage Colors:
402-Sugarbush Red   404-Autumn Gold   406-Spruce Blue
403-Pine Cone   405-Holly Green

Crafted in solid pine and selected veneers.
OCCASIONAL TABLES AND DECORATIVE ACCENTS.

CAMPAIGN CHEST COLLECTION

No. 12-9512
Secretary Top. 24" x 10" x 43" H. Two adjustable shelves behind Antiqued Glass doors, wooden mullions. Back is wood-grained balanced hardboard. Use with No. 12-9511.
*No. 24-9512 Same item in American Foliage Colors.
see page 227

No. 12-9720
Barnstable Rocker. 20" x 24" x 45" H.
No. 14-9720
Same item in Decorated Finish 610.
see page 259

No. 13-8001
Military End Table. 19" x 24" x 22" H.
see page 113

No. 12-9513
Three Drawer Roll Top Desk. 40" x 21" x 43" H. Letter compartments behind roll top.
*No. 24-9513
Same item in American Foliage Colors.
see page 226

No. 13-8002
Military Chest Table. 19" x 24" x 22" H. Three drawers.
see page 113

No. 12-9514
Folding Cellarette. 28" x 18" x 37" H. Opens to 36" x 12". One drawer. Three storage shelves. Stain-resistant Melamine plastic top.
see page 223

No. 13-8003
Military Cocktail Table 48" x 22" x 16" H. Three drawers.
see page 113

No. 12-9515
Chair Table. Shown as table: 40" diameter x 29" H.
#*No. 24-9515 Same item in American Foliage Colors. Pine Cone color top.
see page 223

No. 13-9005
Military Bar Table. 16" x 18" x 23" H. Shown closed.
see page 113

No. 12-9516
Etagere. 34" x 17" x 83" H. Bonnet top is selected veneer. Finished paneled back.
*No. 24-9516
Same item in American Foliage Colors.
see page 224

No. 13-9005 Same item shown open. Compartmentalized stain resistant melamine plastic interior with storage for bottles and glassware.

No. 12-9517
Oval Framed Mirror. 28" x 38" H. Heavy molding with shadowbox frame.
*No. 24-9517
Same item in American Foliage Colors.
see page 225

No. 13-9006
Military Wellington Chest. 18" x 15" x 42" H. Seven drawers.
see page 113

No. 12-9518
Credenza Console. 52" x 15" x 28" H. Door panels are selected veneer. Finished interior. One adjustable shelf behind doors.
*No. 24-9518
Same item in American Foliage Colors.
see page 225

No. 12-9519
Roll Top Desk. 55" x 28" x 48" H. Three drawers in top desk. Seven drawers below. Roll top has lock.
see page 226

All of the preceding items are Solid Pine with selected veneers and inlays where noted. All items are Antiqued Pine in Old Tavern finish skillfully shaded and hand-distressed to achieve an authentic "aged" look.

All items in Military Campaign Chest collections are selected figured Yew wood veneers over solid Mahogany.

*No. 14-6011
Thumb Back Chair. 35" H. Decorated Finishes 400, 409, 411, 604 or 610.

No. 10-6011 Same item in Nutmeg finish.

see page 261

*No. 14-6110 Side Chair
*No. 14-6110A Arm Chair
Hitchcock Chairs. 33" H. Fiber seat. Decorated Finishes 601, 603 or 609.

No. 10-6110; No. 10-6110A. Same items in Nutmeg finish.

see page 255

*No. 14-8300
Pedestal Table. 15" diameter x 23" H. Decorated Finish 609.

see page 263

---

*No. 14-6040
Comb Back Mate's Chair. 30" H. Decorated Finishes 400, 409, 411, 604 or 610.

No. 10-6040 Same item in Nutmeg finish.

see page 261

*No. 14-6111
Button Back Hitchcock Chair. 33" H. Fiber seat. Decorated Finishes 601, 603, 609, 612, 614 or 616.

No. 10-6071 Same item in Nutmeg finish.

see page 255

*No. 14-8340
Spoonfoot Cocktail Table. 42" x 20" x 15" H. Decorated Finish 610.

No. 10-8340 Same item in Nutmeg finish.

see page 262

---

*No. 14-6041 Side Chair
*No. 14-6041A Arm Chair
Ladderback Chairs. 44" H. Fiber seat. Decorated Finishes 601, 603, or 609.

*No. 12-6041 No. 12-6041A
Same items in Antiqued Pine, finishes 212 and 618.

see page 260

*No. 14-6120
Hitchcock Chair. 16" x 16" x 34" H. Decorated Finishes 601 or 611.

No. 12-6120 Same item in Decorated Finish 618.

see page 259

*No. 14-8344
Spoonfoot Drop Leaf End Table. 18" x 25" x 24" H. Opens to 36" with leaves extended. Decorated Finish 610.

No. 10-8344 Same item in Nutmeg finish.

see page 262

---

*No. 14-6072 Side Chair
*No. 14-6072A Arm Chair
Duxbury Chairs. 39" H. Decorated Finishes 601, 604 or 610.

No. 10-6072 No. 10-6072A
Same items in Nutmeg finish.

see page 261

*No. 14-6155
Hitchcock Bench. 24" x 15" x 19" H. Fiber seat. Decorated Finishes 601, 603 or 609.

see page 255

*No. 14-8350
Spoonfoot Harvest Drop Leaf Cocktail Table. 44" x 18" x 15" H. Opens to 32" with leaves extended. Decorated Finish 610.

No. 10-8350 Same item in Nutmeg finish.

see page 262

---

*No. 14-6080
Bannister Side Chair. 45" H. Fiber seat. Available in Decorated Finishes 601, 603, 609, 612, 614 or 616.

see page 260

*No. 14-6170
High Chair. Decorated Finish 601.

see page 259

*No. 14-8355
Spoonfoot Cloverleaf Lamp Table. Opens to 27" diameter with leaves extended. Decorated Finish 610.

No. 10-8355 Same item in Nutmeg finish.

see page 262

---

*No. 14-6085
Drop Leaf Tea Wagon. 19" x 32" x 29" H. Opens to 42" x 32" with leaves. Large artillery wheels and swivel casters. Handle swings under cart. Decorated Finishes 604, 610. Matching plastic wheels.
No. 10-6085. Same item in Nutmeg Finish.   see page 262

*No. 14-6182
Deacon's Bench. 42" x 20" x 34" H. Decorated Finishes 604 or 610.

see page 255

*No. 14-9019
Cloverleaf Magazine Rack. 18" x 12" x 15" H. Decorated Finishes 601, 603 or 609.

No. 10-9019 Same item in Nutmeg finish.

see page 263

---

*No. 14-6092
Chancellor's Chair. 46" H. Decorated Finishes 601, 612, 614 or 616.

see page 261

*No. 14-6301
Farmhouse Chair. 33" H. Decorated Finishes 601, 603, 604, 609, 610, 612, 614 or 616.

No. 10-6301 Same item in Nutmeg finish.

see page 260

*No. 14-9022
Gossip Bench. 33" x 16" x 29" H. Decorated Finishes 604 or 610.

No. 10-9022 Same item in Nutmeg finish.

see page 255

---

*No. 14-6106
Dry Sink. 34" x 18" x 40" H. One drawer. Adjustable shelf behind doors; felt-lined silver compartments. Decorated Finishes 604 and 610.

No. 10-6106 Same item in Nutmeg finish.

see page 254

*No. 14-8200
Hearth Stools. 14" diameter x 17" H. Decorated Finishes 604 or 610.

see page 263

*No. 14-9026
Library Bookstacks. 30" x 14" x 80" H. Two shelves. Back panel only is wood-grained balanced hardboard. Single shelf behind doors. Decorated Finishes 604, 610.

No. 10-9026 Nutmeg finish.

see page 254

---

*Description of Decorated Finishes: 212—Old Tavern; 400—Alabaster White; 409—Antiqued Blue; 411—Daffodil Yellow; 601—Nutmeg Decorated; 603—White Decorated; 604—White Decorated with Nutmeg; 609—Black Decorated; 610—Black Decorated with Nutmeg;

*No. 14-9042
Cigarette Pedestal Table. 15" diameter x 21" H. Decorated Finishes 601, 603, 609.
No. 10-9042 Same item in Nutmeg finish.
see page 254

*No. 14-9704
Salem Rocker. 24" x 28" x 42" H. Decorated Finishes 601, 603, 604, 609, 610, 612, 614 or 616.
No. 10-9704 Same item in Nutmeg finish.
see page 256

*No. 14-9216
Console Cabinet. 30" x 13" x 30" H. One drawer, one adjustable shelf. Decorated Finishes 604 or 610.
see page 254

*No. 14-9705
Child's Rocker. 17" x 21" x 29" H. Decorated Finishes 601, 603, or 609.
No. 10-9705 Same item in Nutmeg finish.
see page 257

*No. 14-9217
Framed Oval Mirror. Overall 24" x 36" H. Decorated Finishes 604 or 610.
see page 254

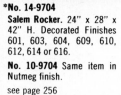

*No. 14-9706
Homestead Rocker. 25" x 28" x 40" H. Scroll Seat. Decorated Finishes 601, 603, 604, 609, 610, 612, 614 or 616.
No. 10-9706 Same item in Nutmeg finish.
see page 258

*No. 14-9218
Square Pedestal Cocktail Table. 19" square x 16" H. Decorated Finishes 604 or 610.
see page 255

*No. 14-9709
Gloucester Rocker, 29" x 19" x 42" H. Decorated Finishes 601, 603, 604, 609 or 610.
No. 10-9709. Same item in Nutmeg Finish.
see page 254

*No. 14-9510
Bookcase. 32" x 11" x 51" H. One adjustable shelf. Decorated Finishes 604 or 610 with Nutmeg back panel. Back panel only is wood-grained balanced hardboard.
No. 10-9510 Nutmeg finish.
see page 255

*No. 14-9710
Litchfield Rocker. 23½" x 19" x 45". Available in Decorated Finishes 601, 609 or 610.
No. 10-9710. Same item in Nutmeg finish.
see page 256

*No. 14-9514
Three Drawer Accent Writing Table. 32" x 18" x 40" H. Pencil tray. Decorated Finishes 604 or 610.
see page 255

*No. 14-9713
Valet Chair. 17" x 16" x 38" H. Decorated Finishes 601, 604, 610, 612, 614 or 616.
see page 259

*No. 14-9702
Cape Cod Rocker. 23" x 28" x 40" H. Decorated Finishes 601, 603 or 609.
No. 10-9702 Same item in Nutmeg finish.
see page 254

*No. 14-9715
Comb Back Rocker. 25" W. x 41" H. Decorated Finishes 601 or 610.
see page 258

*No. 14-9703
Boston Rocker. 24" x 28" x 40" H. Decorated Finishes 601, 603, 604, 609, 610, 612, 614 or 616.
No. 10-9703 Same item in Nutmeg finish.
see page 255

*No. 14-9720
Barnstable Rocker. 20" x 24" x 45" H. Decorated Finish 611.
No. 12-9720 Same item in Decorated Finish 618.
see page 256

611—Black Decorated with Old Tavern; 612—Red Decorated;
614—Green Decorated; 616—Blue Decorated; 618—Old Tavern Decorated.

CLASSIC MANOR COLLECTION

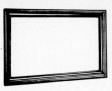

No. 15-5200
Framed Mirror. 45" x 35" H. Use over pieces 51" to 61" long.

see page 117

No. 15-5215
Four Drawer Chest on Chest with Doors. 42" x 20" x 58" H. Three permanent compartments and two drawers behind doors. Removable partitions in top.

see page 114

No. 15-5634
Tall Headboard. 39½" H. Available in 4'6"-5' combination size and 6'6" size.

see page 117

No. 15-5202
Seven Drawer Double Dresser. 56" x 21" x 33" H. Removable partitions in middle drawers.

see page 117

No. 15-5216
Commode Night Table. 25" x 16" x 26" H. One drawer.

see page 115

No. 15-5637
Cornice Headboard. 42½" H. Available in 4'6", 5' and 6'6" sizes.
No. 10-5637. Same item in Nutmeg finish.

see page 117

No. 15-5203
Nine Drawer Triple Dresser. 66" x 21" x 33" H. Removable partitions in top and middle outer drawers.

see page 116

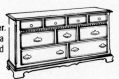

No. 15-5220
Pediment Mirror. 54" x 41" H. Use over pieces 60" to 70" long.

see page 116

No. 15-5643
Pediment Headboard. Overall 53½" H. Available in 5' size.

see page 118

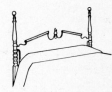

No. 15-5204
Six Drawer Chest. 38" x 20" x 47" H. Removable partitions in third and fourth row drawers.

see page 117

No. 15-5224
Seven Drawer Lingerie Chest. 23" x 17" x 52" H. Top drawer is fitted with felt-lined compartments.

see page 118

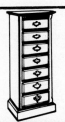

No. 15-5655
Cane Headboard. 41" H. Available in 5' and 6'6" sizes.

see page 115

No. 15-5205
Eight Drawer Chest on Chest. 40" x 20" x 55" H. Removable partitions in fourth and fifth row drawers.

see page 116

No. 15-5230
Tall Crown Mirror. 27" x 48" H. Use two over pieces 60" or longer.

see page 115

CLASSIC MANOR DINING ROOM

No. 15-5206
Cabinet Night Table. 22" x 16" x 26" H. One drawer. Back is selected veneer.

see page 116

No. 15-5612
Pediment Bed. Overall 53½" H. Available in 4'6" or 5' sizes.
No. 10-5612. Same item in Nutmeg finish.

see page 116

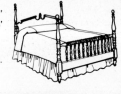

No. 15-6001 Side Chair
No. 15-6001A Arm Chair
Queen Anne Chairs, 42" H., upholstered seat.

see page 101

No. 15-5210
Framed Mirror. 55" x 35" H. Use over pieces 61" to 71" long.
No. 10-5210. Same item in Nutmeg finish.

see page 118

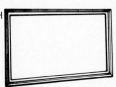

No. 15-5625
Cornice Bed. 42½" H. Available in 3'3", 4'6" and 5' sizes.

see page 119

No. 15-6003
44" Round Extension Table. Shown without leaves.

see page 103

No. 15-5213
Eight Drawer Triple Dresser. 72" x 21" x 33" H. Removable partitions in top outer drawers and middle center drawer. Two tray drawers behind right door.

see page 115

No. 15-5627
Sliding Door Bookcase Headboard. 38" H. Available in 6'6" size. Back is selected veneer.
No. 10-5627. Same item in Nutmeg finish.

see page 119

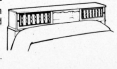

No. 15-6003
Same as above. Opens to 44" x 80" with two 18" aproned filler leaves. Seats 8-10. Aprons only, selected veneers. Shown with leaves.

---

*No. 15-5996 Two Swing-Away Bed Frames for King size Headboards with two twin mattresses and box-springs. All dressers and chests are shipped with swivel casters.

Beds available in 5' (Queen) size are automatically shipped with 81" extra long rails. If you wish to order extra length bed rails, please specify **No. 15-5999** 81" Extra Length Bed Rails along with the number of your bed.

All items are Solid Maple and/or Birch and selected matching veneers where noted in richly shaded and hand-distressed Classic Manor finish.
All bedrails are metal with matching wood-grain finish.

BEDROOM, DINING ROOM, OCCASIONAL TABLES AND DECORATIVE ACCENTS

No. 15-6004
Oval Extension Table.
Shown without leaves.
see page 101

No. 15-6004
Same as above. 44" x 66" x 102" with two 18" aproned filler leaves. Seats 10-12. Aprons only, selected veneers. Shown with leaves.

No. 15-6006
Three Door Buffet. 56" x 19" x 30" H. Removable and adjustable shelf behind two right doors; three tray drawers behind left facing door. Upper drawer fitted with Pacific cloth silver tray.
see page 103

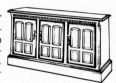

No. 15-6007
Four Door Buffet. 66" x 19" x30" H. Removable, adjustable shelves behind end doors. 3 pull-out tray drawers behind center doors. Top center drawer divided and lined with Pacific cloth for silver storage.
see page 99

No. 15-6008
China Cabinet. 56" W. Adjustable framed glass shelves behind crowned glass doors; grooved base plate rails for display of dishes. Built-in light. For use with No. 15-6006.
see page 103

No. 15-6010 Side Chair
No. 15-6010A Arm Chair
Cane Back Chairs, 38" H., upholstered seat.
see page 100

No. 15-6011 Side Chair
No. 15-6011A Arm Chair
Ladderback Chairs, 44" H., upholstered seat.
see page 102

No. 15-6012 Side Chair
No. 15-6012A Arm Chair
Cane Back Chairs, 42" H., upholstered seat.
see page 99

No. 15-6013
Double Pedestal Extension Table.
Shown without leaves.
see page 99

No. 15-6013
Same as above. 42" x 68" x 104" with two 18" aproned filler leaves. Equalizer slide operation allows for easy opening by one person. Seats 10-12. Shown with leaves.

No. 15-6015
Cabinet Server. 42" x 21" x 33" H. Opens to 63" x 21" with top extended. Finished sides and back. Melamine plastic work surface beneath Birch veneer flip-top. Tray drawer with felt-lined compartments. Adjustable shelves. Swivel casters.
see page 100

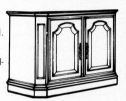

No. 15-6016
Buffet. 44" x 16" x 30" H.

*No. 25-6016
Same item in Antiqued Colors.
see page 100

No. 15-6018
China Cabinet. 66" W. Adjustable wood-framed glass shelves behind crowned glass doors; grooved base plate rails for display of dishes. Built-in light. For use with No. 15-6007.
see page 99

No. 15-6019
China Cabinet. 45" x 17" x 50" H.

*No. 25-6019
Same item in Antiqued Colors.
For use with No. 15-6016.
see page 100

No. 15-6021 Side Chair
No. 15-6021A Arm Chair
Cane Back Chairs. 38" H. Upholstered seat.

*No. 25-6021
*No. 25-6021A
Same items in Antiqued Colors.
see page 105

No. 15-6023
42" Octagonal Extension Pedestal Table.
Shown without leaves.
see page 102

No. 15-6023
Same as above. Opens to 42" x 72" with two 15" aproned leaves. Equalizer slide operation allows for easy opening by one person. Seats 6-8. Shown with leaves.

No. 15-6026
Two Door Buffet. 66" x 19" x 30" H. Removable and adjustable shelves behind two paneled doors. Three drawers in center of case, upper drawer fitted with Pacific cloth silver tray.
see page 101

No. 15-6028
Grilled China Cabinet. 66" W. x 46" H. Removable and adjustable shelves of wood-framed glass behind four doors, with grooved plate rail and decorative grill work. Built-in light. For use with No. 15-6026.
see page 101

No. 15-6033
Dining Table. 40" x 60". Opens to 40" x 96" with two 18" aproned filler leaves. Top is selected veneer with molded polyester plastic edge. Shown with leaves.

*No. 25-6033 Same item in Antiqued Colors.
see page 100

CLASSIC MANOR OCCASIONAL TABLES AND DECORATIVE ACCENTS

#No. 15-8300
Rectangular Cocktail Table. 60" x 26" x 16½" H. Available in finish 229 only.
see page 108

#No. 15-8301
Rectangular Cocktail Table. 68" x 32" x 16" H. Available in finish 229 only.
see page 109

#No. 15-8302
Lamp Table. 25¼" x 25¼" x 22" H. Available in finish #229 only. One drawer.
see page 108

---

*Description of Antiqued Colors
423-Antiqued White   425-Antiqued Yellow
424-Antiqued Blue   426-Antiqued Green

Cabinet doors are equipped with magnetic catches; finished interiors.
All China backs are selected veneer.

#Made of Solid Birch and/or Maple with matched veneers and cross banded borders; moulded polyester edge.

Ethan Allen
AMERICAN TRADITIONAL INTERIORS

CLASSIC MANOR COLLECTION

All items are Solid Maple and/or Birch and selected matching veneers where noted in richly shaded and hand-distressed Classic Manor finish.

#No. 15-8303
End Table. 23¾" x 27" x 23" H. Available in finish #229 only. Two drawers.
see page 108

No. 15-8434
Pembroke Drop Leaf Table. 21" x 27" x 22" H. Opens to 36" x 27" with leaves extended. One drawer. Available only in Classic Manor finish 204.
see page 111

#No. 15-8673
Square Coffee Table. 30" x 30" x 17" H. Available in finish 229 only. Inlaid marquetry top.
see page 112

#No. 15-8304
Square Corner/Cocktail Table. 32" x 32" x 19" H. Available in finish 229 only.
see page 109

†No. 15-8660
Rectangular Cocktail Table. 60" x 22" x 16" H. Wood top is selected veneer.
†No. 15-8660P
Same item with simulated natural cleft slate top.
see page 110

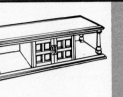

†No. 15-8674
Rectangular End Table. 23" x 27" x 22" H.
see page 112

#15-8305
Pedestal Snack Table. 22" x 22" x 16" H. Available in finish 229 only.
see page 109

†No. 15-8661
Pedestal Cocktail Table. 20" x 20" x 17" H. Top is selected veneer.
†No. 15-8661P
Same item with simulated natural cleft slate top.
see page 110

†No. 15-8675
Octagonal Book Table. 21" x 26" x 22" H.
see page 112

#No. 15-8306
Nest of Tables. 28" x 18" x 22" H. Available in finish 229 only.
see page 108

†No. 15-8664
Rectangular Commode End Table. 28" x 20" x 22" H. Three removable record partitions. Top is selected veneer.
†No. 15-8664P
Same item with simulated natural cleft slate top.
see page 110

†No. 15-8676
Nest Tables. Large (top) table—22" x 26" x 22" H. Small (bottom) table—15" x 23" x 22" H.
see page 112

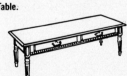

No. 15-8420
Two Drawer Cocktail Table. 56" x 22" x 16" H.
see page 111

†No. 15-8665
Square Commode Lamp Table. 28" x 28" x 22" H. One adjustable shelf. Wood top of selected veneer.
†No. 15-8665P
Same item with simulated natural cleft slate top.

†No. 15-9000
Bonnet Top Curio Cabinet. 25" x 25" x 79" H. 3 adjustable glass shelves. Concealed interior light. Adjustable wood shelf in base. Back is selected veneer.
*No. 25-9000. Same item in Antiqued Colors.
see page 105

No. 15-8421
Square Pedestal Cocktail Table. 20" x 20" x 17" H. Available only in Classic Manor finish 204.
see page 111

†No. 15-8666
Hexagonal Commode Table. 25" x 25" x 22" H. Storage compartment with half shelf. Top is selected veneer.
†No. 15-8666P
Same item with simulated natural cleft slate top.
see page 110

†No. 15-9001
Pier Curio Cabinet. 17" x 14" x 72" H. Three adjustable glass shelves with concealed interior light in top. Back is selected veneer.
*No. 25-9001. Same item in Antiqued Colors.
see page 104

No. 15-8424
Rectangular End Table. 23" x 27" x 22" H. One drawer. Available only in Classic Manor finish 204.
see page 111

†No. 15-8670
Rectangular Cocktail Table. 60" x 22" x 17" H.
see page 112

No. 15-9007
Tall Mirror. 20" x 38" H. overall. Available only in Classic Manor finish 204.
No. 10-9007
Same item in Nutmeg finish.
see page 107

No. 15-8425
Square Lamp Table. 26" x 26" x 22" H. One drawer. Available only in Classic Manor finish 204.
see page 111

†No. 15-8671
Rectangular Bunching Table. 30" x 21" x 16" H.
see page 112

No. 15-9009
Library Book Stand. 26" x 17" x 32" H. Features ratchet-operated adjustable top. Mounted on concealed swivel casters. One adjustable shelf. Finished on all sides. Available only in Classic Manor finish 204.
see page 107

#Made of Solid Birch and/or Maple with matched veneers and cross banded borders; moulded polyester edge.

Cabinet doors are equipped with magnetic catches; finished interiors.

†Classic Manor Tables and Accents, except where otherwise noted available in: Finish 204-Classic Manor; Finish 229-Classic Manor Custom—see pages 108 and 109.

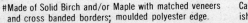

†**No. 15-9010**
Writing Table. 58" x 26" x 30" H.
see page 112

†**No. 15-9046**
Paneled Tall Mirror. Overall: 25" x 46" H.
see page 110

No. 15-9035
Two Door Console Commode. 39" x 14" x 28" H. Adjustable shelf behind doors. Available only in Classic Manor finish 204.
No. 10-9035
Same item in Nutmeg finish.
see page 107

†**No. 15-9200**
Two Door Cabinet. 34" x 17" x 28" H. Adjustable shelf behind doors.
see page 106

No. 16-6000
Bowback Windsor Side Chair. 38" H.
see page 125

†**No. 15-9037**
Console Table. 46" x 12" x 29" H.
*No. 25-9037. Same item in Antiqued Colors.
*No. 25-9037P. Same with simulated marble top.
see page 105

†**No. 15-9201**
Three Drawer Chest. 34" x 17" x 28" H.
see page 106

No. 16-6000A
Bowback Windsor Arm Chair. 42" H.
see page 125

†**No. 15-9038**
Console Cabinet. 40" x 15" x 29" H. One adjustable shelf behind doors.
*No. 25-9038. Same item in Antiqued Colors.
*No. 25-9038P. Same with simulated marble top.
see page 99

†**No. 15-9202**
Library Bookstack. 34" x 14" x 52" H. Back is selected veneer. For use with No. 15-9200 and 15-9201.
see page 106

No. 16-6001
Ladderback Side Chair. 38" H. Fiber seat.
see page 124

†**No. 15-9039**
Accent Mirror. 24" x 48" H.
*No. 25-9039.
Same item in Antiqued Colors.
see page 99

†**No. 15-9203**
Upper Cabinet with Grilled Doors. 34" x 14" x 52" H. Lighted interior. Back is selected veneer. For use with No. 15-9200 and 15-9201.
see page 106

No. 16-6001A
Ladderback Arm Chair. 42" H. Fiber seat.
see page 124

†**No. 15-9040**
Etagere. 34" x 16" x 82" H. One adjustable shelf behind doors. All shelves and end panels are selected veneer.
*No. 25-9040
Same item in Antiqued Colors.
see page 102

No. 15-9500
Seven Drawer Library Desk. 56" x 26" x 30" H. Two file drawers. Finished back has simulated center drawer. Available only in Classic Manor finish 204.
No. 10-9500
Same item in Nutmeg finish.
see page 107

No. 16-6002
Captain's Chair. 30" H.
see page 124

†**No. 15-9041**
Game Table. 34" x 34" x 29" H. Top is selected veneer.
*No. 25-9041
Same item in Antiqued Colors.
see page 105

No. 15-9506
Nine Drawer Secretary Desk. 36" x 19" x 41" H. Five drawers. Drop-lid only is selected veneer. Available only in Classic Manor finish 204.
No. 10-9506
Same item in Nutmeg finish.
see page 107

*No.16-6003**
Rectangular Extension Table. 42" x 66". Top is selected veneer. Shown without leaves.
see page 122

†**No. 15-9045**
Console Commode. 32" x 12" x 30" H. Adjustable shelf behind doors. Top and door panels are selected veneer.
No. 15-9045P. Same with simulated natural cleft slate top.
see page 110

No. 15-9507
Grilled Secretary Top. Overall 76" H. Adjustable shelves behind doors. Selected veneer back panel. For use with No. 15-9506. In Classic Manor finish 204 only.
No. 10-9507
Nutmeg finish.
see page 107

No. 16-6003
Same as above. Opens to 102" with two 18" aproned filler leaves. Equalizer slide-operated top. Seats 10-12. Shown with leaves.

*Description of Antiqued Colors
423-Antiqued White   425-Antiqued Blue
424-Antiqued Yellow   426-Antiqued Green

All items with prefix 16- are Solid Oak with selected veneer where noted and are deeply distressed and hand padded to a glowing patina in a handsome Royal Charter finish.

*No. 16-6004
Octagonal Pedestal Table. 44" x 44". Shown without leaves.

see page 124

No. 16-6011A
High Back Arm Chair. 43" H. Upholstered seat & back panel.

see page 122

No. 16-8004
Hexagonal Commode Table. 22" x 22" x 22" H.

see page 129

No. 16-6004
Same as above. Opens to 74" with two 15" aproned filler leaves. Equalizer slide-operated top. Seats 8-10. Shown with leaves.

*No. 16-6013
Flip-Top Table. 72" x 20" x 30" H. Top is selected veneer.

see page 127

No. 16-8005
Hi Lo Cocktail Table. 40" diameter adjusts to 3 heights. 18" x 26" x 29" H. Adjustable heights.

see page 126

No. 16-6005
Drop Leaf Server. 36" x 18" x 35" H. Top extends to 60" Melamine plastic work surface on top.

No. 16-6013
Same as above. Opens to 72" x 40". Top slides and flips. Seats 8-10.

No. 16-8006
End Table. 22" x 26" x 23" H. Two drawers.

see page 129

No. 16-6006
Huntboard Buffet. 72" x 17" x 31" H. Three drawers. Lower shelf and back are selected veneer.

see page 122

No. 16-6017
Corner China. 42" x 22" x 76" H. 20" along each wall. Lighted interior, adjustable shelves with glass inserts. Back is selected veneer.

see page 126

No. 16-8007
Rent Table. 24" x 24" x 23" H. Storage space behind door. One drawer. Back is selected matching veneer.

see page 128

No. 16-6007
Buffet. 56" x 19" x 32" H. Three doors. Adjustable shelf behind doors. Three drawers. Drawer bottoms are selected veneer.

see page 124

ROYAL CHARTER OCCASIONAL TABLES AND DECORATIVE ACCENTS

No. 16-8008
Square Commode. 24" x 24" x 23" H. One drawer. Back is selected veneer.

see page 129

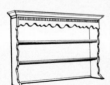

No. 16-6008
Huntboard Deck. 75" x 11" x 47" H. Three drawers. Back is selected veneer. For use with No. 16-6006.

see page 122

No. 16-8000
Refectory Cocktail Table. 42" x 20" x 18" H. Opens to 62" with two 10" draw-end slides.

see page 131

No. 16-8010
Rectangular Table. 60" x 24" x 17½" H. Two drawers.

see page 129

No. 16-6009
China Top. 56" x 15" x 43" H. Leaded glass doors. Back is selected veneer. For use with No. 16-6007.

see page 124

No. 16-8002
Gateleg End Table. 11" x 24" x 21" H. Opens to 30" x 24" x 21" H.

see page 131

No. 16-8900
Pub Set. 40" table diameter. Four stools are 18" H. with brass-studded vinyl upholstered seats.

see page 130

No. 16-6011
High Back Side Chair. 41" H. Upholstered seat & back panel.

see page 122

No. 16-8003
Nest Tables. 22" x 15" x 21" H.

see page 131

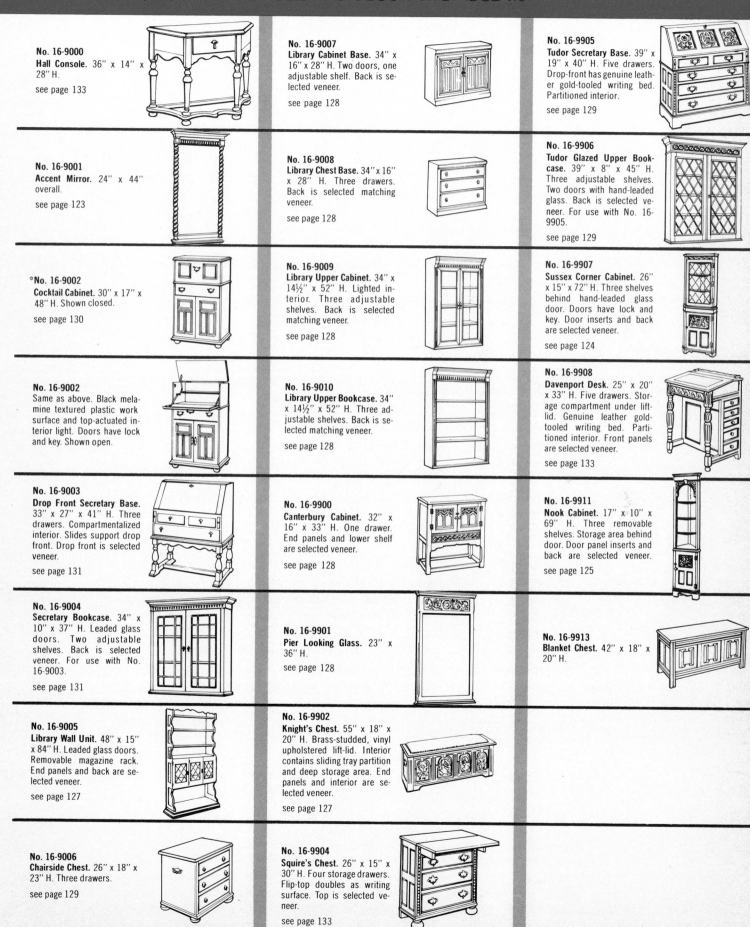

DINING ROOM, OCCASIONAL TABLES AND DECORATIVE ACCENTS

No. 16-9000
Hall Console. 36" x 14" x 28" H.

see page 133

No. 16-9001
Accent Mirror. 24" x 44" overall.

see page 123

***No. 16-9002**
Cocktail Cabinet. 30" x 17" x 48" H. Shown closed.

see page 130

No. 16-9002
Same as above. Black melamine textured plastic work surface and top-actuated interior light. Doors have lock and key. Shown open.

No. 16-9003
Drop Front Secretary Base. 33" x 27" x 41" H. Three drawers. Compartmentalized interior. Slides support drop front. Drop front is selected veneer.

see page 131

No. 16-9004
Secretary Bookcase. 34" x 10" x 37" H. Leaded glass doors. Two adjustable shelves. Back is selected veneer. For use with No. 16-9003.

see page 131

No. 16-9005
Library Wall Unit. 48" x 15" x 84" H. Leaded glass doors. Removable magazine rack. End panels and back are selected veneer.

see page 127

No. 16-9006
Chairside Chest. 26" x 18" x 23" H. Three drawers.

see page 129

No. 16-9007
Library Cabinet Base. 34" x 16" x 28" H. Two doors, one adjustable shelf. Back is selected veneer.

see page 128

No. 16-9008
Library Chest Base. 34" x 16" x 28" H. Three drawers. Back is selected matching veneer.

see page 128

No. 16-9009
Library Upper Cabinet. 34" x 14½" x 52" H. Lighted interior. Three adjustable shelves. Back is selected matching veneer.

see page 128

No. 16-9010
Library Upper Bookcase. 34" x 14½" x 52" H. Three adjustable shelves. Back is selected matching veneer.

see page 128

No. 16-9900
Canterbury Cabinet. 32" x 16" x 33" H. One drawer. End panels and lower shelf are selected veneer.

see page 128

No. 16-9901
Pier Looking Glass. 23" x 36" H.

see page 128

No. 16-9902
Knight's Chest. 55" x 18" x 20" H. Brass-studded, vinyl upholstered lift-lid. Interior contains sliding tray partition and deep storage area. End panels and interior are selected veneer.

see page 127

No. 16-9904
Squire's Chest. 26" x 15" x 30" H. Four storage drawers. Flip-top doubles as writing surface. Top is selected veneer.

see page 133

No. 16-9905
Tudor Secretary Base. 39" x 19" x 40" H. Five drawers. Drop-front has genuine leather gold-tooled writing bed. Partitioned interior.

see page 129

No. 16-9906
Tudor Glazed Upper Bookcase. 39" x 8" x 45" H. Three adjustable shelves. Two doors with hand-leaded glass. Back is selected veneer. For use with No. 16-9905.

see page 129

No. 16-9907
Sussex Corner Cabinet. 26" x 15" x 72" H. Three shelves behind hand-leaded glass door. Doors have lock and key. Door inserts and back are selected veneer.

see page 124

No. 16-9908
Davenport Desk. 25" x 20" x 33" H. Five drawers. Storage compartment under lift-lid. Genuine leather gold-tooled writing bed. Partitioned interior. Front panels are selected veneer.

see page 133

No. 16-9911
Nook Cabinet. 17" x 10" x 69" H. Three removable shelves. Storage area behind door. Door panel inserts and back are selected veneer.

see page 125

No. 16-9913
Blanket Chest. 42" x 18" x 20" H.

Ethan Allen

UPHOLSTERED FURNITURE

INFORMATION AND HELPFUL FACTS

The complete collection of Ethan Allen upholstered furniture is described in detail on the following pages. Here are some general guidelines and information pertaining to the quality features, construction, seat cushion content, finishes, and fabrics which will be helpful when ordering.

SEAT CUSHION CONTENT

Seat cushion content for Ethan Allen upholstered designs is generally designated as follows:

> Last digit —1 is Urethane Foam
>
> Last digit —5 is Polyester Fiber and Urethane Foam

All designs are not offered in both qualities. See detailed specifications for options.

FABRICS

All Ethan Allen Fabrics except Olefin Fibers are protected with stain repellent finish.

DECK AND PROTECTIVE ARM SLEEVES

All items include self-covered decks under the reversible cushions except items covered in velvet, leather, vinyl or crewel.

Matching arm sleeves are included on most fully upholstered items.

All styles feature expert tailoring.

CHOICE OF SKIRTS

On all designs where Skirt is available, we offer the following:

> Boxed Pleats (XP)   Kick Pleats (KP)

Please specify type of skirt by using the appropriate designation when ordering.

FINISHES

Finishes on upholstered furniture with exposed wood frames are designated by prefix numbers as follows:

> Prefix 10— . . . . Nutmeg (211) or Old Tavern (212) finish unless otherwise noted.
>
> Prefix 12— . . . . Old Tavern (212) finish.
>
> Prefix 13— . . . . Patina (209) finish—a warm *Fruitwood* color.
>
> Prefix 14— . . . . Hand Decorated or Decorator Finishes (see detailed listing on appropriate pages).
>
> Prefix 16— . . . . Royal Charter (220) finish.
>
> Prefix 20— . . . . Patina (209) or Nutmeg (211) unless otherwise noted.
>
> Prefix 21— . . . . As noted in detailed specifications.
>
> Prefix 24— . . . . American Foliage Colors (see listing on appropriate pages).

QUILTED FABRICS

Quilted fabrics and quilting are available for an additional cost. Consult your Ethan Allen Gallery for full details.

CONTRASTING WELTS

Any upholstered design can be ordered with contrasting welts. Any fabric except leather can be used in combination with another. Consult your Ethan Allen Gallery for additional cost.

TRAPUNTO

Trapunto embroidery technique is available at additional cost on all fully upholstered, loose pillowback sofas and loveseats only. It will be applied only to one side of each back pillow. It is recommended only on solid color, soft, pliable, smooth fabrics and should be avoided on tweedy, heavy, fuzzy or velvet fabrics. Prints should be outlined quilted not Trapunto embroidered. Consult your Ethan Allen Gallery for full information.

SOFAS AND CHAIRS

All Ethan Allen fabrics except Olefin Fibers are protected with stain-repellent finish.

No. 10-7771-1
Club Chair. 31" x 34" x 35" H. Nutmeg or Old Tavern Finish.

No. 12-7623-1
Three Cushion Sofa. 74" x 34" x 35" H. Old Tavern Finish.

No. 12-7624-1 Three Cushion Sofa. 84" x 34" x 35" H. Old Tavern Finish.

*No. 24-7623-1 *No. 24-7624-1 American Foliage Colors.

see page 51

No. 10-7772-1
Two Cushion Wing Loveseat. 56" x 34" x 35" H. Nutmeg or Old Tavern Finish.

No. 12-7628-1
Tray Ottoman. 24" x 20" x 16" H. With removable cushion. Old Tavern Finish.

*No. 24-7628-1 Same item in American Foliage Colors.

see page 46

No. 10-7773-1
Three Cushion Wing Sofa. 81" x 34" x 35" H. Nutmeg or Old Tavern Finish.

No. 10-7774-1
Three Cushion Wing Sofa. 73" x 34" x 35" H. Nutmeg or Old Tavern Finish.

see page 50

No. 12-7630-1
High Back Rocker. 30" x 36" x 40" H. Old Tavern Finish. Seat cushion not available in -5.

*No. 24-7630-1 Same item in American Foliage Colors.

see page 46

No. 10-7778-1
Tray Ottoman. 25" x 20" x 17" H. With removable cushion. Nutmeg or Old Tavern Finish.

No. 12-7631-1
High Back Arm Chair. 30" x 36" x 40" H. Old Tavern Finish.

*No. 24-7631-1 Same item in American Foliage Colors.

see page 70

No. 10-7780-1
High Back Wing Swivel Rocker. 31" x 35" x 39" H. Nutmeg or Old Tavern Finish.

No. 12-7671-1
Skipper's Lounge Chair. 30" x 31" x 32" H. Old Tavern Finish.

*No. 24-7671-1 Same item in American Foliage Colors.

see page 70

No. 10-7781-1
High Backed Wing Chair. 31" x 35" x 39" H. Nutmeg or Old Tavern Finish.

No. 12-7672-1
Two Cushion Skipper's Loveseat. 52" x 31" x 32" H. Old Tavern Finish.

*No. 24-7672-1 Same item in American Foliage Colors.

No. 12-7621-1
Club Chair. 30" x 34" x 35" H. Old Tavern Finish.

*No. 24-7621-1 Same item in American Foliage Colors.

No. 12-7673-1
Three Cushion Skipper's Sofa. 74" x 31" x 32" H. Old Tavern Finish.

*No. 24-7673-1 Same item in American Foliage Colors.

see page 47

No. 12-7622-1
Two Cushion Loveseat. 52" x 34" x 35" H. Old Tavern Finish.

*No. 24-7622-1 Same item in American Foliage colors.

see page 51

No. 13-7125-5
Sheraton Loveseat. 60" x 34" x 34" H. Seat cushion available in -5 only. Loose pillow back.

see Front Cover

Items with prefix 10- are Solid Maple and/or Birch. Items with prefix 12- are Solid Pine with some structural parts of selected hardwood.

All items on page 393 are available only with Urethane Foam seat cushions, last digit -1, except No. 13-7125-5.

*Description of American Foliage Colors:
402-Sugar Bush Red 403-Pine Cone 404-Autumn Gold
405-Holly Green 406-Spruce Blue

393

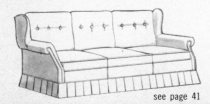

No. 13-7126-5
Sheraton Sofa. 88" x 34" x 34" H.

see Front Cover

No. 16-7431-5
Club Chair. 27" x 33" x 34" H. Royal Charter finish (220) only.

No. 16-7432-5
Loveseat. 50" x 33" x 34" H. Royal Charter finish (220) only.

see page 49

✔**No. 16-7433-5**
Sofa. 71" x 33" x 34" H. Royal Charter finish (220) only.

see page 49

No. 16-7438-1
Ottoman. 25" x 21" x 19" H. Royal Charter finish (220) only.

see page 131

No. 16-7441-5
High Back Chair. 27" x 37" x 39" H. Royal Charter finish (220) only.

No. 20-7020-5
Swivel Rocker. 31" x 34" x 33" H.
No. 20-7021-5
Club Chair. 31" x 34" x 33" H. Seat cushions in -1 or -5 only.

No. 20-7022-5
Three Cushion Sofa. 73" x 34" x 33" H.
No. 20-7023-5
Three Cushion Sofa. 81" x 34" x 33" H.
No. 20-7024-5
Three Cushion Sofa. 89" x 34" x 33" H. Seat cushions in -1 and -5 only.

see page 41

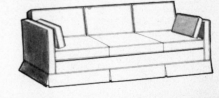

No. 20-7028-5
Two Cushion Loveseat. 52" x 34" x 33" H. Seat cushions in -1 and -5 only.

No. 20-7030-5
High Back Swivel Rocker. 31" x 35" x 37" H.
No. 20-7031-5
High Back Chair. 31" x 35" x 37" H. Seat cushions in -1 and -5 only.

No. 20-7032-5
High Back Three Cushion Sofa. 73" x 35" x 37" H.
No. 20-7033-5
High Back Three Cushion Sofa. 81" x 35" x 37" H.
No. 20-7034-5 High Back Three Cushion Sofa. 89" x 35" x 37" H. Seat cushions in -1 and -5 only.

see page 40

No. 20-7039-5
High Back Two Cushion Loveseat. 52" x 35" x 37" H. Seat cushions in -1 and -5 only.

✔**No. 20-7042-5**
Tuxedo Loveseat. 62" x 34" x 30" H. Design matches No. 20-7048-5 Tuxedo Sofa. Arm pillows included.

see page 53

No. 20-7044-5
Three Cushion Wing Sofa. 96" x 37" x 34" H. Arm pillows included.

see page 32

✔**No. 20-7048-5**
Three Cushion Tuxedo Sofa. 90" x 34" x 30" H. Arm pillows included.
✔**No. 20-7049-5**
Two Cushion Tuxedo Sofa. 78" x 34" x 30" H. Arm pillows included.

see page 24

No. 20-7061-5
Wing Club Chair. 33" x 36" x 35" H.

Items with prefix 16- are Solid Oak with some structural parts of selected hardwood.

Items are listed with Urethane Foam seat cushions, last digit -1 or a combination of Polyester Fiber and Urethane,

All Ethan Allen fabrics except Olefin Fibers are protected with stain-repellent finish.

No. 20-7062-5
Two Cushion Wing Loveseat.
55" x 36" x 35" H.

see page 39

No. 20-7077-5
Tuxedo Sectional Loveseat.
Right arm facing. 58½" x 34" x 30" H. No left arm.

see page 15

No. 20-7064-5
Three Cushion Wing Sofa.
81" x 36" x 35" H.
No. 20-7068-5
Three Cushion Wing Sofa.
89" x 36" x 35" H.

see page 39

No. 20-7078-5
Tuxedo Center Section. No arms. 58½" x 34" x 30" H.

see page 15

No. 20-7071-5
High Back Wing Chair. 33" x 38" x 39" H.

No. 20-7082-5
Two Cushion Loveseat. 60" x 36" x 31" H. With matching arm pillows.

see page 23

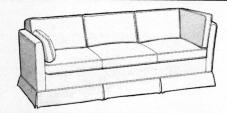

No. 20-7072-5
Tuxedo Sectional Sofa.
Regular left arm facing. 90" x 34" x 30" H. Pillow included. Right arm same angle as back.

see page 15

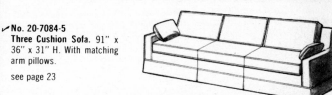

No. 20-7084-5
Three Cushion Sofa. 91" x 36" x 31" H. With matching arm pillows.

see page 23

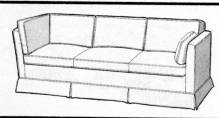

No. 20-7073-5
Tuxedo Sectional Sofa.
Regular right arm facing. 90" x 34" x 30" H. Pillow included. Left arm same angle as back.

see page 15

No. 20-7092-5
Slope Arm Loveseat. 60" x 34" x 29" H. Design matches No. 20-7097-5 Sofa.

see page 42

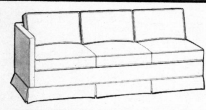

No. 20-7074-5
Tuxedo Sectional Sofa. Left arm facing. 80" x 34" x 30" H. No right arm.

see page 15

No. 20-7094-5
Three Cushion Tuxedo Sofa.
90" x 36" x 30" H.

see page 22

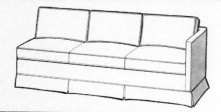

No. 20-7075-5
Tuxedo Sectional Sofa. Right arm facing. 80" x 34" x 30" H. No left arm.

see page 15

No. 20-7095-5
Faceted Sofa. 84" x 41" x 30" H. Trapunto treatment sketched is optional.

see page 18

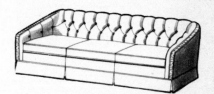

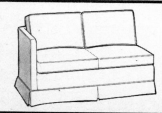

No. 20-7076-5
Tuxedo Sectional Loveseat.
Left arm facing. 58½" x 34" x 30" H. No right arm.

see page 15

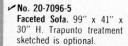

No. 20-7096-5
Faceted Sofa. 99" x 41" x 30" H. Trapunto treatment sketched is optional.

see page 30

Matching arm sleeves are included on most fully upholstered items. Where skirt is available, please specify type in your order: Box Pleats (XP), or Kick Pleats (KP).

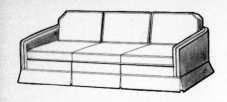

✔ **No. 20-7097-5**
Slope Arm Sofa. 85" x 34" x 29" H.

see page 42

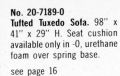

No. 20-7189-0
Tufted Tuxedo Sofa. 98" x 41" x 29" H. Seat cushion available only in -0, urethane foam over spring base.

see page 16

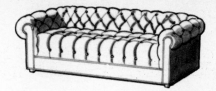

No. 20-7122-5
Chippendale-style Loveseat. 57" x 33" x 34" H. Available also in crewel.

see page 17

No. 20-7191-5
Wing Club Chair. 33" x 36" x 32" H.

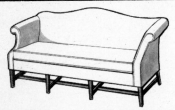

No. 20-7124-5
Chippendale-style Sofa. 81" x 34" x 35" H. Available also in crewel.

see page 27

No. 20-7192-5
Two Cushion Loveseat. 55" x 36" x 32" H.

see page 37

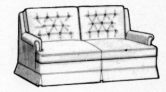

No. 20-7161-5
Lawson Chair. 33" x 36" x 33" H.

No. 20-7193-5
Three Cushion Wing Sofa. 72" x 36" x 32" H.
No. 20-7194-5
Three Cushion Wing Sofa. 84" x 36" x 32" H.

see page 37

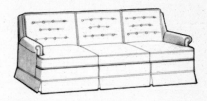

✔ **No. 20-7162-5**
Two Cushion Lawson Loveseat. 55" x 36" x 33" H.

see page 38

No. 20-7242-5
Two Cushion Cap Arm Loveseat. 57" x 35" x 31" H.

see page 34

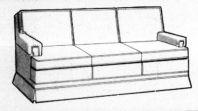

✔ **No. 20-7163-5**
Three Cushion Lawson Sofa. 82" x 36" x 33" H.
✔ **No. 20-7164-5**
Three Cushion Lawson Sofa. 89" x 36" x 33" H.

see page 38

No. 20-7243-5
Two Cushion Cap Arm Sofa. 72" x 35" x 31" H.

see page 34

✔ **No. 20-7182-5**
Slope Arm Loveseat. 57" x 35" x 31" H. Design matches No. 20-7184-5 Sofa.

see page 29

No. 20-7244-5
Three Cushion Cap Arm Sofa. 86" x 35" x 31" H.

see page 34

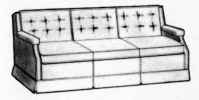

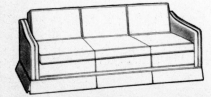

✔ **No. 20-7184-5**
Three Cushion Sofa. 89" x 35" x 31" H.

see page 29

No. 20-7245-5
Two Cushion Cap Arm Sofa. 96" x 35" x 31" H.

see page 34

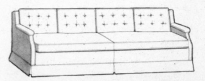

All items on 396 and 397 are available only with -5 Polyester Fiber and Urethane seat cushions except where otherwise noted.

SOFAS AND CHAIRS

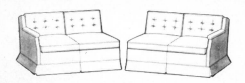

No. 20-7246-5
Right Arm Facing Sectional.
54" x 35" x 31" H.
No. 20-7247-5
Same item. Left Arm Facing Sectional.

see page 35

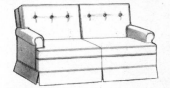

No. 20-7332-5
Two Cushion Lawson Love-seat. 57" x 36" x 31" H.

see page 36

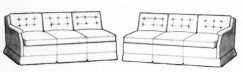

No. 20-7248-5
Right Arm Facing Sectional.
82" x 35" x 31" H.
No. 20-7249-5
Same item. Left Arm Facing Sectional.

see page 35

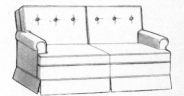

No. 20-7333-5
Two Cushion Lawson Sofa.
73" x 36" x 31" H.

see page 36

No. 20-7260-5
Crescent Tufted Sofa. 99" x 43" x 30" H.

see page 4

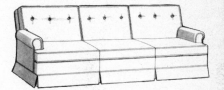

No. 20-7334-5
Three Cushion Lawson Sofa.
83" x 36" x 31" H.

see page 36

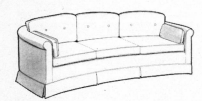

✔**No. 20-7262-5**
Crescent Sofa. 92" x 42" x 30" H.

see page 25

No. 20-7341-5
Wing Club Chair. 30" x 34" x 33" H.

No. 20-7264-5
Chesterfield Tufted Sofa.
103" x 36" x 28" H.

No. 20-7342-5
Two Cushion Wing Loveseat.
51" x 34" x 33" H.

see page 48

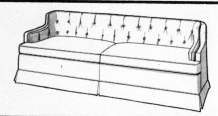

No. 20-7266-5
Pillow Back Sofa. 81" x 31" x 28" H.

No. 20-7343-5
Three Cushion Wing Sofa.
80" x 34" x 30" H.

see page 48

✔**No. 20-7268-5**
Sofa. 89" x 38" x 32" H.

No. 20-7350-5
High Back Wing Swivel Rocker. 30" x 35" x 37" H.
No. 20-7351-5
High Back Wing Chair. 30" x 35" x 37" H.

No. 20-7331-5
Lawson Chair. 33" x 36" x 31" H.

No. 20-7361-5
Club Chair with Scroll Wing.
31" x 35" x 33" H.

Matching arm sleeves are included in most fully upholstered items. Where skirt is available, please specify type in your order: Box Pleats (XP), or Kick Pleats (KP).

No. 20-7362-5
Two Cushion Loveseat with Scroll Wing. 52'' x 35'' x 33'' H.

see page 36

No. 20-7743-5
Three Cushion Lawson Sofa. 83'' x 35'' x 31'' H.
No. 20-7744-5
Three Cushion Lawson Sofa. 89'' x 35'' x 31'' H. Also available with -1 seat cushions of urethane foam.
see page 33

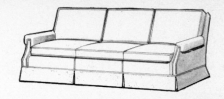

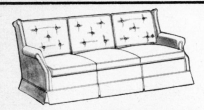

No. 20-7363-5
Three Cushion Sofa with Scroll Wing. 73'' x 35'' x 33'' H.
No. 20-7364-5
Three Cushion Sofa. 81'' x 35'' x 33'' H.
see page 36

No. 20-7861-5
Club Chair. 32'' x 37'' x 34'' H. Old Tavern finish (212) only.
No. 20-7871-5
Hi-Back Club Chair. Same item 39'' H.

No. 20-7370-5
High Back Swivel Rocker with Scroll Wing. 31'' x 36'' x 37'' H.
No. 20-7371-5
High Back Chair with Scroll Wing. 31'' x 36'' x 37'' H.

No. 20-7862-5
Loveseat. 55'' x 37'' x 34'' H. Old Tavern finish (212) only.
see page 44

No. 20-7381-5
High Back Wing Club Chair. 35'' x 39'' x 37'' H.

No. 20-7863-5
Sofa. 82'' x 37'' x 34'' H. Old Tavern finish (212) only.
see page 44

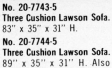

No. 20-7383-5
Three Cushion Wing Sofa. 84'' x 39'' x 37'' H.

No. 20-7870-5
Platform Rocker. 32'' x 39'' x 39'' H. Old Tavern finish (212) only.
see page 18

No. 20-7443-5
Pillow Back Sofa. 88'' x 36'' x 33'' H. Scroll turnings and base trim in Royal Charter finish (220) only. Includes bolsters.
see page 19

No. 20-7881-5
Low Back Club Chair. 31'' x 34'' x 34'' H. Nutmeg or Old Tavern Finish.

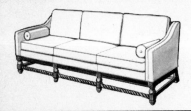

No. 20-7741-5
Lawson Club Chair. 33'' x 35'' x 31'' H. Also available with -1 seat cushion of urethane foam.

No. 20-7882-5
Two Cushion Loveseat. 52'' x 34'' x 34'' H.
see page 45

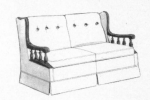

No. 20-7742-5
Two Cushion Lawson Loveseat. 55'' x 35'' x 31'' H. Also available with -1 seat cushion of urethane foam.
see page 33

No. 20-7883-5
Three Cushion Sofa. 81'' x 34'' x 34'' H.
see page 45

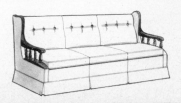

All items on page 398 are available only in -5 Polyester Fiber and Urethane seat cushions.

Matching arm sleeves are included in most fully upholstered items. Where skirt is available, please specify type in your order: Box Pleats (XP), or Kick Pleats (KP).

All Ethan Allen fabrics except Olefin Fibers are protected with stain-repellent finish.

Exposed wood on upholstery is selected hardwood, finished as noted.

SOFAS AND CHAIRS

No. 20-7890-5
High Back Swivel Rocker. 31" x 36" x 38" H.

No. 20-7891-5
High Back Wing Chair. 51" x 36" x 38" H.

OCCASIONAL CHAIRS AND LOVESEATS

No. 20-7892-5
High Back Loveseat. 52" x 34" x 38" H.

see page 45

No. 10-7421-5
Ladderback Club Chair. 26" x 31" x 34" H. Available in finishes 209 Patina or 211 Nutmeg.

#No. 14-7421-5
Available in Bone White 427.

see page 69

No. 20-7956-5
Lawson Sofa. 83" x 34" x 32" H. Available in genuine leather only.

see page 71

No. 10-7422-5
Ladderback Loveseat. 47" x 31" x 34" H. Available in finishes 209 Patina or 211 Nutmeg.

#No. 14-7422-5
Available in Bone White 427.

see page 43

No. 10-7426-5
High Back Wing Chair. 26" x 33" x 39" H. Available in finishes 209 Patina or 211 Nutmeg.

#No. 14-7426-5
Available in Bone White 427.

see page 69

No. 10-7501-1
Spindle Arm Chair. 26" x 30" x 32" H.

see page 45

No. 10-7704-1
Pub Chair. 25" x 30" x 28" H. Available also in leather.

see page 70

No. 12-7516-1
High Back Chair. 26" x 29" x 32" H.

*No. 24-7516-1
Same item in American Foliage Colors.

see page 70

#Description of Decorator finishes:
427-Bone White 428-Azure Blue 429-Mimosa Yellow
430-Celadon Green 431-Celery

*Description of American Foliage Colors:
402-Sugar Bush Red 403-Pine Cone 404-Autumn Gold
405-Holly Green 406-Spruce Blue

No. 12-7517-1
High Back Library Chair. 27" x 36" x 44" H.

*No. 24-7517-1
Same item in American Foliage Colors.

see page 70

Items on page 399 have seat cushions of Urethane Foam, last digit -1 or a combination of Polyester Fiber and Urethane, last digit -5, and are available only as listed.

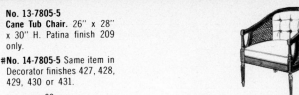

No. 12-7705-1
Pub Chair. 25" x 30" x 28" H. Available also in leather.
***No. 24-7705-1** Same item in American Foliage Colors.
see page 70

No. 13-7805-5
Cane Tub Chair. 26" x 28" x 30" H. Patina finish 209 only.
#No. 14-7805-5 Same item in Decorator finishes 427, 428, 429, 430 or 431.
see page 69

No. 13-7110-5
Cabriolet Arm Chair. 22" x 21" x 32" H. Cane back.
#No. 14-7110-5 Same item in Decorator finishes 427, 428, 429, 430 or 431.
see page 68

No. 13-7806-5
Cane Tub Chair. 23" x 23" x 31" H. Patina finish 209 only.
#No. 14-7806-5 Same item in Decorator finishes 427, 428, 429, 430 or 431.
see page 69

No. 13-7111-5
Trianon Wing Chair. 28" x 30" x 40" H.
#No. 14-7111-5 Same item in Decorator finishes 427, 428, 429, 430 or 431.
see page 68

No. 13-7807-5
Arm Chair. 25" x 28" x 32" H. Cane sides. Patina finish 209 or Georgian Court 225.
#No. 14-7807-5 Same item in Decorator finishes 427, 428, 429, 430 or 431.
see page 69

No. 13-7112-0
Devon Arm Chair. 24" x 26" x 38" H. Seat is urethane foam over spring base.
#No. 14-7112-0 Same item in Decorator finishes 427, 428, 429, 430 or 431.
see page 68

No. 16-7514-1
Pub Chair. 25" x 28" x 30" H. Available also in leather.
see page 70

No. 13-7113-5
Embassy Scroll Arm Chair. 26" x 29" x 36" H.
#No. 14-7113-5 Same item in Decorator finishes 427, 428, 429, 430 or 431.
see page 68

No. 20-7171-5
Cap-Arm Mr. Club Chair. 30" x 35" x 31" H.
see page 65

No. 13-7114-5
Dubarry Wing Chair. 26" x 25" x 42" H.
#No. 14-7114-5 Same item in Decorator finishes 427, 428, 429, 430 or 431.
see page 68

No. 20-7178-5
Cap-Arm Mrs. Club Chair. 28" x 33" x 30" H.
see page 65

No. 13-7115-5
Hampton Wing Chair. 26" x 25" x 42" H.
#No. 14-7115-5 Same item in Decorator finishes 427, 428, 429, 430 or 431.
see page 68

No. 20-7201-5
Barrel Chair. 28" x 29" x 30" H.
No. 20-7202-5
Swivel Barrel Chair. Same item as above, but with swivel mechanism.
see page 67

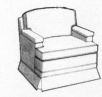

No. 13-7119-0
Low Ladderback Chair. 25½" x 29" x 28" H. Seat is urethane foam over spring base.
#No. 14-7119-0 Same item in Decorator finishes 427, 428, 429, 430 or 431.

No. 20-7204-5
Chippendale Wing Chair. 32" x 33" x 42" H. Available also in leather.
see page 61

---

400 #Description of Decorator finishes:
427-Bone White 428-Azure Blue 429-Mimosa Yellow
430-Celadon Green 431-Celery

Matching arm sleeves are included on most fully upholstered items. Where skirt is available, please specify type in your order: Box Pleats (XP), or Kick Pleats (KP).

Items on page 400 have seat cushions of Urethane Foam, last digit -1, or a combination of Polyester Fiber and Urethane, last digit -5, and are available as listed, unless

OCCASIONAL CHAIRS AND LOVESEATS

No. 20-7208-5
High Back Fireside Chair. 31" x 34" x 33" H. With skirt.

see page 61

No. 20-7312-0
Host Chair. 25" x 27" x 42" H. Available also in Crewel. Seat cushion urethane foam over spring base.

see page 18

No. 20-7213-0
Host Chair. 25" x 28" x 43" H. Cabriole leg. Available also in crewel. Seat cushion urethane foam over spring base.

see page 101

No. 20-7314-5
Barrel Swivel Chair. 29" x 33" x 32" H. Semi-attached back.

see page 67

No. 20-7215-5
Curved Button Back Chair. 31" x 32" x 31" H.

see page 67

No. 20-7315-5
Curved Button Back Swivel Chair. 31" x 32" x 31" H.

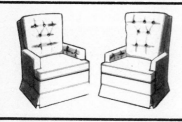

No. 20-7302-5
Mr. Swivel Rocker. 29" x 35" x 40" H.

No. 20-7303-5
Mrs. Swivel Rocker. 29" x 35" x 38" H.

see page 65

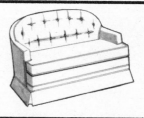

No. 20-7401-5
Loveseat. 52" x 33" x 32" H.

see page 21

No. 20-7304-5
Barrel Chair. 29" x 33" x 32" H. Semi-attached back.

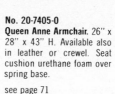

No. 20-7403-5
"T" Cushion Chippendale Wing Chair. 33" x 34" x 44" H. Available also in leather or crewel.

see page 61

No. 20-7305-5
Club Chair. 31" x 34" x 32" H. Semi-attached back.
No. 20-7306-5
Swivel Rocker. 31" x 34" x 32" H.

see page 65

No. 20-7405-0
Queen Anne Armchair. 26" x 28" x 43" H. Available also in leather or crewel. Seat cushion urethane foam over spring base.

see page 71

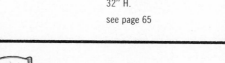

No. 20-7307-5
Mr. Club Chair. 30" x 35" x 37" H.

see page 64

No. 20-7406-5
Oak Lounge Chair. 31" x 39" x 34" H. Wood trim is selected hardwood in Royal Charter finish (220) only.

see page 62

No. 20-7308-5
Mrs. Club Chair. 30" x 34" x 32" H.

see page 64

No. 20-7408-5
Oak Hi-Back Wing Chair 28" x 33" x 48" H. Wood trim is selected hardwood in Royal Charter finish (220) only. Available also in leather or crewel.

see page 60

otherwise noted.
All items on 401 available only with -5 Polyester Fiber and Urethane Foam seat cushions unless otherwise noted.

Wood trim on upholstered items is selected hardwood available in choice of Patina (209) or Nutmeg (211) unless otherwise noted.

No. 20-7409-5
Lounge Chair. 34" x 38" x 32" H. Available in leather without skirt.

see page 15

No. 20-7507-5
Lounge Chair. 36" x 38" x 34" H. Loose pillow back.

see page 66

No. 20-7410-5
Hi-Back Mr. Club Chair. 30" x 37" x 39" H.

see page 64

No. 20-7508-5
Chair. 31" x 34" x 33" H. Tufted back.

see page 66

No. 20-7411-5
Low-back Mrs. Club Chair. 29" x 33" x 34" H.

see page 64

No. 20-7509-5
Swivel Chair. 29" x 30" x 27" H.
No. 20-7510-5
Same item without swivel feature.

see page 66

No. 20-7412-5
Curved Back Lounge Chair. 32" x 38" x 37" H.

see page 62

No. 20-7511-5
Swivel Rocker. 30" x 34" x 34" H.
No. 20-7512-5
Same item without swivel and rocking features.

see page 66

No. 20-7414-5
Roll Back Man's Chair. 29" x 40" x 39" H. Available also in leather.

see page 62

No. 20-7514-5
Chair. 30" x 36" x 34" H.

No. 20-7501-5
Swivel Chair. 29" x 31" x 27" H.
No. 20-7502-5
Same item without swivel feature.

see page 66

No. 20-7516-5
Chair. 31" x 36" x 33" H.

No. 20-7503-5
Swivel Rocker. 32" x 33" x 35" H.
No. 20-7504-5
Same item without swivel and rocking features.

see page 66

No. 20-7605-5
High Back Fireside Chair. 28" x 32" x 46" H. Available also in crewel.

see page 62

No. 20-7505-5
Swivel Rocker. 31" x 35" x 36" H.
No. 20-7506-5
Same item without swivel and rocking features.

see page 66

No. 20-7606-5
Queen Anne Wing Chair. 29" x 33" x 46" H. Available also in leather or crewel.

see page 61

Wood trim on upholstered items is selected hardwood available in choice of Patina (209) or Nutmeg (211) unless otherwise noted.

All items on pages 402 and 403 are available only with -5 Polyester Fiber and Urethane seat cushions unless otherwise noted.

OCCASIONAL CHAIRS AND LOVESEATS

No. 20-7607-5
High Back Fireside Chair. 20" x 32" x 45" H. With Skirt.

see page 61

No. 20-7710-5
Club Chair. 28" x 33" x 32" H.

see page 63

No. 20-7616-5
Queen Anne High Back Chair. 32" x 34" x 44" H. Available also in crewel.

see page 59

No. 20-7711-5
High Back Swivel Rocker. 35" x 38" x 38" H.

see page 63

No. 20-7618-5
Tapered Back Chair. 28" x 31" x 34" H.

see page 63

No. 20-7810-5
Man's Lounge Chair. 34" x 38" x 37" H. Available also in leather. Also available with -6, cushion 75% down, 25% duck feathers.

see page 62

No. 20-7619-5
Sheraton Loveseat. 51" x 30" x 31" H. Available also in crewel.

see page 30

No. 20-7937-5
London Club Chair. 31" x 33" x 32" H. Available also in leather. Available with -6 cushion, 75% down, 25% duck feathers.

see page 62

No. 20-7703-5
High Ladderback Chair. 29" x 35" x 45" H. Available also in crewel.

see page 60

No. 20-7706-5
High Back Wing Chair. 33" x 33" x 46" H.

see page 60

No. 20-7707-5
Tufted Back Chair. 28" x 31" x 34" H.

see page 63

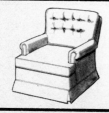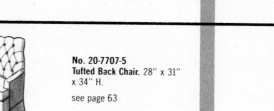

No. 20-7708-5
Barrel Back Chair. 33" x 35" x 35" H.

see page 63

Matching arm sleeves are included in most fully up-holstered items. Where skirt is available, please specify type in your order: Box Pleats (XP), or Kick Pleats (KP).

ETHAN ALLEN DAY BEDS

✓ **No. 10-7504-1**
Double Day Bed. 80" x 34" x 30" H. Opens to sleep two on separate beds. Thick Urethane mattresses.

see page 56

✓ **No. 10-7505-1**
Single Day Bed. 80" x 34" x 30" H. Same item as above except sleeps one.

see page 56

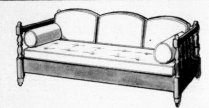

✓ **No. 12-7507-1**
Double Day Bed. 80" x 34" x 30" H. Opens to sleep two on separate beds. Thick Urethane mattresses. Matching bolsters included.

see page 56

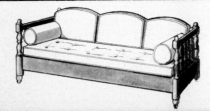

✓ **No. 12-7508-1**
Single Day Bed. 80" x 34" x 30" H. Same item as above, except sleeps one. Matching bolsters included.

see page 56

ETHAN ALLEN "AND-A-BED"® SLEEPER SOFAS

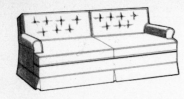

No. 21-7002-5
Two Cushion Lawson Sleeper. 55" x 35" x 31" H.
No. 21-7003-5
Two Cushion Lawson Sleeper Sofa. 75" x 35" x 31" H.

see page 54

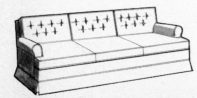

No. 21-7004-5
Three Cushion Lawson Sleeper Sofa. 81" x 35" x 31" H.

see page 54

No. 21-7012-5
Sleeper. 52" x 35" x 34" H.
No. 21-7013-5
Two Cushion Roll Arm Wing Sleeper Sofa. 72" x 35" x 34" H.

see page 57

No. 21-7014-5
Three Cushion Sofa. Same as above. 78" x 35" x 34" H.

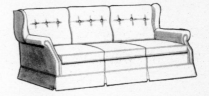

No. 21-7022-5
Sleeper. 52" x 35" x 37" H.
No. 21-7023-5
Two Cushion Sleeper Sofa. 72" x 35" x 37" H. Wood trim is selected hardwood. Old Tavern finish (212) only.

see page 55

No. 21-7024-5
Three Cushion Sleeper Sofa. 78" x 35" x 37" H. Wood trim is selected hardwood. Old Tavern finish (212) only.

see page 55

✓**No. 21-7033-5**
Two Cushion Sleeper Sofa. 75" x 35" x 34" H.
✓**No. 21-7034-5**
Three Cushion Sleeper Sofa. 81" x 35" x 34" H.
✓**No. 21-7035-5**
Four Cushion Sleeper Sofa. 87" x 35" x 34" H.

see page 56

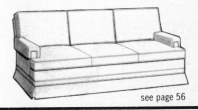

✓ **No. 21-7043-5**
Two Cushion Tuxedo Sleeper Sofa. 74" x 35" x 31" H.

see page 56

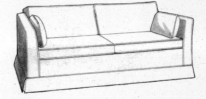

✓**No. 21-7044-5**
Three Cushion Tuxedo Sleeper Sofa. 80" x 35" x 31" H.
✓**No. 21-7045-5**
Three Cushion Tuxedo Sleeper Sofa. 86" x 35" x 31" H.

see page 56

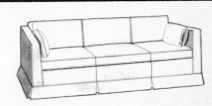

No. 21-7052-5
Two Cushion Lawson-style Loveseat. 52" x 35" x 30" H. Has 36" x 72" mattress.
No. 21-7053-5
Two Cushion Lawson-style Sleeper Sofa. 72" x 35" x 30" H.

see page 57

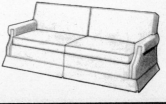

✓Loose pillow back.

Matching arm sleeves are included in most fully upholstered items. Where skirt is available, please specify type in your order: Box Pleats (XP), or Kick Pleats (KP).

Items shown are available with seat cushions of Urethane Foam, last digit -1, or a combination of Polyester Fiber and Urethane Foam, last digit -5, and are available only

All Ethan Allen fabrics except Olefin Fibers are protected with stain-repellent finish.

Wood trim on upholstered items is selected hardwood finished as noted.

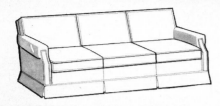

No. 21-7054-5
Three Cushion Lawson-style Sleeper Sofa. 78" x 35" x 30" H.

see page 57

ETHAN ALLEN RESTOCRATS RECLINING AND ROCKING CHAIRS

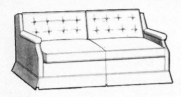

No. 21-7063-5
Two Cushion Cap Arm Sleeper Sofa (full size). 72" x 35" x 31" H.

see page 54

No. 21-7900-1
Wing Restocrat Recliner. 31" x 37" x 40" H.

see page 72

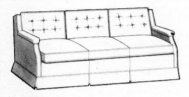

No. 21-7064-5
Three Cushion Cap Arm Sleeper Sofa (Queen size). 78" x 35" x 31" H.

see page 54

No. 21-7910-1
Wing Restocrat Rocker. 31" x 37" x 40" H.

see page 73

No. 21-7073-5
Sleeper Sofa. 70" x 35" x 33" H. Old Tavern finish (212) only.

No. 21-7074-5
Sleeper Sofa (Queen size). 78" x 35" x 33" H. Old Tavern finish (212) only.

see page 55

No. 21-7911-1
Wood-trim Restocrat Rocker. 31" x 37" x 38" H. Patina (209) or Nutmeg (211) finish.

see page 72

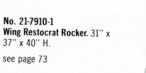

No. 21-7912-1
Restocrat Rocker. 31" x 37" x 38" H. Pine wood arm and wing. Old Tavern finish (212) only.

see page 72

No. 21-7921-1
Wing Restocrat Rocker. 35" x 36" x 40" H.

see page 73

No. 21-7922-1
Restocrat Rocker. 31" x 37" x 38" H. Old Tavern finish (212) only.

see page 73

No. 21-7924-1
Restocrat Rocker. 31" x 37" x 38" H. Royal Charter finish (220) only.

as listed.
Sleeper Sofas are available with optional set of casters on front legs. Please specify No. 21-7999 when ordering.

Ethan Allen
AMERICAN TRADITIONAL INTERIORS

UPHOLSTERED FURNITURE

No. 21-7928-1
Restocrat Rocker. 30" x 37" x 38" H.
see page 73

No. 21-7943-5
Restocrat Recliner. 31" x 37" x 33" H. Back features "pop-up" head rest.

No. 21-7930-1
Restocrat Rocker. 31" x 37" x 37" H.
see page 72

OTTOMANS, FOOTSTOOLS AND BENCHES

No. 21-7931-1
Restocrat Rocker. 29" x 37" x 37" H.
see page 73

No. 10-7428-5
Ottoman. 26" x 21" x 17" H. Cushion available in -5 only. Available in finishes 209 Patina or 211 Nutmeg.
No. 14-7428-5 Available in 427 Bone White.

No. 21-7933-1
Restocrat Recliner. 31" x 37" x 37" H.
see page 72

No. 10-7429-5
Bench. 47" x 21" x 17" H. Cushion available in -5 only.
No. 14-7429-5 Available in 427 Bone White.
see page 69

No. 21-7934-1
Restocrat Recliner. 29" x 37" x 37" H.
see page 73

No. 10-7500-1
Stackables 17" x 17" x 9" H. Cushion available in -1 only and vinyl cover.
No. 12-7500-1 Same item in Old Tavern finish (212).
see page 70

No. 21-7936-1
Restocrat Rocker. 32" x 38" x 40" H. Wood trim is Old Tavern finish (212) only.

No. 16-7438-1
Ottoman. 25" x 21" x 19" H. Royal Charter finish (220) only.
see page 131

No. 21-7941-5
Restocrat Recliner. 31" x 38" x 33" H. Back features "pop-up" head rest.

No. 16-7439-5
Tufted Bench. 45" x 19" x 17" H. Royal Charter finish (220) only.
see page 132

No. 21-7942-5
Restocrat Recliner. 29" x 38" x 33" H. Back features "pop-up" head rest.

No. 20-7101-1
Semi-Attached Pillow Ottoman. 21" x 30" x 15" H.

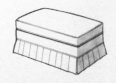

Items that are listed with Urethane Foam Seat Cushions, last digit -1, or a combination of Polyester Fiber and Urethane Foam, last digit -5, and are available only as listed unless otherwise noted.
Items with prefix 16- are Solid Oak in Royal Charter finish (220) with some structural parts of selected hardwood.

All Ethan Allen fabrics except Olefin Fibers are protected with stain-repellent finish.

Exposed wood on Ottomans is selected hardwood, finish as noted.

ETHAN ALLEN RESTOCRATS, OTTOMANS, FOOTSTOOLS AND BENCHES

No. 20-7102-1
Ottoman. 17" x 22" x 15" H. Available only in -1 Urethane Foam cushion.

see page 67

No. 20-7104-1
Square Ottoman with casters. 24" x 24" x 15" H. Available only in -1. Urethane Foam cushion.

see page 67

No. 20-7106-1
Ottoman. 21" x 30" x 15" H. Available also in Leather. Available only in -1 Urethane Foam cushion.

see page 67

No. 20-7404-0
Ottoman. 25" x 18" x 17" H. Available also in Leather.

see page 71

No. 20-7407-1
Ottoman. 29" x 21" x 18" H. Available only in -1. Urethane Foam cushion.

see page 62

No. 20-7868-1
Ottoman. 21" x 28" x18" H. Old Tavern finish (212) only. Available only in -1 Urethane Foam cushion.

No. 20-7938-0
London.Club Ottoman. 27" x 20" x 16" H. Available also in Leather. Cushion is cotton felt over spring base.

see page 62

THE TREASURY OF
Ethan Allen
AMERICAN TRADITIONAL INTERIORS
DETAILED INDEX BY SERIES STYLE NUMBER
FURNITURE, TV, BEDDING, LAMPS, CLOCKS, ACCESSORIES, WALL DECOR

Ethan Allen
AMERICAN TRADITIONAL INTERIORS

TREASURY BOOKSHELF
ORDER BLANK

FOLD HERE

MAIL ORDER

POSTAGE WILL BE PAID BY

ETHAN ALLEN TREASURY BOOKSHELF
ETHAN ALLEN DRIVE
DANBURY, CONNECTICUT 06810

BUSINESS REPLY ENVELOPE
NO POSTAGE STAMP NECESSARY IF MAILED IN THE UNITED STATES

FIRST CLASS
PERMIT NO. 449
DANBURY, CONN.

FROM

FOLD HERE

FOLD HERE

Ethan Allen
AMERICAN TRADITIONAL INTERIORS

TREASURY BOOKSHELF
ORDER BLANK

ETHAN ALLEN TREASURY BOOKSHELF
ORDER BLANK

HOW TO ORDER

This order blank has been designed for quick, efficient and accurate handling. Your order will be processed and shipped directly from your entries on the form. Please print all information. Be sure to include check or money order. Please add local sales tax if applicable.

1. Fill in the order blank according to the details specified. Keep in mind that the "Ordered By," or "Shipped To" sections will be used as a shipping label.

2. If the order is to be sent as a gift to another person, please print the name in the "Ship To" section, and your name in the "Ordered By" section. More blanks are available for the asking, or add your own list if you prefer.

PLEASE NOTE

Your order will be filled promptly by our Ethan Allen Treasury Bookshelf distribution center.

In the far West, allow three weeks for delivery. In the mid-West and the East allow two weeks.

Be sure to indicate the name of the Ethan Allen store from who you received this Treasury in the space provided below.

All sales are final. We cannot make exchanges or accept returns (unless books are defective).

Ethan Allen
AMERICAN TRADITIONAL INTERIORS

HOW MANY	CATALOG NO.	TITLE	PRICE EACH	TOTAL
	98-1001	American Heritage History of American Antiques	13.95	
	98-1003	Golden Treasury of Early American Houses	29.95	
	98-1004	American Glass	14.95	
	98-1005	Index of American Design	11.95	
	98-1006	Wallace Nutting Furniture Treasury	18.50	
	98-1007	American Needlework	15.00	
	98-1008	Treasury of American Clocks	12.95	
	98-1009	Fine Points of Furniture—Early American	3.95	
	98-1011	Antiques Treasury of Furniture and Other Decorative Arts	15.00	
	98-1012	American Folk Painting	Discontinued	
	98-1013	Pine Furniture of Early New England	10.00	
	98-1014	American Country Furniture 1780-1875	7.95	
	98-1020	The American Heritage Cookbook	6.95	
	98-1021	America's Historic Houses	8.50	
	98-1022	Heritage of Early American Houses	12.50	
	98-1023	America's Folk Art	8.50	
	98-1024	Treasure Rooms of America's Mansions	15.00	
	98-1025	Treasury of American Design (2 vols.)	49.95	
	98-1026	Crafts for Fun & Profit	6.95	
	98-1027	Polly Prindle's Book of Patchwork and Quilts	12.95	
			SUB TOTAL $	
		Add Local Sales Tax, if Applicable		
		Make Check or Money Order Payable To: "ETHAN ALLEN TREASURY BOOKSHELF"	TOTAL	

IMPORTANT: Please indicate the store name and city that appears on the back of your Treasury.

STORE NAME _____ CITY _____

ETHAN ALLEN TREASURY BOOKSHELF
ETHAN ALLEN DRIVE
DANBURY, CONN. 06810

ORDERED BY

PLEASE PRINT

NAME

ADDRESS

CITY · STATE

ZIP CODE

If order is to be sent as a gift to another person, fill in "Ship To" information below.

SHIP TO

PLEASE PRINT

NAME

ADDRESS

CITY · STATE

ZIP CODE